Stitch

Stitch

Mark Morris

PIATKUS

Copyright © 1990 by Mark Morris

First published in Great Britain in 1991 by
Judy Piatkus (Publishers) Ltd of
5 Windmill Street, London W1

British Library Cataloguing in Publication Data

Morris, Mark
  Stitch.
  I. Title
  823.914[F]

  ISBN 0−7499−0045−8

Phototypeset in Compugraphic Times 11/12 pt by
Action Typesetting Limited, Gloucester
Printed and bound in Great Britain by
Butler & Tanner Ltd, Frome and London

Dedication

This book is dedicated to Nicholas (The Boy) Royle who drove through Hell with only a mannequin for company. 'Blimey, sarge, it's a real pea-souper out there.'

Acknowledgements

I'd like to thank my wife, Nel, for her love, support and understanding during the writing of this book. I'd like to thank Nick Royle and Wendy Howitt for allowing me to read them extracts which prompted constructive and encouraging responses. I'd like to thank Kevin Mullins for providing me with university insights, Nigel Daniel for his medical pointers and Stephen Laws for a small but vital detail. And in a more general vein, thanks to John Gilbert, Dave Hughes, Phil Nutman and the BFS, flag-wavers all.

Part One

The Crack

'What sickness is it that keeps sending me kids and followers? It's your world out there that does it.'

Charles Manson

Taken from *Without Conscience – Charles Manson in his Own Words*, as told to Nuel Emmons

1

Light slithered over him, shaping the blue-white putty of his face, throwing zebra stripes of shadow across his shirt front. The TV, from which the light issued, droned and muttered, occasionally exhaling music. Apart from that the room was dark. He sat cross-legged on the floor, hunched over, his breath shallow, the index finger of his right hand twitching slightly now and again. There was an unmade bed behind him, upended Reeboks on the floor, a damp crumpled towel strewn over a chair back.

On the screen Charlotte was dying. She lay prettily in a hospital bed, hooked to the obligatory drips and monitors, though with not a hair out of place. Concerned relatives were draped aesthetically around her, murmuring platitudes of reassurance, masking true feelings which were all too apparent in the close-ups of their liquid eyes. Knowing glances flickered back and forth as Charlotte whispered, 'When I'm better ...' She paused to wince; then the pain passed and she stretched out a hand to stroke the flaxen hair of a perfect child. The hand wavered; her eyes sighed closed; the hand drifted to the blanket like an autumn leaf and she was gone. Relatives bowed their heads. With perfect timing someone wept. The credits overlaid Charlotte's still hand and the signature tune began.

He sniffed, felt his eyes filling, and laughed with embarrassment though he was alone in the room. These kinds of things always got to him. He was a sucker for sentimentality. He knuckled the tears back into his eyes, shook his head ruefully, and pushed himself, groaning, to his feet. He picked up the towel and flung it over the nearest radiator, then plodded through to the kitchen.

He opened the refrigerator door, light spilling out and pooling around him like milk. He lifted out a carton of grape juice, took a swig, put back the carton and closed the door. Opening the cupboard above the fridge, he considered for a moment, then lifted out a tin of baked beans, a loaf of sliced brown bread and a large bag of taco shells. He put bread in the toaster, opened the tin and

3

dumped its contents into a pan. As his toast browned and his beans bubbled he slouched against the counter, popping shell after shell into his mouth, crunching, chewing, swallowing at speed as if he were in a competition.

'Olé,' he muttered as the bread jumped from the toaster's hot jaws, slightly blackened, smoking gently. He put the half-eaten bag of tacos back into the cupboard, gingerly lifted out the slices of toast and dropped them quickly on to a plate.

He tutted as he scraped beans from the bottom of the pan, turned on the hot water tap, waited until the water was scalding, then put the pan underneath. He opened the cutlery drawer, took what he needed, then carried his plate back to the TV. The news was on. He watched it as he ate, shaking his head at government cutbacks, listening silently to reports of rail crashes, terrorist attacks, kidnaps, hijacks, murders. As always he used only a fork to eat with. Even now, after all these years, he still could not abide the feel of a knife in his hand.

2

Where the hell were they? He felt a complete prat sitting here on his own. As the pub door opened, admitting petrol fumes, Dan Latcher twisted his head. One of the bikers who entered caught the movement and glanced at him. Dan turned quickly away, hunching over until the bikers had been swallowed by the crush at the bar.

Sighing, he looked at his watch. It was almost ten to nine. He'd been sitting here for an hour now, nursing half a lager, getting some very funny looks. There was nothing worse, he thought, than sitting alone in a pub surrounded by people who were having a good time. Especially when those people happened to be dressed in leathers and biker's boots, as opposed to his own red- and grey-checked suit and maroon suede winkle-pickers. He adjusted his bootlace tie, smoothed a slender white hand over the nape of his bristling neck. He'd had the flat-top done specially for the new term in order to create an impression.

Startled, he looked up as laughter burst over him. A group of bikers were passing his table with frothing pints. One of them had obviously made some comment: they were smirking through their curtains of lank hair, lingering perhaps in the hope that he would retaliate. Dan didn't; instead he picked up his lager and took a sip. He stared through the glass at the greasy table-top until the soily smell of the bikers had dissipated.

'Excuse me.'

He jerked upright in his seat. Though softly spoken the voice was unexpected. He stared wild-eyed at a man holding a pint of Guinness. Gathering himself, he managed, 'Er . . . yes?'

'I was wondering, is this seat taken?'

Dan stared at the seat the man had indicated. It occurred to him to joke, 'Yes, by the invisible man,' but he shook his head.

'Er . . . no,' he said. 'No, I don't think so.'

'Ah,' said the man, satisfied, and sat down.

Surreptitiously Dan eyed the man as he took off his jacket and glanced around. He was fiftyish, squat and paunchy, his bald pink head appearing to sprout direct from his shoulders. Though clean, his clothes were worn and drab. His face was unusual − full-lipped, pug-nosed, and yet somehow . . . feline. Maybe it was the eyes, Dan thought. They were a soft twinkling green, long-lashed, slightly slanted.

The man lifted his pint and took a swig, eyes hooded in ecstacy as though he'd spent all day toiling beneath a desert sun and had been longing for this moment. At last he lowered his glass, a full third of the Guinness gone, and licked away the creamy moustache. Catching Dan's eye, he murmured, 'Ambrosia, that's what this is. Food of the Gods.'

Dan smiled, tight-lipped, but made no comment, a gesture of polite discouragement. He took another sip of his drink, glanced at his watch. He'd go in a minute − Bongo and that lot wouldn't be coming now. There was a late show on at the Gala Cinema − *Withnail and I*. Maybe he'd go to that. There'd be a more civilised crowd there than in this shithole of a place.

'My word, aren't you . . .? You are! You're Daniel Latcher!'

Dan reared back, surprised. The man was grinning at him, waggling an index finger. Before Dan could say anything the man was rooting in the pocket of his jacket which was draped over his seat, a pinpoint of white light gleaming on his smooth pink scalp. He twisted back, podgy hands smoothing a magazine which had been folded in his pocket.

Realising how the man had recognised him, Dan felt a blend of alarm, embarrassment and delight. In his spare time he wrote short stories, though of the twenty-two he had written so far only one had been published — pleasingly in a glossy mass-market magazine called *Fear*. On the table before him now was the very issue in which his story appeared. Tongue-tied, he could only mutter, 'Oh, I see ... Well, yeah.'

'Daniel Latcher,' the man murmured as if he had just met the American President. He thumbed through the magazine until he came to Dan's story, *Fingers*. 'Sign this for me, would you?'

Dan could feel his ears and cheeks burning, was half-aware that the smile on his face must look sickly. A miniature of that face stared back at him from the page — solemn and sallow, with dark eyes, a narrow nose, a thin-lipped mouth. It was rather an insipid face, though Dan preferred to think of it as delicate, sensitive. Girls tended to regard him as either very attractive or something of a wimp.

'I ... er ... I don't seem to have a pen,' he said, tapping his pockets. He was ashamed of the confession — proper writers were supposed to carry pens and a notebook everywhere with them, weren't they?

'No problem,' said the man effusively, 'I have one.' He produced a blue felt tip from the hip pocket of his jacket. Dan couldn't help thinking that felt tips were somewhat childish — didn't they give them to the mentally disturbed to draw pictures with? Or were they only allowed crayons? The man was looking at him shrewdly as though guessing his thoughts. Quickly Dan took the pen, uncapped it, and scribbled his name next to his photo.

'Thank you,' said the man, taking the pen. The magazine lay open on the table between them, and though Dan knew it was to let the ink dry it made him feel as though he were flaunting himself. He was relieved when the man closed the magazine, folded it carefully and replaced it in his pocket.

'Allow me to introduce myself,' the man said, extending a hand. 'My name is Peregrine Stitch.'

Unwillingly Dan took the hand. He expected it to be damp and fleshy, and was therefore suprised to find it dry, almost scaly in texture. The man squeezed his hand a little tighter than was necessary, making Dan feel uncomfortable.

'I thought your story was interesting,' Stitch said when they had settled back in their seats. 'I felt it showed a surprising subtlety for one so young. How old are you? Twenty, is it?'

'Twenty-three.'

'Twenty-three.' He shook his head in admiration. 'And what

brings you to Maybury? Isn't it Liverpool you hail from?'

'Yes,' said Dan. How did the guy know that? From his accent? Then he remembered the bio in *Fear*. 'I go to the Uni in Maybury. I'm a student here. Fourth year honours.'

He kept his voice low. He doubted that students would be very popular in a pub such as this. Stitch, however, seemed oblivious to his discomfort.

'A student, eh? And what is it you study?'

'Psychology,' Dan muttered, thinking, "Shut up, shut up."

'Psychology? A fascinating subject. I'm something of a psychologist myself.'

'Oh, yeah?' said Dan wearily.

'Yes indeed. Psychology — the study of the human mind. I observe people, you know. Watch them. Sometimes one can deduce an individual's thoughts and feelings simply by scrutinising his or her body language. I pride myself on being a very good judge of human character.'

He grinned, and for the first time Dan saw his teeth. They were alarmingly pointed, as though he'd had his molars and incisors replaced exclusively with canines. He picked up his glass and poured the rest of his pint down his throat. Dan was reminded of a snake stretching its jaws wide to swallow prey whole.

'Would you like a drink?' Stitch asked, jabbing a plump finger at Dan's glass. Dan balked at the offer but appeared to consider it. Casually he looked at his watch.

'Erm . . . I'd like to but I think I'd better get going. I wanted to make the late show at the Gala.'

'*Withnail and I*? What a coincidence, I'm going there too! Great minds think alike, eh? We can go together.'

'Oh. Yes,' said Dan, and forced a smile to pretend he liked the idea.

'But the film doesn't start for over an hour yet. Time for a couple more drinks first, eh?'

Dan struggled for an excuse to get away but his wits deserted him. He shrugged and grimaced.

'What'll you have?'

'Er . . . just an orange juice please,' Dan said, feeling as though by accepting anything stronger he would somehow be making a commitment to this man.

Stitch pushed himself up from his seat and clumped to the bar, clutching his glass. Dan stared unseeingly at the video playing on a screen above his head — Guns n' Roses — and wondered desperately what he should do. Maybe he should have said he was

7

meeting someone, a girlfriend perhaps. Surely not even Stitch would be so thick-skinned as to suggest accompanying him then. But the moment had passed now. It was no use thinking what he should have done. What could he do now? Feign illness and go home? Sneak out of the pub while Stitch was still at the bar? Ultimately his indecision resulted in his doing nothing. He was still sitting there when Stitch returned with the drinks.

'Thanks,' said Dan, and gulped at his orange juice though he didn't really want it. Maybe he ought to try and look as bored as he could, reply in monosyllables; maybe that would make the man go away. But even as he thought it he knew he wouldn't be able to carry it through. He was too nice a guy; he didn't like upsetting people. No, like a true Brit he supposed he would simply have to sit and suffer in silence. For God's sake the man was friendly enough – why not just enjoy his company? But there was something about him, an aura, that set Dan's nerves on edge.

The next hour hobbled, crawled, at times threatened to curl up and die. Stitch wove words around Dan, coaxed answers and opinions from him, manipulated the conversation to his own ends. They 'discussed' philosophy, the cinema, literature – and Dan himself. As the two of them stepped from the smoky heat of the pub into the cool drizzly September night, it suddenly occurred to Dan just how much information he had given the bald man. It felt almost as though Stitch's true intention had been to extract as many personal details from Dan as possible, as though the rest of their conversation had been a fabrication, a smoke-screen, to disguise his true motive.

It was rather a paranoid idea, Dan knew, but nevertheless it was one that persisted. On the ramshackle bus that took them to the cinema, he replayed the conversation in his mind. Somehow Stitch had persuaded Dan to yield up details of his life and background, his family, friends, political and social views, even his bloody Liverpool and Maybury addresses! Shit, how had that happened? He squirmed uncomfortably in his seat, sneaked a glance at Stitch sitting beside him. Why did Dan always think of animals where he was concerned? The man was cat-like, wolf-like and reptilian in equal measure, and he smelled ... somehow cold.

The film was good but Dan found he could not enjoy it. The homosexual uncle gave him the creeps, reminded him disquietingly of his companion. Maybe that was it, maybe Stitch was gay, maybe he wanted to get inside Dan's boxer shorts. But no, there was something more to him than that, something that Dan could not quite put his finger on.

8

'Nightcap?' Stitch suggested when they had left the darkness of the cinema and stood blinking in the foyer.

"Fucking hell, just piss off and leave me alone!" Dan thought. 'Er ... no thanks. I'm rather tired. I'd like to go home to bed.'

'Just a quick one then,' Stitch compromised. 'We get off at the same stop. I live just round the corner from you.'

Dan's stomach turned over. Would this evening never end? Stitch's persistence, indeed his very presence, was disturbing. However Dan forced himself to smile and turned resignedly to walk to the bus stop, Stitch at his shoulder. He toyed with the idea of suddenly making a break for it, bolting across the road, but he knew that he wouldn't.

The bus was full of drunken students, back for the start of the new term tomorrow, but unfortunately there were none that Dan recognised. If only Bongo and Carl and Johnny-boy had turned up he wouldn't be in this predicament now. Tomorrow, he thought, they would laugh about this, he'd have a story to tell in the coffee bar. It was all part of life's rich tapestry. An experience. "Did I ever tell you about the night I met the weirdo in the pub?"

The area where Dan lived − where they both lived − was called Royston, and was situated one and a half miles from the University. It was a tightly packed maze of terraces and back-to-backs, the focal point of which was an incongruously new shopping complex. They stepped off the bus into a heavy drizzle which had varnished slate roofs and tarmaced roads. Somewhere a dog was barking mournfully. The bus pulled away with a grumbling "Whoosh".

They started downhill, their shadows shimmering darkly around their heels. Street lamps weaved ahead, a snake of lights. Student houses were distinguishable by their overgrown gardens, their ill-painted doors and windowsills. One house blared light and music; people stood drinking in the garden despite the rain. Though Dan had felt himself outgrowing this aspect of student life in the past year or so, he suddenly wished that he could be there among them: laughing, partying, getting smashed.

'Here we are,' Stitch said a few minutes later, 'this is where I live.'

The street sign, hanging askew, read Blackmoor Place. It *was* only a couple of streets from the house Dan shared with four others, but the way he felt it might as well have been the other side of town.

'I ... um ...' he began, intending to have one last attempt at crying off. Stitch, however, as though guessing his intention, had clumped away out of earshot, was rooting noisily through his pockets, presumably for keys. Sighing, Dan hurried to catch up with him. By the time he did so, Stitch was shoving open a squealing gate, was trudging up a path towards a house that looked shabbier than most.

'Mr Stitch,' Dan gasped as the bald man thrust a key into the lock of the front door. Stitch didn't turn, didn't even acknowledge him, merely twisted the key and pushed the door open. 'Mr Stitch, I really am very tired. If you don't mind, I think I'd like to go home.'

Now Stitch paused, his foot on the doorstep. He turned, his face half in shadow, half illuminated by street lamps. Dan thought he looked like a hunchback from an old Universal horror film. Softly he said, 'But we're here now. You might as well have a coffee before you go.'

Dan hovered, anguished by indecision. Why didn't he just walk away? What right did this fucking weirdo have to dictate to him? He looked into Stitch's strange green eyes, drew a deep breath which tasted of fumes. Already the situation had become awkward. Dan's stomach churned with embarrassment.

'Look, I —' he began, but suddenly Stitch darted back into the light and placed a hand lightly on his shoulder.

'Come in,' he ordered. His voice was soft, but was there a threat in there somewhere? A hint of venom?

Dan's shoulders slumped. Stitch's touch seemed to drain resistance from him. He ran a hand through his hair, which was like hedgehog spines beaded with water. In a small voice he muttered, 'All right, all right ... just a quick coffee ... and then I'll go.'

Stitch smiled and led the way into a dingy hallway that smelled thickly of fish and unwashed linen. The dark bowled towards them, enveloping as a cloud, until the bald man flicked a switch, dispelling it. The weak bulb illuminated a stained ceiling and faded wallpaper, a payphone clamped to the wall beside a table scattered with junk mail. Ahead of them red-carpeted stairs led upwards. To the left of the stairs a narrow corridor led presumably to the basement.

Dan started as a toilet flushed and a door at the end of the corridor was snatched open. A scrawny figure emerged, clad only in jeans, ribs jutting through his pasty frame, his hair bleached white. He paused to nod at Stitch, to glare at Dan with red-rimmed eyes; then he darted away. Dan heard his bare feet descending, slapping stairs like Gollum in *Lord Of The Rings*.

Stitch plodded up the stairs, round a corner, up another short flight. Dan followed, trying to work out what he was doing here. The bald man halted at a door numbered 6, unlocked it, entered.

He stood to one side like a butler, inclining his head slightly. When Dan was inside he closed the door behind them.

'Sit down, make yourself comfortable,' Stitch invited, waving Dan towards a sad-looking armchair upholstered in emerald-green draylon. Dan did so gingerly; he had the impression he were lowering himself into an enormous fleshy leaf. The only light in the room came from a lamp like a pale brown mushroom that had been on when they'd entered. Stitch crossed to a small gas cooker, lifted a kettle from one of the rings and began to fill it at a cracked sink.

Dan looked around. The room was murky, bordering on squalid. The indeterminately covered walls were blotched with either grime or shadows. The carpet was threadbare, as were the curtains. The G-plan furniture — a wardrobe, table, chair, bed and a chest of drawers — looked to have been salvaged from a rubbish tip and hastily cleaned. The whole place smelled fusty, a haven for dust-mites and spiders.

Stitch struck a match and held it over the hissing gas ring. Blue flame blossomed like a flower. The bald man set the kettle on the ring, then clumped across the room and pulled the chair from beneath the table. He sat down, grunting, making the chair creak in protest.

'Nice place,' Dan said lamely.

Stitch looked around, then shook his head. 'Not really. I haven't been here long.'

That much was obvious from the lack of adornment. Stitch had made no attempt whatsoever to make the place homely. The lamp, a rug, two boxes of books, a few kitchen implements and the bedclothes appeared to be his sole contribution to the decor. Dan glanced at the books. They looked old, bound in thick dull leather. Something about them bothered him.

'You know, Daniel,' Stitch said, leaning towards him, 'you're a very special young man. Very special indeed. I sense it in you.'

Dan recoiled a little, stared at his host. Then he shrugged, tried to laugh off the comment. 'What makes you say that?' he ventured.

Stitch took the magazine from his pocket and dropped it on the table. 'I just know,' he said. 'Believe me, you're going to be somebody.'

The magazine, that's what was bothering Dan. The books Stitch owned were old, antiquarian even, completely at odds with the lurid glossy publication he had been carrying. So what did that mean? Had Stitch somehow contrived their meeting, had he followed Dan to the pub? And if so, for what purpose? He surely couldn't be a fan?

11

The only explanation Dan could come up with disturbed him deeply. Stitch had happened across his photograph in the magazine and had become obsessed with him. The bald man himself had admitted that he had not lived here long — and he didn't speak with a local accent. Was it possible that he had tracked Dan across the country, made enquiries, hunted him down?

It was not cold in the room but suddenly Dan was shivering. "Fucking hell," he thought, "I'm in big, big trouble." Stitch was smiling at him, eyes like jade. Why had Dan not realised before just *how* crazy this guy looked? How the fuck had he got himself into this situation? He gripped the arms of the chair and wondered what his next move should be. Ought he to bolt for the door? Casually stand up and dismiss himself? Play it cool by drinking his coffee and then leaving so as not to antagonise his host? He felt a tic jumping at the corner of his eye, a weight curl in his bowel. The vision of his own bed, rumpled duvet and all, swam in his mind's eye like heavenly enticement.

Stitch was still leaning forward, plump hands clasped between his knees. 'Destiny,' he murmured unexpectedly. 'Is that a concept you believe in, Daniel?'

'I ... I don't know,' Dan managed to stammer. He tried to push himself up but his arms lacked strength. 'Look ... I ... I really think I'd better go. I have to get up early in the morning.'

'Not yet, not yet,' the bald man soothed. 'Just a few more minutes.' He stood up and stepped towards Dan, making the student flinch. He grinned savagely, pointed teeth zigzagging between his lips. 'I will make you a fisher of men,' he murmured, and chuckled.

The kettle began to squeal as his hands reached up to his face.

3

As Ian eased the car through the University's entrance gates he wondered again whether he was doing the right thing. He'd had a secure job in Leeds, despite rumours of privatisation, and teaching was not exactly the healthiest profession to enter just now, was it? The gateman jabbed pointedly at a sign reading 5mph and Ian responded with a wave. As the car crawled towards the car park, lurching over sleeping policemen, he reassured himself by thinking: "Vocation".

That was why he'd come here. The Civil Service was okay for some, but never once in his seven years' employment had Ian felt truly contented. He'd always wanted a job where the rewards were more personal, where he could integrate with others, see and appreciate the fruits of his labours. In the Civil Service there was always a barrier between himself and the public. Those who appealed to him for financial support did not seem real: they were faceless and therefore soulless, nothing but despairing entreaties on sheets of paper. It was easy to become blasé, even cynical, about them. An example of this was his colleague, Ray Collins', photocopying of correspondence he received from the truly destitute and passing it round for amusement. Because the senders were homogeneous, the catalogue of despair they recounted often seemed (to Ray at least) unbelievably and hilariously funny.

Ian tucked the car neatly into a space between a white Nissan Micra and a yellow-and-black Mini called Cyril, and cut the engine. He got out and stretched, pressed a clenched fist into the small of his back as he surveyed his surroundings. Maybury University was one of the smallest in the country, the Halls of Residence and lecture theatres enclosed within a single campus. Surrounding the University were fields and farmland: from a distance the place looked like an ugly industrial sculpture − all concrete, brick, tarmac, glass, steel − nestling in the centre of a glowing green carpet. On his way here Ian had passed through Maybury itself, which lay a mile and a half to his left. It was a largish market town, history proclaiming it as once the site of a battle which might possibly have involved King Arthur and his Knights of the Round Table.

Taking his suitcase from the boot of the car, Ian approached the main entrance. Despite himself he felt nervous, and wiped his fingers across his forehead; they came away shiny and wet. The large glass doors hummed open, surprising him, as he stretched out a hand to push them. He entered, and was assailed by signs pointing this way and that: "Dining Room", "Auditorium", "Bars", "Library" he read before he saw the one he was looking for. A hand-written sign in the shape of an arrow read: "Freshers' Registration".

He took a deep breath, tightened his grip on his suitcase and followed the arrow. The smell that enclosed him was of fresh paint and new carpets, floor polish and burnished wood. In a strange way the restoration was daunting; it made Ian feel he would need to be razor-sharp to match his surroundings. At the moment he felt anything but – his cheeks were burning, his shirt was sticking to his armpits, his suitcase was bumping against his leg. He hauled the case up a short flight of steps towards double doors panelled in glass. On the glass, through which Ian could see people milling about, was taped a piece of paper on which: "Senior Common Room – Registration" had been written in red.

Ian entered a swell of chatter. A crocodile of people meandered back from a long table at the far end of the room. Behind the table sat three students wearing bright yellow t-shirts emblazoned with the words: "Welcoming Committee". Some of the new students were with their parents, some alone. Ian felt like an over-age imposter. He tagged on to the end of the queue and put down his suitcase. To his left, floor-to-ceiling windows displayed a quadrangle dominated by an ornamental fountain; to his right a wall of notice boards exhibited a mass of information. Ian shuffled forward with the rest of the queue, picking up his suitcase, putting it down again. When he reached the front he grinned and said, 'Hi,' to the pretty blonde behind the desk.

The girl glanced at him, gave a vacuous smile, and replied, 'Hi. What name is it, please?'

'Ian Raven. English Lit. and Teaching.' He watched as she flipped over pages, as her red-painted fingernail slid down the list of names.

'Ah, yes, here we are. You're in Lancelot Hall, room seventeen. Stu here will show you where it is. You get your keys from the hall warden who lives on the first floor. Here's your Uni information pack. Hope you settle in okay.'

'Thanks,' Ian said, taking the cardboard folder the girl was holding out to him. He turned to Stu, who was perched on the edge of the table, arms folded. Ian smiled and Stu nodded, though it was obvious from his expression that he considered freshers (even those older than him) an inferior race. His thick-muscled arms and

14

military crewcut gave him the air of a bouncer rather than a guide. Without a word he slid from the edge of the table and pushed through the crowd towards another set of double doors.

'Excuse me ... sorry ... excuse me,' Ian said as he tried to follow with his suitcase. Stu led him through a coffee bar where students chatted around tables littered with styrofoam cups. At the pool table Stu paused to exchange vociferous greetings with the players, ignoring Ian's presence completely. Ian began to feel annoyed. Fucking bonehead! Who the hell did he think he was? He was just trying to formulate some scathing remark when Stu glanced at him, muttered, 'Come on,' and strutted away.

More double doors, more corridors. A world of angles and efficiency, of bureaucracy and academe. Ian followed Stu's broad yellow back whilst at the same time trying to digest the barrage of information that was assailing him from all sides. The bank there, the Union office here, and there a sign pointing to the gymnasium. "Freshers' Ball, Gary Glitter + Guests". "*Rainman* starring Dustin Hoffman and Tom Cruise, Tonight in the Auditorium". Ian was beginning to wheeze a little now. He would have to have a blast on his inhaler when he reached his destination.

'It's a bigger place than it looks,' he said conversationally.

Stu shot him a cursory glance which contained more than a hint of derision, and answered, 'Yeah.'

Oh, sod you, Ian thought wearily. He was neither impressed nor intimidated by Stu's hard-man act. The thick-set student swung round a corner and thrust out an arm, jolting open a pair of double doors through which daylight poured. He didn't bother holding the doors open for Ian; they swung back as he stepped through, almost trapping his suitcase.

'Thanks,' he said sarcastically, feeling anger redden his face.

Stu looked surprised, then scowled. 'I volunteered for this so I could meet some birds,' he muttered, 'but so far I've met fuck-all.' He glared at Ian as though contemplating whether to take the issue further, then swung back. 'That's Lancelot,' he said, pointing. 'Duncan Westey lives in the downstairs flat, number one. He'll give you your keys.' Without waiting for a reply he stalked away, taking his frustration out on the door once again.

Ian watched him go, shaking his head. 'Welcome to Maybury. Have a nice day,' he muttered, and chuckled hollowly. Lancelot Hall, like all the rest, was a rectangular red box studded with windows. Flanking the hall was a small car park, a grey structure with a black and red sign that proclaimed "Performance Centre", and a cluster of other buildings.

15

Ian plodded towards it, sweat scampering down his chest, itching between his shoulder blades. The lobby was dark and cool, carpeted in brown with beige walls. A blond-haired man in a track-suit was leaning against a noticeboard, talking animatedly into a telephone. He had his eyes closed and his left hand pressed against his ear as if surrounded by a cacophony of noise.

'Look, Janice, I never promised anything ... For Christ's sake, I'm only human, aren't I? ... Well, that's hardly my fault, you shouldn't have gone off to Brazil like that ... What do you mean? I only – oh shit, there go the pips again.'

Ian slunk away before he could be accused of eavesdropping. The Hall appeared to be comprised of narrow corridors twisting around a central staircase. Ian had a choice of turning either left or right. He hesitated a moment, then turned left. He ascended three stairs, passed a door marked "Bathroom", another marked "Kitchen". Then he came to three numbered doors – 2, 3 and 4.

He tutted and retraced his steps, turning right where he had turned left before. This corridor was similar to the first – another door marked "Bathroom", one marked "Laundry", but there was only a single bedroom door, labelled "1. Hall Warden – Duncan Westey".

He grunted, satisfied, put down his suitcase and rapped on the door. From within he could hear the beat of music, the song familiar but elusive. He heard a creak and padding footsteps. The door opened.

'Hello there. What can I do for you?'

Duncan Westey was in his thirties. He had a large domed fore-head, accentuated by his receding hairline, and a scrappy beard. He wore flared jeans, a waistcoat and a Hawkwind t-shirt that had once been black but was now grey. His feet were bare, and so white they appeared translucent. He was smoking a roll-up.

'Hi,' said Ian. 'My name's Ian Raven. I just arrived today. Could I have the keys to my room, please? Number seventeen.'

Westey grinned. 'Oh, right, come in.' He loped into the room, reminding Ian of a puppet plucked to life by strings. Ian wrinkled his nose at the smoky haze, breathed surreptitiously into his hand so the smoke wouldn't trigger his asthma. Westey leaned over a table, sifting a finger through keys which were piled like treasure.

'Here we go,' he said. 'Shit, these bitches are a little tangled.'

As he untangled them, Ian looked round the room. Clothes were strewn on the settee, records stacked haphazardly in a corner. A bright pink surfboard, like a flattened shark, was propped against a wall dominated by an enormous poster – a black and white

Bob Dylan profile. The door at the back of the room, on which hung an ancient-looking dartboard, led presumably to the rest of Westey's flat.

'Got it!' Westey exclaimed, drawing Ian's keys from the pile. He handed them over, blinking rapidly as the smoke from his roll-up drifted into his eyes. 'Hey,' he said, 'you're a mature student, right?'

Ian laughed. 'Is it really that obvious?'

Westey laughed with him. 'You just don't look like a schoolkid, that's all. How old are you anyway?'

'Twenty-five.'

Westey nodded slowly as though Ian had made a suggestion he was now pondering. 'Right. So what brings you here?'

Ian shrugged. 'I got bored with my job, that's all. Civil Service. I'm training to be a teacher now.'

Westey whistled. 'Dangerous profession. You ought to try the army, it's safer.'

Ian was growing sick of people telling him that classrooms were no-go areas these days. A friend of his who taught biology at a large comprehensive in Leeds, had assured him that schools were no more violent than they ever had been. He was even writing an article – "Tabloid Tales Out of School" – for *The Independent* in order to try to prove his point.

'What about you?' Ian said, changing the subject. 'What do you do here?'

'I'm what is known as a fly in the ointment,' Westey said with satisfaction. 'I do a little lecturing, a little research, but my main task is to establish a fully operative television and recording studio right here on campus.' He sucked on his cigarette, barked a laugh that was full of blue smoke. 'I'll tell ya, the authorities are busting a gut over my status. They don't know whether to call me a lecturer, a technician or an auxiliary. It creases me up, truly it does.'

Ian smiled at Westey's mirth. The warden said, 'Hey, man, you wanna smoke or something?'

Ian shook his head. 'No thanks. To tell you the truth, I'm an asthmatic.'

Westey adopted an expression of concern and immediately stubbed out his cigarette. 'Hey, you should have said. You want me to open a window or something?'

'No, it's okay. I'll, er ... go and dump this stuff in my room.'

'Yeah, you do that. Hey, any time you want to drop in for a beer, just feel free. The door's always open.'

17

Ian grinned, grateful for the offer. 'Thanks. I might take you up on that.'

By the time he reached the third floor he was wheezing. Room 17 was to the left of the staircase, beside the bathroom. Ian put down his suitcase and the Uni information pack and fitted his key into the lock. '*Voilà,*' he muttered as the door swung open.

It was a nice-sized room, containing a bed, a desk, a chair, and tucked behind the door, a large wardrobe, built-in cupboards and sink unit. The far wall was dominated by a window which gave a view of the back of the Performance Centre, sports fields, tennis courts, and the dark spiky roofs of Maybury in the distance. Ian tossed the cardboard folder on to the bed and propped his suitcase against it. He wandered over to the window, looked at the view for a moment, then pulled the chair from beneath the desk and sat down. He was struggling for breath a little now, and closed his eyes, trying to calm himself, to breathe deeply. If that didn't work he'd have a blast on his inhaler, though he tried to use it only as a last resort.

After a couple of minutes his breathing began to ease and he opened his eyes. All at once he felt completely out of place, felt as though he'd made some dreadful and irredeemable mistake. Don't be stupid, he told himself. You're doing the right thing. Of course you are.

He walked across to the sink unit to wash his hands, and looked at himself in the mirror. He was handsome in a way, he supposed, or at least not unpleasing. His hair was thick and dark, his eyes brown. His bone structure gave his face an attractive angularity. At first glance he appeared a little scrawny, though in truth he was more athletic than he looked. His arms were thin but tight with sinew; certainly strong enough, despite his asthma, to make him useful at tennis and squash.

He dried his hands on the back of his jeans and slipped off his bulky black jacket. Heaving his suitcase on to his bed, he laid it flat and unzipped it. The contents swelled to escape as the pressure was released. The next twenty minutes were spent unpacking, finding a space for his belongings, claiming this strange new territory as his own.

That done, he stripped off his shirt and draped a towel across his shoulders, deciding to try out the bathroom next door. He was delighted to discover there was a shower as well as a bath, and spent a glorious quarter-hour in the steam-soaked cubicle, jets of hot water beating the tension from his shoulders, the smell of sweat from his hair. Back in his room he changed into fresh jeans, trainers and his favourite red sweater. It was almost four-thirty. What time was dinner?

He withdrew the Prospectus from the information pack he'd been given and flicked through it. Ah, here it was under Dining Room — the evening meal was served between 5 and 7 p.m. That meant he could explore for an hour or so before going to eat. And there was a map of the campus here too, so he wouldn't have to wander aimlessly.

Okay, he thought, plan for the evening. Unpack the rest of his stuff from the car; look around for an hour; eat; go see this film *Rainman*; make his way to one of the bars.

He tried to cast aside his doubts as he slipped his wallet and inhaler into the inside pocket of his jacket and zipped it up. He *was* doing the right thing. He *was*. In years to come he was going to look back on this as the best decision of his life.

4

'Whoooopeeee!'

The girl swept into the room, pink suitcase in one hand, large carpet bag in the other. Annie, who had been dozing, was snatched into wakefulness, and for one brief confused moment wondered what this stranger was doing in her bedroom. Before she could decide, the girl had dumped her bags and was bounding across, face glowing, slides threatening to shake loose from her rust-coloured hair.

'Hi,' she said, 'I'm your room-mate, Stephanie Peele. But you can call me Steph. Everyone else does.'

'Oh ... er, hi,' said Annie, blinking, looking around. Memory returned, as did the crushing homesickness she'd been trying to avoid through sleep. 'My name's Annie. Annie O'Donnell. Er ... you don't know what time it is, do you?'

Steph consulted her watch. 'Almost five. Christ, my dad drives so slowly! I was *dying* to get here. What time did you arrive?'

Annie sat up, still feeling a little woozy. The top bunk above

19

her head bore down like her depression, made her feel she were in a cage. She scrambled out and stood up, her thoughts floating. 'Er ... about half-past three. Sorry, what did you say your name was again?'

'Steph,' repeated her room-mate, 'Steph Peele.' She skipped across to the window and looked out. 'Isn't this brilliant? I've been looking forward to it all summer. Freedom at last, eh? God, I can't believe I'm really here.'

'Hmm,' said Annie non-committally. At that moment she was wishing she was anywhere *but* here. The homesickness, the sense of disorientation she already felt, was exacerbated by the hormonal blues of her period. However, making an effort to be civil, she asked, 'Where have you come from?'

'Chidwell,' replied Steph, 'it's a little village in Surrey. Pretty but so-o-o boring.' She turned from the window. 'How about you? No, don't tell me, let me guess. I'm good with accents. Somewhere near Manchester, I'd say.'

'Close,' said Annie, smiling a little. 'Preston actually.'

'Well, that's virtually Manchester. What course are you doing?'

'English Lit. How about you?'

'Drama. Have you seen the Performance Centre? Isn't it brilliant!'

Annie shook her head to say, no, she hadn't seen it, but Steph was talking again. 'I was chatting to one of the Welcoming Committee – Robert, his name was. Pretty hunky, actually. And funnily enough, he does drama too, only he's in the third year. Anyway he was telling me they're putting on a musical at Christmas, *Oh What A Lovely War*, and they'll be auditioning in a couple of weeks. So I think I'll go in for that. Do you think I'll get a part? I mean, me being a fresher and everything?'

She paused for breath and looked at Annie. Though Annie was not aware of it, her face must have betrayed the sense of inadequacy she was feeling. The red-haired girl rolled her green eyes, wrinkled her freckled nose.

'Uh-oh, listen to me. I'm talking too much, aren't I? I'm sorry, Annie, I always get like this when I'm excited. Look, just tell me to shut my gob, okay? I won't get offended, honest. It's this huge thespian ego of mine. I just like the sound of my own voice.'

She flung up her hands to convey a sense of exasperation at herself. Despite the nugget of misery that perched in the pit of her stomach, Annie smiled.

'God, I'm starving. Let's go get something to eat. Check out the talent,' suggested Steph.

Annie shrugged, shook her head. 'No thanks. I'm not really that hungry. I think I'll just stay here for a while.'

She sat on the bed. Steph sat beside her. 'Hey,' said the red-haired girl, her voice suddenly gentle, 'are you okay?'

Annie smiled, then crossed her arms defensively. 'Yeah, I'm fine.'

Steph shook her head. 'No, you're not.' She took Annie's hand, thrust out her bosom and drew in her neck to give the impression of double chins. 'Now, lovey, come on,' she said in an affected husky voice, 'you tell your Aunty Claire Rayner what the problem is.'

Annie barked a laugh, then put a self-conscious hand to her mouth.

'That's better,' said Steph. 'I'm determined you're not going to be miserable while I'm around.'

Annie shrugged. 'Oh, I'm not miserable,' she said, 'not really. I'm just a bit ... I don't know ... homesick, I suppose.'

Steph squeezed her hand. 'So are ninety per cent of the people here,' she said. 'You'll soon get over it. Honest you will.'

'You're not,' Annie said.

'Yeah, well, you've never lived in Chidwell.' Steph grinned.

'It's just ... leaving all my friends behind. My family. I've never lived away from home before.'

'You'll make new friends,' said Steph. 'Me for one. I know it's hard at the moment, but try to think of this as a time of opportunity, independence, a time when you can ... can become your own person.' She wrinkled her nose. 'Does that sound corny?'

Annie shrugged.

'It's an adventure, Annie,' said her room-mate earnestly. 'I promise you, a week from now you'll be having a great time. I'll make sure of it.'

Annie smiled weakly. 'Thanks, Steph.'

'Feeling better?'

Annie wasn't but she nodded. 'A bit.'

'Good,' said Steph. She jumped up from the bed, making the springs protest. 'Tell you what, we'll unpack first, make this place a bit more homely, *then* we'll go get something to eat. Okay?' She was already flinging open the lid of her suitcase, dragging out clothes, books, knick-knacks wrapped in tissue paper. Annie watched her but made no move to follow her example. She pressed her hands into her lap and sighed.

'Okay,' she agreed reluctantly.

5

Catriona was worried. She had the distinct impression that Dan was not telling her the truth. She stood and glared at his closed bedroom door, as though in the belief that if she stared long and hard enough she would develop X-ray vision and penetrate the woodwork.

She knocked. 'Dan,' she said for the third time, 'I'm making a cuppa. Do you want one?'

Again it seemed she would receive no answer. She clenched her fists in frustration. She felt like screaming at him, battering on the door until he came out. Then a small groaning voice said, 'No.'

Allelujah, she thought, so there *is* life after all! 'Are you sure?' she said. 'It won't be any trouble.'

Another pause, one in which she might or might not have heard a sigh like crumpling linen. Then:

'No,' the voice murmured. 'I mean ... I'm sure. Thanks.'

She made an exasperated sound, hovered a moment, then turned and headed for the kitchen. Okay, she thought, if that's the way you want it, you can just bloody well sod off.

She crashed about the kitchen — making the kettle clank against the tap as she filled it; causing the mugs to scrape harshly together as she snatched one from the cupboard; dropping the tea pot lid on the counter so that it echoed like a small cymbal. She felt satisfied at the din: it seemed to express her anger somehow. She only hoped that Dan could hear it too, and more, that he could read her anger in it.

'See if I care then,' she muttered as she carried her steaming Snoopy mug into the lounge, 'see if I bloody care!'

But she did care. It was caring, and having her concern rejected, that made her so annoyed.

She slumped on to the settee, grabbed the copy of *Cosmopolitan* that Emma had left on the floor and began to leaf through it. As she gazed unseeingly at the pages she thought about Dan. What was wrong with him? Why was he behaving like this? It was especially galling after the way they had been last term, the hard time she had had over her parents' divorce and the way he had helped her through it.

"Is Your Man A Considerate Lover?" the magazine asked her. She snorted and flung it to the floor. What *was* wrong with him? Why was he refusing even to see her? Maybe the summer break had made him realise how close they'd been getting, maybe he was now embarrassed by their tenderness and was trying to avoid her. In which case, she thought, living in the same house would be difficult, to say the least.

She sipped her coffee, drew up her legs. But no, she didn't believe he would simply avoid her. It wasn't as if they'd made any commitment, after all; they'd left things hanging, had tacitly and mutually given themselves the summer to think their feelings through. And if one or the other decided that they didn't want to carry this any further, then fine, it could be dropped casually and easily, with no nasty scene, no awkward dénouement. They could still be friends, confidantes even. They could be tender without being intimate, loving without being lovers.

So why, she thought, was he behaving like a schoolkid, shunning her as if she was a bad smell? She made herself comfortable, had another sip of coffee. Well, he couldn't stay in there forever; he had to come out eventually. And when he did, she would confront him.

She had arrived in Maybury an hour ago, brimming with news and expectation. The house she shared with four others — Dan, Neville, Julie and Emma — had been silent, which she had assumed meant she was first back. She had taken her bags up to her room, thrown herself on to her bed with a sigh, and then almost in the same movement had jumped up and prowled about the house, acquainting herself with it once again.

Neville, who lived in the attic bedroom, was definitely not back. Dust flew at her when she opened his door; a snarling zombie promoting Iron Maiden glared from the wall; the windowsill had become a summer morgue for flies. There was no sign of Julie either, who had the room next to hers on the middle floor, though Emma — who lived next to the bathroom and was forever complaining about the smell Nev made in the toilet — had been and gone (probably to Uni, Catriona thought, to check out the freshers).

She had trooped downstairs to make a cup of tea, giving Dan's door a perfunctory rap as she did so. His room was at the front of the house on the ground floor, back to back with the lounge. But he hadn't returned yet, she was sure of it. When her taxi had pulled up in front of the house his curtains had been closed, and she'd made enough noise entering the house and hauling her luggage upstairs to wake the dead.

She was surprised, therefore, to hear a scuffle of movement from his room, so slight that had she coughed she'd have missed it.

'Dan?' she said uncertainly. 'Dan, are you in there?'

23

She was already thinking of mice, even rats, when a pale brittle voice said, 'Yes.'

'Dan, it's me – Catriona. Can I come in?'

This time the reply was more urgent, almost panicky. 'No! I mean ... it's not a good idea.'

'Why not? What's the matter? Are you all right?'

A pause that stretched and stretched. Then: 'No ... I'm not well ... I ... I've got flu.'

Catriona laughed. 'Oh, is that all? Well, I'll look after you. I'll make you a lemon drink.'

'No ... I'm all right ... Just ... just leave me alone.'

Not surprisingly she was perplexed by his rejection, but attempted to make light of it. 'Well, that's a fine welcome, I must say.'

No answer. Catriona frowned, her patience beginning to wear a little thin.

'Come on, Dan, come and talk to me. You can lie on the settee. I'll put the fire on. I'll even make you some hot chocolate if you're good.'

It was a bone of contention that had developed into a running joke between them; Dan was forever stealing Catriona's hot chocolate. However there was no expected chuckle from his room, no answer of any sort.

'Come on, Dan,' she said, a little snappish. 'I haven't seen you for ages. Look, we don't have to talk or anything. We can just keep each other company.'

She heard a barely suppressed groan, then the voice muttered, 'Go away.'

Anger flared in her. 'All right,' she barked, 'piss off then. You can rot for all I care!'

She had stormed upstairs, unpacked furiously, then had gone to the corner shop to buy milk, slamming the front door behind her. Let him stew in his own juice for a while she had thought. He'll soon see what a shit he's being.

But it was now an hour later and still he had not emerged. Catriona gulped the last of her coffee, then clumped through to the kitchen to make another. While she was scooping Café Hag from the jar, the doorbell rang.

Who was this? Scatter-brained Julie who always managed to pack her doorkeys under ten tons of luggage? Leather-clad Nev, rat-arsed as usual? She half-ran down the hall, eager to renew dormant friendships, anxious to share her misgivings about Dan. She twisted the catch, dragged open the door – and recoiled.

A stranger stood there, the kind of person she always crossed the street to avoid. He was maybe twenty but looked haggard and sick and old. Pasty acned skin was stretched tight over his narrow skull. Eyes like flecks of grit darted in bruised sockets. His black clothes were filthy. His body smelt of rank sweat, his breath of glue. When he opened his mouth her gaze shifted from his bleached hair, to his brown teeth, to the sores around his lips.

'Is Dan in?' he muttered.

'Er ... Dan who?' she said. Surely he couldn't mean *her* Dan?

'Latcher. Dan Latcher. Is he in?'

She had an urge to lie. The prospect of admitting this guttersnipe into the house was almost unbearable. However his eyes bored into hers and she found herself admitting, 'Er ... yes. Yes, he is. But he's in bed. He's ill. He's not seeing anyone.'

'He'll see me,' the glue-sniffer said and stepped into the house. Instinctively Catriona moved back to avoid him, thus allowing him easy access.

'Who are you?' she said, noting the needle-marks in his arms, the death's-head tattoo on his shoulder half-hidden by his t-shirt.

'A friend,' he said, and grinned at her. His gums were grey as death.

Nervously she retreated as he advanced into the house, bringing his stink with him. He stopped at Dan's door, knocked twice, said, 'Dan, it's me. Spider.'

There was a momentary pause before the door was jerked open and a voice said, 'Come in.'

Catriona caught a glimpse of Dan's frightened pale face before Spider slipped inside and the door snapped shut behind him.

25

6

The potatoes were soily. Ian pushed them to the side of his plate and concentrated on the fish. Around him knives scraped on crockery, an occasional burst of laughter breaking free from the tangle of voices. He was sitting at the end of a table set for eight, browsing through his Prospectus. At the other end of the table two guys were telling each other sick jokes about babies and spitting food as they laughed.

Ian had spent over an hour exploring and had been largely impressed by what he'd seen. The sports and library facilities were first-class; the television and recording studios that Duncan Westey was initiating appeared almost complete. He had been drawn into conversation with one of the librarians, Barbara, a middle-aged local with a prickly manner. She had reeled off a list of new equipment purchased by the Uni over the summer in a quietly disapproving voice, as though each item constituted a mortal sin.

'New squash courts, a multi-gym, an all-weather pitch, new seats in the Auditorium, new curtains and carpets everywhere, a new computer system for the library, electronic typewriters, photography equipment, recording equipment, video equipment for the History Department, new telephones in all the halls ...' She shook her head, earrings sparkling. 'I mean, I ask you! They're thinking of putting a swimming pool in next year, not to mention replacing the plumbing in the girls' halls. And they talk about education cuts!' She rolled her eyes as though party to some vast confidence trick. 'It's a joke, it really is.'

Oh, well, better than spending money on bombs, Ian felt like saying but bit back the words. He smiled understandingly, made his excuses and left, the librarian still tutting behind him like a clock.

'A baby in a microwave,' one of the guys at the end of the table said, and the other whooped, spraying custard. Ian groaned and pushed the remains of his meal aside, grey potatoes and a greasy pile of bones and fish skin. He sipped his glass of water, leaving a buttery smear on the rim. Though he generally avoided dairy products because of his asthma, he reached for the plate of cheese and biscuits he had selected in lieu of dessert.

He hoped he wasn't going to be too old to enjoy himself here. He wasn't afraid of loneliness – he had lived alone in bedsit land in

Leeds for over six years and was content with his own company —
but he did feel he ought to take the opportunity to make the most of
all that the University had to offer, both educationally and socially.
It was strange: there were times in the office when he'd felt like
a kid, listening to the woes of marriages and mortgages; but here
he felt almost smugly mature, a man-of-the-world surrounded by
giggling juveniles.

He glanced up from his Prospectus as a tray of food was placed
before him on the table. Another tray was placed beside the first,
and then the owners were dragging out chairs and sitting down.
The girl who sat opposite Ian was plumply curvaceous, her green
eyes sparkling and dancing as they absorbed their surroundings, her
red hair seeming to fizz with energy. Her companion was the classic
English Rose: slim, fair-skinned, with long straight golden-brown
hair, pale grey-blue eyes and delicate long-fingered hands. She
glanced at Ian and immediately he picked up on her uncertainty, her
sense of dislocation. He smiled reassuringly and her lips twitched
back in an almost-smile.

'It *is* okay to sit here, isn't it?' the red head asked. 'I mean,
you're not waiting for someone or anything?'

Ian spread his hands. 'No. I mean, be my guest.'

The red head beamed. 'Thanks. I'm Steph, this is Annie. We just
arrived today. It's so exciting.'

'I'm Ian,' Ian replied. 'I arrived today too.'

Steph paused in the act of impaling a forkful of asparagus.
'Really? You look too old to be a fresher.'

The girl called Annie giggled abruptly, surprising Ian. Steph
realised what she'd said and a mortified expression appeared on
her face.

'Oh, look, I didn't mean you looked old or anything. I just
meant you looked ... mature. Yeah, that's it. I wasn't trying to
be funny.'

Ian grinned, not least because Annie was now beginning to giggle uncontrollably. He recognised that her laughter was more a
release of tension than because she found Steph's faux pas genuinely hilarious.

'That's all right,' he said, 'no offence taken. Actually I am pretty
ancient: twenty-five, would you believe? It's taken me this long to
decide what I want to do with my life.'

'And what's that? Steph asked.

Ian glanced at Annie, whose giggles had completely overtaken her
now. A clenched fist was pressed to her mouth, her shoulders were
heaving, her face red. Ian realised that if Annie started weeping

27

she would look no different. And he realised too that only the narrowest of lines separated the two extremes.

'Teach,' he replied in answer to Steph's question, and then turning to Annie he asked, 'Hey, are you okay? Would you like some water?'

Annie looked up at him. There were tears in her eyes. She took the proferred glass, emitting a bubble of sound that Ian guessed was the word, "Thanks".

'You'll have to excuse my friend,' Steph said. 'They only released her yesterday.'

Annie sipped water, and gradually her giggles subsided. When she was able she said, 'Sorry about that. I don't know what's wrong with me.'

'Nerves, I expect,' said Ian. 'Coming to a strange place, meeting new people. It's bound to set you a bit on edge.'

His presumption sounded a little pompous in his own ears, but Annie looked grateful for his understanding. She flickered a smile at him, to which Ian responded.

'So what course are you doing?' Steph asked. 'With your teaching, I mean?'

'English Lit.,' replied Ian.

'Hey, so's Annie. It looks like you two were destined to meet, doesn't it?'

Annie looked a little embarrassed. She began to pick at the salad on her plate, carefully slicing her lettuce as though steeling herself to eat it. Ian did not know quite how to respond to Steph's comment. In the end he shrugged and said, 'What about you? What course are you doing?'

'Drama,' Steph said. 'I can hardly wait to get started. I went to see the Performance Centre earlier. It's brilliant, just like a real theatre. Have you seen it?'

Ian told her he could see it from the window of his room but admitted he hadn't yet been inside. Steph told him he should. Ian said he would. Annie ate her salad slowly and silently.

'What were you doing before you came here?' Steph asked. When Ian told her she screwed up her face and said, 'Bo-o-oring.' Then the apologetic expression reappeared and she said quickly, 'Oh look, I didn't mean that to sound rude either. God, it's always the same with me. Open my mouth and put my foot in it.'

Ian glanced at Annie who smiled shyly at him. She was pushing the food around on her plate with her fork, like a prospector searching for nuggets of gold. 'No, it *was* boring,' he said. 'God knows how I stood it for seven years. You just get caught

28

up in the routine of it, I suppose, don't notice the time passing.'

Steph shook her head. 'I could never do anything like that. I'm going to be an actress, I'm totally determined.'

Quietly, as though unsure whether she should be saying so, Annie pointed out, 'Actresses spend of lot of time out of work, you know, Steph.'

'Yeah, I know, but I'll still find plenty to do. I'll read loads, improve my mind. And I'll go to dancing lessons and to the theatre. And I'll keep fit, and maybe learn a musical instrument.'

'What about money?' said Annie. 'How will you live?'

'I'll get a bar job or something in the evenings,' Steph said. 'And I'll still be able to sign on, you know, I'll be okay. Anyway, that question won't arise. As soon as I'm discovered I'll get floods of offers. I'll have to turn down dozens every week.'

She grinned, though Ian guessed she was only half-joking. Steph really did believe she was going to be a star. He found her unshakeable confidence both admirable and naive. Annie seemed to withdraw into her shell again, too insecure to pursue the discussion further.

'Are you going to eat that or what?' Steph said, nodding at her friend's half-eaten salad. Somehow she had managed to devour chicken pie, potatoes, mushrooms and asparagus whilst still enjoying the lion's share of the conversation.

Annie looked at the food, then pushed the plate away and shook her head.

'You'll waste away,' Steph warned her. 'You've got to eat you know, Annie.'

Annie pulled a "So what?" face. Intrigued by their unlikely friendship, Ian asked. 'How did you two meet?'

'We're room-mates,' Steph said. 'Don't you have one?'

He shook his head.

'Charming,' Steph proclaimed. 'We girls have to share while you guys get a room to yourself. Oops, no offence, Annie.'

'Maybe it's because I'm a mature student,' Ian suggested. 'Perhaps that's one of our privileges.'

'Yeah, maybe. I guess you need the extra room for your walking frame, pacemaker, stuff like that.'

They all laughed, Annie included. Ian looked at his watch and said, 'Hey, I was going to see this film, *Rainman*, and then have a drink in the bar. Do you two fancy joining me?'

'Yeah, great,' said Steph. She turned to Annie. 'Okay?'

Annie nodded. Ian guessed that the idea of sitting watching a film for a couple of hours appealed to her; it would take her out

29

of herself and give her a break from the uncomfortable procedure of forging new relationships.

'Okay,' he said. 'Well, it starts in ten minutes. We'd better get going.'

They piled their crockery together on to a tray and got up to leave, Steph munching an apple. The Auditorium was about two-thirds full when they arrived, people sitting in clusters of twos, threes, fours. Everywhere Ian looked tentative friendships were getting underway, some that would last a day, some a lifetime. As a result conversation was subdued and attentive, laughter polite.

'Let's sit over there,' Steph said, pointing, and led the way. She chose three seats in almost the exact centre of the Auditorium. They sat down – Steph, then Ian, then Annie. Ian enjoyed sitting between the two of them; he hadn't had a female friend since breaking up with Christine nine months ago.

Before the film, the Union President, Tim Millward, made a short and amusing speech welcoming them to the University. He was lanky as a stork, with a thatch of black hair shaved to stubble at the sides, and large hands which he clasped together like a priest. At the culmination of his speech, two Welcoming Committee members made up like clowns ambushed him with plastic buckets full not of water but of condoms. There was a ripple of laughter, much of it self-conscious, though Ian was aware of Steph beside him guffawing heartily.

Then came the film. Afterwards Steph was full of awe at Hoffman's performance. 'He's so *inspiring*,' she kept saying, 'God, he was breathtaking, don't you think?'

Both Ian and Annie did think so. Yet so enthusiastic was Steph that their opinions seemed almost half-hearted.

They found a table in the bar and sat down. The atmosphere in the room was convivial but restrained. As time wore on, however, and inhibitions were loosened by alcohol, the almost cocktail-party ambience was superceded by something altogether more raucous, more open. Ian was aware of Annie relaxing by degrees; it was like watching iron soften. Steph became even louder than normal. Her strident laughter drew amused and astonished glances, was so infectious it set off chains of laughter round the bar like an echo.

'How are you going to cope with her?' Ian asked Annie when Steph had gone to buy drinks. He was buzzing happily, already full of affection for these two very different women.

Annie smiled a little. 'I don't know,' she said. 'I honestly don't.' She looked down at her glass, still smiling, and ran her fingertip slowly round its rim.

30

'What do you think of the reading list for the course?' Ian asked, then immediately thought: Boring question.

Annie, however, seemed eager to talk; conversation was far less awkward than silence. She frowned as she searched for the right word. At last she said, 'Formidable.'

'Yeah,' Ian agreed, glad that he wasn't the only one to think so.

'Mind you,' she continued, 'I've already read about six of the books, so that should take the pressure off a bit.'

'Oh, yeah?' said Ian, impressed and a little alarmed. 'Which ones have you read?'

Annie reeled off the titles.

'You sound as though you read a lot,' Ian said.

'Oh, I love it. How about you?'

Ian nodded. 'Curling up by the fire with a good book — it's one of my greatest pleasures.'

'What do you read?'

'Oh, anything. From ... Raymond Chandler to Stephen King. D.H. Lawrence to ... Maeve Binchy.'

'Oh, I love Maeve Binchy!' Annie exclaimed. A spark of enthusiasm lit her eyes. 'I think her books are so ... I don't know ... full of light. I loved *Firefly Summer*. Have you read that?'

'Yes,' said Ian. 'I think *Echoes* is my favourite one of hers.'

They began to talk books, and all at once the words were spilling out, overlapping, interrupting one another.

'Hey, gang, there's a disco at eleven. Bop till you drop,' announced Steph, reappearing with a double handful of drinks and two more people. To Ian's disappointment her arrival curtailed his and Annie's conversation, though the two of them shuffled closer to allow Steph's new friends room to sit down. Steph announced she had "just met them at the bar", and Ian laughed, admiring her ability to pick up new friends as most people would pick out clean underwear for the morning.

Steph made the introductions. Ian and Annie said hello to Emma Chettle from Wimbledon, who looked like a model, smoked perfumed cigarettes and seemed to brandish her gums when she laughed; and to Neil Gardener from Starmouth, who was dark-haired and solidly built and who obviously fancied Steph.

The five of them got on well, though Ian found Emma somewhat affected. He was also painfully aware that Annie was withdrawing into her shell again, intimidated by the introduction of yet more strangers. They had a few more drinks; Ian arranged to play squash with Neil; at eleven o'clock they pushed back their chairs and stood up, Ian half-jokingly offering his arm to Annie.

31

Annie smiled, and though she didn't take his arm she allowed her hand to linger on his shoulder for a few seconds.

'Sorry to be a party-pooper,' she said, 'but I think I'll give the disco a miss if you don't mind. I don't really feel up to it.'

Ian was surprised at how disappointed he felt. 'Are you sure? You don't want to come just for an hour or so?'

Annie shook her head. 'No. I've had a nice evening, really. I've just . . . got a bit of a stomach upset, that's all.'

'Oh,' said Ian. 'Okay. Do you want me to walk you back to your hall?'

'No, you go with the others. I'll see you at the introductory lecture tomorrow morning.'

They exited the bar, said goodnight and went their separate ways. Annie's departure had evened the group up − two girls, two boys − but Ian felt it had somehow unbalanced it. He was surprised to find he still had bags of energy − at work he'd often felt drained, thoroughly exhausted by the evening, though at the office he did nothing more demanding than answering telephones and dealing with correspondence. Entering the room where the disco was being held was like stepping into a sauna. Music pulsed off the walls, so loud it seemed to beat thickly against Ian's throat and chest.

Steph immediately paired off with Neil and the two of them began to dance, Steph flamboyantly, Neil a little stiff-legged. Emma smiled at Ian, flashing her gums, her face yellow as jaundice under the lights. 'Dance?' he mouthed and Emma nodded willingly. They weaved their way through the crowd until they found a space that suited them.

Time passed in fractured spasms. So total was the music it seemed to cram Ian's senses, including his sight. In a strange way it was like being deaf; after a while the music became a wall of noise, his limbs plucked into movement by a beat that was almost subliminal. It was an exhilarating feeling; he couldn't remember when he had last felt so completely free. Towards the end he smooched with Emma, though it was more because he didn't want to break the mood than because he found her attractive.

When the music stopped and the lights came on they broke apart almost guiltily, as though a spell had been broken. All at once Ian felt tired and a little asthmatic; his ears hummed. They located Steph and Neil, who were snuggled up to one another, soporific smiles on both their faces. Their obvious contentment made Ian even more acutely aware of the distance between himself and Emma.

'Wasn't that *brilliant*!' Steph enthused. Her voice seemed oddly flat and distorted.

'Yes,' said Ian, 'it was good. God, I haven't danced so much since I was about sixteen.'

'We're going back to my place for a coffee,' said Neil. 'Do you two want to come?'

Ian didn't like the presumption that he and Emma were now a couple. 'Not for me, thanks,' he said. 'I need some sleep. I'm an old man, remember.'

They teased him a little about his age, but Ian had the impression Neil and Steph wanted to be alone anyway. He said goodnight, made vague arrangements to meet up with them tomorrow, and made his way back to his hall.

Tiredness seemed to settle ever more heavily inside him with each step. By the time he entered his room and locked the door behind him he felt shattered. He looked at his watch and was astounded to see it was almost 2:15. He crossed the room, drew the curtains, then flopped on to his bed. He could smell the smoke from Emma's perfumed cigarettes on his clothes. His throat seemed to have closed to a tiny aperture; his breath laboured in his chest like an animal in a sack. He fumbled his inhaler from his jacket pocket and took two long steady blasts. It seemed to act like an anaesthetic, and within seconds he was tumbling, fully-clothed, towards sleep.

7

The window rattled in its frame. Rain began to tap almost idly on the glass. Dan Latcher's face was rigid, his eyes focussed inward. His skin was pastry-white in the light from the angle-poise lamp.

It was almost three a.m. and the house was encased in sleep. Dan was unaware of the time, or of the comings and goings of the other household members, or of the infrequent taps on his door, the voices by turn concerned, cajoling, angry. He was aware of little but the sheets of paper on the desk in front of him, the pain that scrabbled at his mind, that blazed white-hot in his arm and his hand. Though he appeared still, his body locked into place, inside he was twisting in agony.

His right hand gripped a pen so tightly that the bones glared like a chalk outline. The pen sped over a blank sheet of paper, scribbling words incredibly fast, so much so that the hand was a blur, impossible to focus upon. Dan watched it, his breath rasping, sweat dribbling unchecked down his face, into the collar of his shirt, beading on his scalp and sleeking his cropped hair. All at once his face creased, his mouth worked torturously.

'No ...' he whispered. 'Please ... please ... no ...'

Yet he continued writing.

8

Two miles away a man sat up suddenly in the darkness, eyes springing open as if someone had jabbed him with a stick. His room seemed to jolt, to waver, a sheet stitched of shadows rippling in the wind. He rubbed his eyes, swallowed, tried to relax limbs that were almost aching with tension. What had woken him? Why was his heart pumping like an overburdened machine? He strained his ears but could hear nothing. His senses seemed muffled with darkness.

He pushed back his bedclothes, lowered his feet to the floor and padded across to the lightswitch. He raised his hand to the switch, then hesitated. Suddenly he was afraid that the light would reveal him too plainly, make him more of a target. A target for what? He was being paranoid, ridiculous. Being plucked from sleep had disoriented him, filled him full of silly night-fears that he would laugh about in the morning. He tried to laugh now but couldn't. The darkness, the silence, were too real, too threatening. Threatening? Why threatening? He was behaving like a child, scared of shadows and dreams and imaginary monsters. The objects in his room were hovering bulks of darkness but they were certainly harmless; his bed was an island, a refuge, somewhere safe.

Leaving the light off, he crossed to the window. Now he could hear the gentle patter of rain. Perhaps that had wakened him? He gripped the edge of the curtain, tugged it back and peered out. A pale wiry figure with a smear of white hair seemed to dart like a timid animal into a nearby clump of shadow.

For a few moments he stood, rigid. Had he really seen that? It had been an almost subliminal impression, nothing more than a flash of uncertain movement. He glared into the shadows until his eyes ached but now there was not even the hint of a figure. Something rose in his memory, unpleasant, distasteful, frightening. All at once he was certain a bulky grinning figure would be standing in the doorway when he turned round.

He turned, breath backing into his throat.

There was no one there.

He expelled a long plume of breath, smiled nervously to himself. Of course there was no one there. He was not a child now, he had come to terms with all that long ago. It was only the shock of waking so suddenly that had brought it back like this. He had to get a grip, set himself firmly in the real world. He crossed purposefully to his bedside cabinet and picked up the clock beside his bed. Almost four in the morning. That seemed to prove something. Nobody would be sneaking around at this hour in the rain, would they?

He considered making himself a coffee, then decided that it was too much trouble and that it would only keep him awake. He opened his bedroom door, peered out and listened: the stillness seemed tight as a vacuum. He crossed back to the window, looked out again, but nothing moved in the monotone landscape except the twitch of rain in gleaming puddles. He returned to bed, smiling at his nervousness. The fact that he could smile showed how well he had reconciled himself to what had happened to him as a child.

The bedclothes were cool but welcoming. He slipped snugly into the hollow that his body had made. A sudden flurry of wind and rain made him jump, but then he smiled and closed his eyes. Less than three minutes later he was asleep.

9

Someone was tap dancing in Ian's head whilst at the same time pushing blunt needles into the backs of his eyeballs. He groaned, rolled over, trying to dislodge the hoofer, but it made no odds. 'For Christ's sake,' he muttered. He reached out a hand to the glass of water he always kept on his bedside table. There was no glass. No bedside table. One eye, a mere slit, cracked open.

'What the ...?' Daylight drenched the room, though it was flooding in through the wrong side, through a thinly-curtained window that had been installed as he slept. And his other window, that had been blocked up, covered by a wardrobe. And his walls! My God, someone had redecorated!

He sat up, rubbing at the glue that sealed his eyelids firmly together. The tap dancer became a football hooligan, kicking him repeatedly in the inside of his skull.

'Shit,' he groaned. Now his stomach was getting in on the act. Last night he must have argued with a wizard who'd changed his room around, put a boot-happy lunatic in his skull, filled his belly with a Force 10 gale. He lay down again and his wayward anatomy settled, though only a little. As sleep drained away, the broken fragments of his memory drifted into alignment.

Maybury, that's where he was. And he would have to get used to the sun's new aspect for this was his home now. His Leeds bedsit was empty, the keys handed back to the landlord for the new tenant, most of his worldly possessions stored in boxes in the guest bedroom of his mother's bungalow. He smiled. Despite this pig of a hangover he felt oddly contented. Opportunities awaited him; challenges; a new life. It felt like the first day of a three-year holiday.

He got up gingerly, padded across the room to his sink and splashed his face with cold water. Christ, how much had he drunk last night? Obviously more than he'd thought. Either that or someone had laced his beer with strychnine. He thought of breakfast and his stomach rolled. Well, maybe he would forego that particular delight. What time was it anyway? His introductory lecture was at ten. He hunted for his watch and eventually found it beneath the chair on which he'd dumped his clothes.

Seven-fifteen. No wonder it was so quiet. His body-clock must have woken him, informing him it was time for work. Ha! he thought. Well, that was one clock he wouldn't be needing any more. Then one of his twinges of apprehension crept up on him, took him unawares. What have I done? He quelled it almost immediately, thought of last night, of the friends he'd made.

Of Annie.

He smiled and it hurt his face. He washed carefully, dressed carefully, loath to upset the bad-tempered ogre that last night's alcohol had created inside him.

And Steph, her booming infectious laugh. And Neil, full of wry smiles and dry humour. And then there was Emma, of course — well, she was okay too. When he swallowed he could still taste her smoky kiss. He felt a little regretful that he had allowed that to happen.

He opened his window, then sat on the chair he'd cleared of clothes and browsed through his information pack. The Extra Curricular Activities (ECA) Society were holding a fair today for the freshers in the Senior Common Room. That should be interesting. He'd go along, see what was on offer. He flicked through a few more pages, then laid the folder on the floor. Reading was making him nauseous, concentrating on those little squiggles of black. He rested his head on the chair back, breathed deeply, closed his eyes. When he opened them again he was surprised to discover it was seventy minutes later.

He felt a little better. Well enough, he decided, to face breakfast. It gave him a good feeling to think that this time last week he was wearing a suit and tie, locking up his bedsit and getting into his car, bracing himself for the stressful Grand Prix that was Leeds rush-hour traffic, the mind-numbing atrophy of the office. He grinned as he laced up his trainers. They were like a symbol of his freedom. He grabbed what he would need for the morning and left his room.

He went downstairs, passing open doors where guys lounged in t-shirts and boxer shorts, some looking as bad as he felt. There was a great deal of banter, though Ian recognised that much of it was bluff — teasing and tomfoolery used to screen homesickness, the uncertainty that came from being with new people, in strange surroundings. A week from now, he thought, the banter will be genuine. He exchanged a few "Hi's", almost collided with a muscle-man who crashed out of a shower room, hair dripping, perfect body steaming like bread fresh from an oven. Someone somewhere was yodelling loudly and tunelessly. Ian shook his head, wincing. As he passed the warden's flat on the ground floor, the door opened.

'Hi,' Ian said as Duncan Westey emerged. The hall warden

jumped, as though at a hand on his shoulder, then he focussed on Ian and smiled shakily.

'Oh, hi,' he replied. 'Shit, man you gave me a shock. I'm a little delicate this morning, you know.'

'Sorry,' Ian said. Westey did indeed look delicate. His skin was white and pinched, the eye sockets dark by contrast. 'Me too,' Ian said. 'Heavy night last night, eh?' The warden looked momentarily uncomfortable, then nodded.

'Yeah,' he agreed, 'heavy night.' He turned and locked his door, pocketed the keys.

'I'm just going for some breakfast,' Ian said. 'Fancy coming?'

Westey hesitated, then shrugged and said, 'Okay, why not? You'll regret it though, I can tell you that. A couple of strips of charcoal and one of those rubber eggs from the joke shop.'

'I was thinking more of tea and toast,' said Ian. 'So where did you go last night? I didn't see you in the bar.'

'Nah, you wouldn't catch me in there,' said Westey. 'Full of bloody little first years.'

Ian looked at him and caught the humour in his red-rimmed eyes. 'Too wild for you, eh, old timer?' he said.

Westey hunched his shoulders, stooped forward and said in a quavery voice, 'What's that, son? You'll have to speak up. My ears aren't what they were.'

The two of them laughed and stepped out into the sunshine. Despite his hangover Ian felt happier than he had in a long time.

10

'Howard! Ho-warrrd!'

Howard Duffy jumped a little. 'Er . . . yes, Mum?'

'Howard, are you up yet? You don't want to be late. Don't you start teaching today?'

He put down his razor as she appeared in the bathroom's open doorway, a tiny wizened woman whose limbs seemed little more than a collection of sticks. The black cardigan draped over her bony shoulders gave her the appearance of a bat, as did the tight shrivelled features, the knobbled claws twisted around the top bar of a metal walking frame.

'Howard, what are you doing?' Her voice was harsh as fingernails on a blackboard; he saw spittle gleam in the spiny white hairs that sprouted from her chin.

He looked at himself in the bathroom mirror and his reflection looked back in blank surprise. 'I'm . . . er, shaving, Mum,' he said, feeling guilty in spite of himself. 'Just shaving, that's all.'

He was a large man in his late thirties with soft blond hair, bright blue eyes, and thick, fleshy, almost girlish lips. At that moment he was wearing a white vest which his paunch stretched tight before spilling over the elasticated waistband of his baggy blue jogging trousers. He had shaving foam smeared liberally over his throat and jowls. He shifted his substantial weight from left foot to right as he twisted his head to regard his mother.

She looked momentarily confused. Her mouth worked, a feeble aperture. Then she muttered, 'Shaving? You? . . . Oh, yes. Yes, of course. I shall want my breakfast soon, Howard. You know I need my breakfast in the morning.'

'Yes, Mum, I know,' Howard said dutifully. 'I won't be long.' He picked up his razor again and poised it above the white mask of foam like a newly-wed about to cut into the thick icing of a wedding-cake. Behind him he heard the clank and thud of the walking-frame being turned towards the top of the stairs, his mother's breath like the wet rattle of pebbles stirred around in a bucket of water.

He frowned, expelled a small sigh. Put down his razor for the second time.

'Um . . . hang on, Mum. Don't try and get down the stairs with that thing. I'll come and help you.'

39

She paused, looked back at him and smiled a toothless smile.

'Help me? Don't be silly, Howard, you've got to get on. No, no, I'll be fine. I'll make some nice bacon and eggs for breakfast, shall I?'

She turned back towards the stairs, jerked forward another few inches like a crippled insect. Howard shook his head, wiped his face on a towel and lumbered towards her. He'd been carrying her up and down stairs for almost a year now, yet every day there was the same palaver – she'd insist that she could manage by herself and he'd have to drop whatever he was doing to go to her aid. He didn't know if it was stubbornness on her part or simply a blind ignorance of her frailty that made her behave like this. What he did know was that if she ever tried to negotiate those stairs without him, both she and her walking-frame would tumble headlong.

He shuddered at this prospect, had waking nightmares about it. So far he'd been lucky, had always been in a position to go to her assistance, but what if one day he couldn't? What if one day he was sleeping, or out in the garden, or sitting on the toilet? Soon, he promised himself, he would override her protests and move all her belongings down to the sitting room. So far he'd refrained from doing so because of the vehemence of her opposition. She said she liked the view from her room, could sleep only in her large old familiar bed, but Howard knew that the real reason was that she regarded a move downstairs as giving up, as an admission that age was taking its toll, that mortality was waiting around a corner not too far away. Persuading her to use the walking-frame and the commode during the day had been hard enough, but actually evicting her from the room she'd slept in for almost fifty years would be like rubber-stamping her infirmity. Howard knew that when the time came he would need tact and courage and an awful lot of patience. So far he hadn't felt up to all that, but each day his mother became more of a liability, more of a burden, and in his heart of hearts he knew that it was now only a matter of time before the truth would have to be faced.

'Come on, Mum,' he said. 'That thing's too heavy for you. Let me give you a hand.' He placed a pudgy arm around her shoulders to support her as he gently lifted the walking-frame aside.

He bent to pick her up, felt her arms encircle him, her dry scaly long-fingered hands chafing the back of his neck. Howard cleaned and ironed his mother's clothes assiduously, yet he could never quite seem to get rid of the musty-bread smell that clung to them.

'Thank you, Howard. You're a good boy. Mummy's little helper.'

He smiled, but judiciously turned his head aside when his mother spoke to him. It seemed from her breath that there was something sour and dead inside her.

He carried her downstairs and set her on the couch in the front room. She was light as a corn dolly; another of Howard's recurrent fears was that one day he would take hold of her arm and the skin would crumble to sawdust beneath his fingers. She sat on the couch and smiled up at him, a small child in a witch's mask. Howard arranged the cushions behind her so that her back was well-supported, then switched on the television where Russell Grant, dressed in a lurid mohair jumper, was reading horoscopes.

'Ooh,' she squealed, clapping her hands together. 'I like him. What's his name again? Frank Bough?'

'Er ... Russell Grant, Mum,' Howard said, but she was waving a hand at him now, urging him to silence.

'Shh, Howard, listen. Scorpio. This is you.'

Howard listened obediently. He was informed that he had plenty of get up and go and that if he looked after the pennies the pounds would look after themselves. When his horoscope was over he said, 'You ... ah, sit here, Mum, while I finish my shave and get dressed, and then I'll make us some breakfast.'

His mother pursed her lips at him. 'Howard, you don't have to speak to me like that, you know. I'm not a child.'

He concealed a sigh. 'No, Mum, I know. I'm sorry.'

'Apology accepted,' she said and turned back to the television to listen to Pisces.

Howard went back upstairs, re-applied his shaving foam and shaved carefully. He thought of what his mother had said: that comment she had made about not being a child was ironic because in many ways that was just what she was. Howard remembered a time when she had been his comforter, his protector, but now life, it seemed, had turned full-circle and he was paying back those dues. He found the responsibility scarey, especially now when her strength and her mind were failing so rapidly. Sometimes she was fine – as lucid and sharp-witted as ever. But at other times she would throw tantrums, wet her bed, giggle like a schoolgirl on a first date, or simply forget who and where she was. At first these changes in her had been barely noticeable, dismissed with a shake of the head, a shrug of the shoulders. But now she was so unpredictable, and consequently a danger to herself, that he was permanently on tenterhooks.

His face looked raw and pink after his shave. Howard carefully applied a little of the rose and wheatgerm moisturiser he had bought for his mother last Christmas, but which she had never used because

41

she said she didn't like the idea of putting germs on her face. He went into his bedroom, carefully folded the clothes he would need for his day's lecturing, and put them in a black zip-up bag. He added a clean towel, a bag of toiletries and the book he was reading, *The Old Devils* by Kingsley Amis.

He pulled on an old blue tracksuit top with frayed elbows, zipped it up, then tied and laced his running shoes. Every day he drove to the University early and ran four laps — a mile — round the track. Though the running never seemed to change his weight at all (he had resigned himself to the fact that he was one of nature's tubbies), it made him feel good, set him up for the day. As well as the physical aspect, Howard liked the solitude of running. The air seemed to feed not simply his lungs but his mind too, seemed to flush out, temporarily at least, all his fears and insecurities.

He went downstairs, hefting the walking-frame in one hand, his bag in the other. He could hear his mother cackling in the sitting room. He stuck his head round the door. 'I'll just make some breakfast, Mum, okay?'

She looked up at him and nodded. 'All right, darling. Porridge for me, please. And don't make my tea too strong.'

It was what she said to him every morning. 'No, Mum,' Howard said and exited the room.

When breakfast was ready he went back into the sitting room and lifted his mother from the couch, letting her go only when her hands were wrapped safely around the top bar of the walking-frame. He preceded her into the kitchen, transferred her porridge from pan to bowl and buttered the toast. He was just lifting the tea cosy from the pot in readiness to pour when she hobbled into the kitchen.

He ate his cornflakes and tried not to look at his mother as she devoured her porridge. As always she was hunched over the bowl, shovelling the slimy grey pulp into her mouth like some scrawny pond creature feeding on frog spawn. The sounds she made were hideous. Howard had grown more or less used to them by now but he still found it embarrassing if someone called — the postman or the milkman — when his mother was eating. She lifted her tea cup and brought it tremblingly to her lips. When she put it down again there was a residue of porridge, like a glob of brain tissue, on the rim.

Howard was just finishing his own tea when a white-haired woman appeared in the kitchen window and waved to them. This was his mother's friend, Mrs Atkins from next door, who sat with her during the day. He stood up to let her in but she had pushed open the door and entered before he could get there.

42

'Coo-ee, it's only me,' she called unnecessarily as she stepped inside.

She had brought her knitting and her *Daily Mirror Crossword Book* with her which the old ladies claimed kept their minds active. Howard installed his mother in the sitting room, fussing round until he was certain she had everything she needed.

'Ah, right, well, um, I'll see you later then,' he said finally. 'You know where everything is, Mrs Atkins, don't you? There's ... ah, tea and coffee in the kitchen, and the number where I can be reached is by the phone. I'll try and pop back at lunchtime but I'm not promising anything. Well ... cheerio.'

The old ladies gave him little wiggle-fingered waves and smiled condescendingly. Howard realised he was being patronised and left the room, blushing. He picked up his bag, carried it outside to his rust-plagued Volkswagen Beetle and tossed it onto the passenger seat before squeezing behind the wheel. As he drove away he felt as he always did − a bright airy sense of release and, paradoxically, an irrational fear that he was leaving that which he most treasured to the mercy of some unknown threat.

11

At number 42 Cramer Road Dan Latcher had been voted the least favourite person in history. Three of the four-strong electorate were now gathered around the breakfast table, each feeling like death warmed up, each engrossed in a private fantasia of murderous thoughts in which Dan was very much the victim.

The fourth member of the quartet, Emma Chettle, was upstairs in bed, snoring gently. She had arrived home around two, been woken like the rest of them at four, and had dragged herself back to bed at seven-thirty when the typing had finally ceased.

That was half an hour ago. Since then coffee had been made and threats muttered. Catriona, Nev and Julie now sat facing each other in bleary exhausted silence, steam wreathing from their cups, corkscrewing into the air like twisted skewers of silent anger.

43

They sat that way for a long time before speech finally passed between them. Nev, clad in a Monsters of Rock t-shirt, studded wristbands, bandanna and patched jeans, roused himself and looked up. Hair swished back from his face like parting curtains. The cross, dangling from his left ear, twinkled like a glimpse of treasure. His hand reached out, curled round the coffee cup and squeezed as though it were Dan's throat.

'I'll kill him,' he muttered, not for the first time. 'I'll fucking kill the bastard.'

Julie nodded, in full accordance with the sentiment, but Catriona, whose anger was tempered with anxiety, still felt compelled to seek justification for Dan's bizarre behaviour.

'I think he's having a breakdown,' she said. 'Or he's in some sort of trouble, drugs or something. He wouldn't behave like this normally.'

Julie's hand pecked at her stylishly cropped hair like a bird re-arranging its nest. 'In that case we should talk to somebody. Call a doctor or something. Speak to his parents.'

There was no such charity in Neville's eyes. 'He'll need a fucking doctor if I get my hands on him, but not to talk to. If he doesn't unlock that door soon, I'll kick the fucker in. I mean it.'

They fell to silence again. Catriona ran her finger round the rim of her coffee cup. Finally Julie said in a tentative, slightly awed voice, 'You don't *really* think it's drugs, do you? I mean ... what sort of drugs would they be?'

Catriona looked at Julie, in part motherly affection, part amusement, part despair. Sometimes Julie was like a wide-eyed child, so naive that people who didn't know her thought she was putting it on. Catriona sometimes wondered whether she'd been raised in some castle in the clouds, protected from corrupting influences such as newspapers, television, the facts of life.

Nev waved a hand as though scattering seeds. 'Heroin, coke, could be anything,' he said. 'Maybe this guy you saw was his supplier, Cat. What did you say he called himself again? Fucking Spider or something?' Catriona nodded.

Julie said, 'But I still don't understand why Dan should start typing at four o'clock in the morning. And so fast! It sounded like a machine gun. I mean, why would he do that? If you're on drugs don't you just sit around having trips and things?'

Nev sniggered but quickly stifled it. Julie got upset if she felt she was being made fun of. 'Maybe it's speed. That fills you full of energy, makes your mind race, you know? There was this guy I knew at school, fucking nutter he was. He took some speed before

44

one of his exams and afterwards he told me the ideas had just flowed out of him; he had so many he couldn't write fast enough to get 'em all down on paper. He was really buzzing, you know? He thought he was gonna be hailed as a genius. Anyway a week later we got the exam papers back and he'd come bottom of the class with thirteen per cent or something. He was really pissed off at first but he soon saw the funny side. He showed us his exam paper and, y'know, it just didn't make sense at all. He'd written twenty-six pages in three hours and it was all just a pile of shit.'

He shook his head, snorting laughter at the memory. Catriona smiled, but Julie just looked bemused.

'So you think Dan's been taking some of this speed stuff?' she said.

Nev tossed his head, flicking hair out of his eyes. 'Dunno. It's a possibility.'

Catriona glanced towards the doorway that led into the corridor where Dan's room was. 'What are we going to do, Nev?' she said, somehow making the entire sentence sound like a sigh. 'I'm really worried about him.'

Nev tried to cultivate the image of a tough guy, but those with whom he lived knew his moody posturing was mostly a sham. His eyes softened a little. He reached out and briefly patted Catriona's hand.

'Don't worry, Cat, he'll be all right. He'll come out sometime – he still needs to eat, doesn't he? And when he does come out, we'll be fucking waiting.'

'You're not going to hurt him, are you?' Julie said, alarmed.

Nev looked embarrassed for a moment. 'Nah. But I'll make him fucking talk to me. Soon as he opens that door, I'll be in there like a fucking shot.'

'But ... but what about Uni?' said Julie. 'You've got lectures today. You can't miss those.'

'Can't I? You just watch me. I reckon this is more important than a few poxy lectures.'

Catriona nodded her agreement, then added, 'But I think if Dan's still not appeared by, say, tea-time we ought to bring someone else in on this. Like Julie says, call his parents or something.'

'Okay,' said Nev. He picked up his cup and downed his coffee in three large gulps.

'I wonder what he's using for a toilet,' said Julie suddenly.

The other two gaped at her. Julie never – but *never* – spoke of such vulgarities.

'*What*?' said Catriona, unable to keep the amazement from her voice.

Julie blushed. Catriona glared at Nev who was trying desperately to quell an eruption of laughter. Mumbling into her cup, Julie said, 'I just wondered with him, y'know, not coming out of his room since yesterday, how he'd been ... I mean what he was using ... y'know ...'

She trailed off, embarrassed. Quickly Catriona said, 'Yeah, that's a point. I wonder what he *is* using.'

'Must've got a bucket or something,' suggested Nev, making a gallant effort to remain deadpan. 'Fuck, it must really stink in there.'

Julie stood up, still blushing, still not looking at them. 'I think I'll ... er ... think I'll go and have a bath,' she said.

She left the room. Catriona and Nev looked at each other for a moment, then Nev dissolved into helpless laughter.

'Shh,' hissed Catriona. 'She'll hear you.'

Nev made a cage of his arms and buried his head in it in an attempt to stifle his mirth.

'Shh,' said Catriona again, but she was laughing now too. 'Shut up, Nev, for God's sake!'

Nev raised his head. Tears were sparkling in his eyes. 'That girl,' he gasped, 'is fucking priceless ... I don't believe her ... I mean ... I just fucking love her.'

'Prat,' grinned Catriona, poking him in the bicep. 'This is serious, Nev, remember.'

Gradually his giggles subsided. He sat up straight, took a deep breath.

'Yeah, I know,' he said. He grinned, was about to add something, when Dan's bedroom door was abruptly plucked open.

The two of them turned and gaped. Catriona felt goosebumps prickle down her arms and wondered momentarily why that should be so. Nev pushed back his chair, half stood, as a figure appeared in Dan's bedroom doorway. They both expected him to be haggard, rumpled, ill-looking. Which was why Nev muttered, 'Fuck me,' when Dan walked into the lounge.

No, not simply walked: strutted, bounced, *leaped*. Dan was dressed in his sharpest outfit (grey zoot-suit, burgundy shirt, white tie, black and white winklepickers) and appeared to be positively crackling with energy. His flat-top was gelled to perfection; his eyes were large and clear and brown. His skin was glowing; his teeth, prominently displayed due to his wide painted grin, seemed to radiate a pure marble light.

Catriona felt more goosebumps sweep across her skin but this time their motivation was not unease but desire.

'Morning, morning, morning,' Dan said effusively. 'And how are we all today?'

There was a stunned silence before Nev gathered at least a portion of his wits. In a voice that was not as cutting as he would have liked, he replied, 'Knackered, thanks to you. What the fuck have you been playing at, Dan?'

Dan's grin never wavered. His sparkling eyes flickered to focus on Catriona. She had to make a conscious effort to stop herself sighing with contentment. This is ridiculous, she thought, but her emotions seemed to refute the observation. Dan's gaze was melting the ice inside her, dissolving the anxiety, the fear, the anger, that his bizarre behaviour had wrought.

In a syrup-sweet voice he said, 'Playing at? Whatever do you mean, Neville? I don't quite follow.'

Nev felt a surge of anger superceding his surprise and was grateful for it. 'Course you fucking follow,' he snapped. 'All this staying in your room, typing at four in the morning, getting social calls from junkies. I mean, what's it all about, Dan? Why are you being so fucking weird?'

Still Dan's grin remained fixed. Still Catriona struggled with emotions like those of a lovesick adolescent confronted with a pop idol.

'Weird?' Dan seemed to spit out the word like a shred of gristle. 'I'm not being weird, Neville, I've merely been working.' He held up a large brown envelope he must have been carrying when he entered the room but which neither of them had noticed. 'A six-thousand word story,' he explained. 'Conceived and executed in a single evening.'

His eyes glittered; his body seemed to generate the menacing buzz of an electricity pylon. 'This year,' he continued, 'will be the making of me.' His eyes stared into the middle distance. Rapture held his face. 'The making of me,' he repeated softly. 'Oh yes. I have a destiny to fulfil.'

Nev looked at Catriona and surreptitiously drew circles at the side of his head with an index finger. Catriona nodded but she felt confused. Part of her wanted to be swept away by Dan's charisma. She forced her thoughts back to the practical.

'But ... but why didn't you at least say hello, Dan? Why did you lock us out?' she heard herself ask.

'I needed solitude,' he replied. 'Creation was weaving its magic within me. I could not allow it to be corrupted.'

47

'Bollocks!' spat Nev. He circled the table, fists bunched, to confront Dan. 'What are you on?' he demanded pointedly.

'On?' Dan said, amused. 'Do I assume, Neville, that you are referring to narcotics?'

'Don't come that shit with me! We know all about you, all about fucking Spider. Look at you, Dan, you're high as a kite. What are you fucking taking?'

Even confronted with outright accusations Dan continued to smile. Mildly he said, 'I'm high on life, Neville, on opportunity. I have seen such sights, experienced such revelations in the past few days. You wouldn't – you *couldn't* – understand.'

'Try me,' Nev said. 'C'mon, what have you seen? Pink elephants floating up to Heaven? Lizards crawling out of the walls? Let's have a look at that story you've written, Dan. Let's see what a literary masterpiece you've produced.'

He made a half-hearted grab for the brown envelope. With astonishing speed Dan's right arm shot out and his hand clamped around Nev's wrist. Nev howled as, with a sharp twist, Dan forced him to his knees.

'Stop it!' cried Catriona, shaken by the sudden violence. 'Stop it, you two! Dan, you're hurting him!'

Dan looked round at her, still smiling. The stink of him suddenly wafted over Catriona, making her eyes water. Eau de cologne, hair-gel, talcum powder, mouthwash. She coughed, dabbed at her eyes. Dan released Nev, who collapsed to the floor, face screwed into a knot of pain.

'I must go,' Dan said softly. 'There is much to do. Destiny beckons.'

His teeth flashed. He turned on his heels and swept from the room, from the house, slamming the front door behind him.

Trembling, Catriona slipped from her chair and knelt on the floor beside Nev. He was curled into a crescent-moon shape, moaning, cradling his wrist. 'Here, Nev, let me look,' she said, and touched him gently on the shoulder, prompting him to turn over. Nev twisted his head to look at her, tried to mask his pain, to blink away his hurt.

'That bastard,' he muttered. 'That fucking bastard. He took me by surprise, Cat. I'll fucking kill him next time.'

'Let me look at your wrist,' Catriona said again. Unwillingly Nev held his arm out for her to see.

She recoiled. Nev's flesh, where Dan had gripped it, was shockingly, impossibly, bruised. Two blue-black fingerprints, tinged in yellow and green, showed the places where Dan's index finger and thumb had dug in. But even more shocking than this was the condition of the wristband that Nev wore. The stiff black leather had been squeezed and pulled out of shape as easily as if it were made of plasticine. Even the studs which jutted from it had been flattened into tiny pats of metal.

12

Each year Paul Carmichael braced himself for the inevitable, and each year was delighted to discover that the inevitable could be postponed for another twelve months. It's bound to happen sooner or later, he thought, but as he drove in through the University gates the prospect of a new academic year filled him with familiar excitement. Not even the attitude of some of his older, more cynical colleagues would deflate his mood today. Sometimes he looked at them and thought: How long before I'm like this? Enthusiasm waning, gradually disappearing, leaving nothing but the endless grind, bitterness, disillusion?

He parked the car and got out, whistling tunelessly to himself. Hefting his briefcase he was about to cross the car park when a red Metro turned the corner and cruised sedately into a parking space, driven by a straight-backed woman whom Carmichael recognised. Being in a good mood, Carmichael waved and received a tight-lipped smile in response. He waited as the woman cut the engine, collected her things together, got out of the car and came towards him.

'Good morning, Miss Trent,' Carmichael said effusively, 'and how are you this fine morning?'

The woman produced another restrained smile in response to his greeting. 'Perfectly well, Mr Carmichael,' she replied.

'Good,' said Carmichael. 'And how was your summer? Did you do anything exciting?'

'My summer was satisfactory, thank you. "Restful" is probably the most appropriate word to describe it.'

'Did you go on holiday this year?'

'Not as such. I spent a week with an old aunt in Cornwall. She has a cottage there. It was most pleasant.'

'Ah, yes,' Carmichael said, 'the Cornish coast is a lovely part of the country. So I take it you're fresh and ready to face the rigours of a new term?'

Miss Trent tilted her head a little and the corners of her mouth twitched into a smile once again. 'As ready as I'll ever be, Mr Carmichael,' she said. 'And how about you? How was your summer?'

They made smalltalk as they crossed the carpark, a somewhat incongruous couple. They were both in their mid-thirties, yet whilst Carmichael looked younger, Jayne Trent projected the image of an ageing spinster. She wore high-necked, long-sleeved dresses that invariably reached her ankles. Her hair was scraped tightly back from her head and drawn into a solid bun at the crown. She wore no make-up on her pale, lightly-freckled face. She taught History, and sometimes Carmichael imagined that she had stepped right out of it, a Victorian governess trapped in an alien twentieth century.

In truth, Jayne Trent intrigued Carmichael; he found her something of an enigma. Whenever he spoke to her he couldn't help but lapse into a formal, slightly archaic mode of speech which he supposed was a kind of gentle mockery. Perhaps it was to do with the impression she gave him that she somehow mocked herself. He had a constant urge to pull the pins from her hair and watch it tumble about her shoulders, wished that just once he could see her dressed in bright, loose, trendy clothes. Though not vain, Carmichael cared about his own appearance; he favoured snug designer jeans, linen suits, bought Lacoste shirts, sweaters from Benetton. He kept his hair and moustache neatly trimmed, thought beard stubble was neither rugged nor masculine but simply an excuse for sloppiness. He wondered if he would have been so image-conscious had he been married. He wondered too what Jayne Trent would look like if she *really* laughed.

Their route took them past a small annexe which served as a music room, and which was linked to the back of the main university building by a high-walled wooden enclosure. The university kitchens backed on to the enclosure, which housed six large industrial dustbins on castors into which all the kitchen refuse was dumped. Normally the door in the wooden fencing was closed, but as the two of them passed Carmichael noticed it was open and he glanced inside. He couldn't quite believe he had seen what he thought he had, and was given no time to confirm his first impression as the door was slammed in his face.

'Hey,' he said, coming to a halt.

Surprised, Jayne Trent stopped too. She had not seen what Carmichael had, and at first thought his exclamation was directed at her. Then she saw him march over to the closed wooden door and reach for the handle. 'Whatever's the matter, Mr Carmichael?' she asked.

Carmichael turned back. He looked both a little confused and a little embarrassed.

'I'm not sure,' he said. 'This door was open when we came past. I looked inside and saw ... something. Or thought I did. But I can't have. It's ... it's ridiculous.'

He turned the handle and pushed the door. It came open easily. He stepped into the kitchen yard, Jayne Trent following. The bins smelled faintly of overripe fruit. The yard was clearly empty; there was nowhere to hide.

'Strange,' said Carmichael, looking around.

Jayne Trent turned her nose up and her mouth down at the smell. 'What is it you thought you saw, Mr Carmichael?' she asked a little tersely.

Carmichael turned to her and abruptly barked a laugh. 'It sounds idiotic ... and pretty unpleasant. It must have been my imagination.'

'What *was* it?' Jayne Trent asked again, evidently beginning to find this whole episode rather tiresome.

'It was ... I looked in here, and I saw ... a boy, a teenager. Pretty scruffy, spiky white hair, tatty clothes. He was squatting by one of these bins, and he had something in his hands and he was eating it.' He stopped and laughed a little half-heartedly, seemingly reluctant to go on.

Jayne Trent appeared singularly unimpressed. 'It's possible, I suppose,' she said, 'a vagrant looking for scraps. There's another door there that leads out on to the playing fields. He must have gone that way.'

Carmichael shook his head as though she'd missed the point. 'No, no,' he said, 'it wasn't the fact that he was here, it was what he was eating.' He waved a hand and grimaced as though in silent, pre-emptive apology. 'It was squirming, Miss Trent. It was alive. I could have sworn it was a rat.'

Jayne Trent seemed to retract her head in disgust, her chin pulling back into her neck. 'That's repulsive, Mr Carmichael,' she said, as if he had just told the sickest joke she had ever heard.

'I know, but you did ask. That was what it looked like.' He shrugged, attempting to make light of the incident, and wandered

51

across to the other door which Miss Trent had indicated. He wasn't particularly interested in catching the boy – he wouldn't know what to do with him if he did – but he did want to satisfy his curiosity. He hoped he'd been wrong about the rat. He must have been, he assured himself, though the split-second image of the boy tearing at the furry, wriggling body with his teeth was sharp as a photograph in his mind.

He reached the other door and pushed it open. A grassy bank sloped gently down to a footpath, a hedge, and then to a level patch of ground on which were the first of the university's three football pitches. A running track circled the pitch, and on the track a single figure – blue as an ink stain, kicking up dust – could be seen ploughing his lonely furrow. However of the rat-eating vagabond there was no sign. In the midst of all this green he should surely have stuck out like a bloodspot on a bedsheet. Carmichael turned his head, aware of Jayne Trent at his shoulder. Her look was sceptical.

'Well?'

'I did see *someone*,' Carmichael insisted. 'I know I did. It wasn't the wind that slammed the door in my face.'

'A member of the kitchen staff perhaps, closing the door before going back inside?'

If she had not sounded so dubious, Carmichael might have let the matter rest. As it was he began to descend the grassy slope towards the jogger, determined to prove that he was not a man given to flights of fancy.

The runner, he saw, was Howard Duffy, an Economics lecturer at the university. He was plodding gamely round the track, red face shiny with sweat, reminding Carmichael of the tortoise whose steadiness won the race with the hare.

'Howard,' Carmichael called, raising a hand as Duffy rounded the bend and came towards him. Duffy glanced up, obviously startled from some reverie. 'Howard, may I have a word? It won't take a minute.'

It was obvious from Duffy's expression that he did not welcome this break in his routine. However he panted to a halt, placing his hands on his knees and bowing his head as if about to throw up. 'What is it?'

Carmichael decided to forego the usual pleasantries. 'Have you seen a boy while you've been running, coming from the direction of the kitchens? White spiky hair, scruffy. He may have been holding an animal in his hands.'

Duffy raised his head and looked at Carmichael a moment as if uncertain whether the request was genuine. Finally he said, 'No, I haven't. I hadn't seen anyone at all before you came along. It's been very peaceful.'

The insinuation was obvious. Carmichael sighed and said, 'All right, Howard, thanks anyway. Sorry to disturb your run.'

Duffy grunted and began jogging again. He looked a little stiff at first but quickly regained his rhythm.

At the top of the slope Jayne Trent was waiting for Carmichael but looked as if she would rather be elsewhere. 'No luck, I take it?'

'No,' admitted Carmichael. 'I don't understand it, I'm certain I saw someone.'

'Ah, well,' said Jayne glibly. 'I'm sure there's some perfectly reasonable explanation.' She looked at her watch, too casual for the gesture to be spontaneous. 'If you don't mind, I really must get on. I have a number of things to prepare before my opening lecture.'

Carmichael nodded. 'Okay. Perhaps I'll see you later. Thanks for humouring me.'

Jayne Trent smiled tightly and hurried away.

For a minute or two after she had gone, Carmichael stood at the top of the slope and turned to look out across the fields once more. A breeze smelling of grass riffled his hair, set bushes murmuring like restless sleepers. Howard Duffy continued to plod around the track, constant as the second hand on a watch. The scene was peaceful, idyllic even, yet Carmichael's earlier mood of well-being had soured a little inside him. The mystery of the white-haired boy, and the unpleasant image that lingered in his mind, made him feel unsettled, a little nauseous. He hoped a few moments spent gazing at nature, breathing it in, would dispel his feeling of distaste — but at last, resignedly, he turned and walked back to the University.

53

13

Ian felt as though he'd been transported ten years back through time. It was so weird sitting in a classroom again. True, the desk on which he rested his elbows was modern, streamlined, graffiti-free, more like the desk in his office than the battered wooden structures he'd been used to at school (inkwells stuffed with pencil shavings, chewing gum and worse stuck on the underside), but there was still more than enough in here to prompt a rose-tinted glow of nostalgia.

The blackboard, for instance, with its ridge at the bottom containing a few sticks of broken chalk and a chunky blackboard rubber; the posters on the walls advertising various RSC productions; the large square cupboards at the back of the room which doubtless contained dog-eared textbooks and the like. Ian smiled secretly as he watched other members of the group enter and sit down. He imagined someone scrawling something obscene on the blackboard before "Sir" arrived, or producing a bendy ruler with which to start flicking paper pellets.

Breakfast had revived him. After the first mouthful of toast Ian had felt his stomach settling, and now his headache was almost gone too. Duncan Westey had been good company, though Ian couldn't help feeling that something was troubling him. More than once, during breaks in their conversation, Ian had glanced up and had caught him sighing deeply or staring into his bowl of cornflakes. Twice Ian had almost asked him if something was the matter but both times had chickened out. If Westey wanted to talk about it, he would, he assured himself. There was no reason to embarrass them both by probing too deeply; after all, he hardly knew the guy.

He looked up with anticipation as the door opened once more, and smiled as Annie walked into the room. She looked uncertain, tremulous even, but returned Ian's smile when she noticed him. If anything she looked paler than yesterday, as though her sleep had not been restful. She moved between the desks, murmuring demure excuse-mes. She was dressed in a white blouse, pale blue cotton trousers and a pale blue cardigan. Over her shoulder she carried a canvas bag emblazoned with the words "World Wildlife Fund" and a drawing of a panda chewing a stick of bamboo.

'I got lost,' she said, slipping the bag from her shoulder and sitting down. 'I was afraid I was going to be late.'

Ian looked at his watch. 'No, perfect timing,' he told her. 'How's the stomach this morning? Any better?'

Annie blushed a little and nodded. 'Yes, thanks,' she said, and bent to rummage in her bag as if she didn't want to discuss it. A young man with a moustache entered the room. At first Ian assumed he was a student. He was surprised when the man perched himself on the edge of the tutor's desk and said, 'Right then. Are we all here?'

The next hour passed quickly and pleasurably, Mr Carmichael proving to be witty, easy-going, instantly likeable. A couple of times during the lecture Ian glanced at Annie, trying to judge whether she was enjoying it as much as he was. He couldn't decide whether she was engrossed in the tutor's words or her own thoughts; she was watching Carmichael talk, her face expressionless, chin resting on her left hand. As they filed out of the room and into the corridor, Ian asked Annie what she had thought of the lecture.

'Oh ... it was good,' she said as if the question had surprised her. 'The course sounds interesting. Mr Carmichael's nice.'

Ian said, 'Are you settling in a bit more now?'

Annie wrinkled her nose. 'I suppose so,' she said unconvincingly. 'How about you?'

'Yeah,' said Ian, 'I think it's great.' Then he cursed himself for sounding so enthusiastic. If Annie thought that everyone but her was having a wonderful time, it could only make her feel worse. In an attempt to change the subject he asked hastily, 'How was Steph this morning?'

'Oh, you know,' said Annie, 'like a whirlwind as usual. Kept going on about how *wonderful* Neil was, how they had hit it off immediately, how he understood her needs. She ...' Annie paused, not sure whether to go on. She did so, but hesitantly. 'She ... well, she was a bit direct for me. I mean ... well ... you know.'

She blushed. Ian said, 'Mmm.' They were silent for a minute.

Then Annie asked, 'How about you? Did you enjoy last night?'

Ian picked up on the veiled tone of the question. He glanced at Annie to see that she was observing the expression on his face. Her blush deepened and she looked away.

'Er ... yes,' he said. 'Yes, it was good. Had a bit of a hangover this morning.'

'I hear that ... well, that is, Steph told me that ... well, that you and Emma seemed to get on quite well.'

Now it was Ian's turn to blush. He cursed Steph's big mouth.

'Well, all right,' he said. 'Y'know, Steph was off with Neil so I talked to Emma, that's all.'

55

Annie made an "Oh-I-see" face. Too casually she asked, 'Will you be seeing her again?'

Ian shrugged. 'I don't think so. That is, we haven't arranged anything.' He wanted to say more, to tell Annie exactly how he felt, but it was too soon: the words stuck in his throat.

'Oh,' she said non-committally. They descended the stairs at the end of the corridor, each pretending they were concentrating too hard on not falling down them to speak. At the bottom they both started talking at once.

'I was going – ' said Ian.

'I said I'd – ' said Annie.

They stopped talking simultaneously. Ian laughed. 'Go on,' he said. 'You first.'

Annie smiled, more convincingly than before. 'I told Steph I'd meet her in the coffee bar at eleven. Would you like to come too?'

'Yeah, sure,' said Ian. 'What I was going to say was: I'd planned to go to this ECA Fair in the Senior Common Room, maybe join a few clubs or something. But the Fair goes on till one, so there'll be time for a coffee first. Maybe we can all go together afterwards?'

'Mm,' said Annie. She turned, flicking a long strand of gold-brown hair behind her ear, and looked around for the sign to the coffee bar. Ian saw it and pointed it out to her, resting a hand lightly on her upper arm as he did so. She didn't flinch from his touch as he'd feared she might. He felt a wriggle of pleasure at even this amount of physical contact.

'Come on then,' said Annie shyly, and hefted the bag into a better position on her shoulder.

They followed the signs until they arrived at the coffee bar, which was a hub of activity. Nevertheless they heard Steph's greeting almost immediately. 'Annie! Ian! Over here!' Her voice carried, encouraging roughly half the people in the coffee bar to turn and stare at the new arrivals. Subjected to such scrutiny the two of them cringed and scurried across the floor, red-faced.

'Did you have to shout like that, Steph?' Annie said in a soft voice as she and Ian reached the table where her room-mate was holding court. 'Everyone looked at us.'

'Sorry,' said Steph, though it was obvious from her expression that she didn't know what the fuss was about. She took Annie's hand and squeezed it, whilst with her other hand she gestured flamboyantly behind her. 'Grab a couple of chairs and come and sit down,' she said. 'Everyone's dying to meet you.'

"Everyone" meant the six or eight people crammed around a

table littered with styrofoam cups, crumpled paper bags, empty crisp packets and chocolate bar wrappers. Annie glanced at Ian with misery in her eyes. He looked at her sympathetically: even he felt a little intimidated by Steph's (entirely innocent) habit of directing attention at you when you were least expecting it. Ian guessed that Annie would probably have been much happier picking her way slowly and carefully through the first couple of weeks, keeping a low profile, developing friendships at her own speed. But with Steph around that was impossible. She was all for cramming as much as she could into the smallest amount of time, and being the scatty, generous soul she was, she liked to share her exhilaration, to carry as many people as she could along on her tide of joy.

'Would you like a drink or anything?' Ian asked Annie.

'I'll have a coffee,' she replied. 'Decaffeinated if they've got it.'

'Milk and sugar?'

'Milk, yes, but no sugar.'

Ian poked Neil Gardener in the back as he walked past. Neil turned and grinned, slapped half-heartedly at the prodding finger. Standing in the queue at the coffee counter, Ian watched Annie as she carried two chairs to the table and set them down to the right of Steph. The red-haired girl waved an arm. Ian heard her cry, 'Shift round everyone,' and smiled as they all complied, marvelling again at Steph's brash self-confidence and sense of guileless manipulation, the aura she exuded which caused people to gravitate towards her.

He returned to the table with two steaming styrofoam cups and a paper bag which was speckled with grease from the doughnut inside. He gave one of the cups to Annie and placed the other on the table in front of him, sliding it along so that it created a furrow in the debris. He took the doughnut from the bag, bit into it and then wished he'd waited. Steph began to introduce her new-found friends; Ian was forced to return greetings with greasy doughnut sticking to his teeth, sugar around his mouth and jam squidging over his fingers.

Once the preliminaries were out of the way he, Annie and Neil were all but excluded from the conversation. The three of them sat and listened to the discussion on drama, their gazes growing blanker by the second. Steph, animated and vociferous, seemed unaware of their detachment. When Ian turned to Annie and murmured, 'I thought they were all dying to meet us,' she merely raised her eyebrows and shrugged, though in truth Ian guessed she was quite content to sit there unobtrusively.

He bought himself a Coke and a Mars Bar and another cup of coffee for Annie. He looked around, lending only half an ear to the conversation, which seemed to be about Mickey Rourke and someone he'd never heard of. He was supposed to keep off junk food due to his asthma, but ten minutes after he'd finished his Mars Bar he bought himself a bag of peanuts from the snack dispenser. On the way back he stopped behind Neil, placed a hand on each of his shoulders and leaned over to speak to him.

'Me and Annie are thinking of going to this ECA Fair in a couple of minutes. Do you fancy coming?'

Neil nodded. 'Gladly. I'll see if Steph wants to come.' He tapped her on the arm to gain her attention and began to speak to her in a low voice.

Two minutes later the four of them were standing up, Steph still talking, still continuing the debate. Ian, Annie and Neil hovered like minders. 'See you later in the bar,' Steph called finally. She waved as though her friends were on a train, disappearing into the distance.

'Yeah, see you, Steph.' 'Bye, Steph.' She grinned and waved again, buoyed by acceptance. 'Er ... nice to meet you too,' a lean, unshaven student with a ponytail told Ian.

'Yeah,' said Ian with a false smile. He couldn't remember whether this was Frank or Simon; he didn't much care. They left behind the smell of cheese burgers and bacon rolls, the click of pool balls, the mindless jangle of video machines. They didn't leave behind the animated chatter of student voices, however. If anything it was louder in the Senior Common Room than it had been in the coffee bar.

The ECA Fair resembled a church bazaar. Tables lined every wall of the large long room, each belonging to a club or society within the university. It was a colourful occasion. Many of the clubs had decorated their stands with streamers or banners or something befitting their status. The Railway Enthusiasts had set their stand on a piece of railway track with an enormous black and white poster behind them depicting the head-on view of a steam train roaring out of a tunnel; the Doctor Who Appreciation Society had a life-sized model TARDIS and a representative dressed as Tom Baker who was offering free jelly babies to the passers-by. The Nasty Film Society, which Ian joined on the spur of the moment, had a seven-foot tall stand-up cardboard model of Pinhead from *Hellraiser*, an enormous poster for Cronenberg's *The Fly*, and was giving away a free rubber monster with each membership.

There were more conventional societies too – political parties, religious groups and sports clubs. Steph eagerly dragged Neil over to the Drama Society stand whilst Ian and Annie perused what the Literary Society had to offer.

Ian picked up a copy of *David Copperfield* bound in soft red leather, the pages edged in gold leaf. 'May I?' he asked the silent po-faced man behind the table. The man nodded, albeit reluctantly. Ian handled the book as if it were a wounded butterfly.

'Look at this, Annie,' he said, passing it to her. 'Isn't it beautiful? Do you fancy joining? It's only ten quid a year.' He hoped he didn't sound over-eager. He'd wanted her to join the Nasty Film Society with him — he'd envisaged comforting her while she clung to him in terror in a dark cinema (very macho!) — but she had declined with a small smile.

'Mm,' she said, 'it's nice.' She gave the book no more than a cursory examination before, to Ian's disappointment, replacing it on the table.

'Not your scene? Too stuffy?' he joked. Apeing the movements of a fawning shop assistant, he stooped, gave a flamboyant "after you" gesture and continued, 'No matter. I'm sure we have something in stock that will suit, madam.'

Annie smiled but half-heartedly. Ian straightened and placed a hand lightly in the small of her back.

'Hey,' he said, 'you all right?'

Annie shrugged, pulled a face. 'Yeah,' she sighed.

'But?' prompted Ian.

She looked at him. His expression was earnest, concerned. Her sudden smile was more genuine than the last but sadder too.

'What do you think of Steph?' she asked cautiously.

Ian was surprised by the question. 'Steph? Well ... I think she's great. Why?'

Annie sighed. 'Do you think she and I will get on?' she said.

Aha, thought Ian, here's the crux. In truth he had been wondering the same thing in the coffee bar. However he said, 'Yeah, of course. Why shouldn't you? She's a bit loud, granted, but you could do a lot worse, you know.'

Annie nodded. 'Yeah, I know. It's just ... well, we're like chalk and cheese. You saw what it was like with all her drama friends. I just couldn't talk to them. I couldn't think of anything to say, and to tell you the truth, I didn't really want to. I'm just worried that we'll start getting on each other's nerves after a while.'

Ian offered what he hoped was a reassuring smile. He felt an urge to hug Annie, but wasn't sure how she would take the gesture. 'I know it's probably not much consolation, but try not to worry about it,' he said. 'I mean, you've only known each other for a day. Things are still pretty weird. It doesn't help that Steph's one of these people who can settle into a new situation straight away and get on with everybody. It makes you feel as though you're sort of trailing behind, doesn't it?' He had been about to say "inadequate" but amended himself at the last second. He saw Annie nodding slightly.

'Give it a couple of weeks, take things slowly, see what happens,' he continued. 'Maybe you two'll come to some sort of compromise. Or maybe you'll just be, y'know, casual friends. You'll live together but you'll see other people, move in different circles, that kind of thing. I mean, just because you're room-mates doesn't mean you have to be bosom buddies, does it? As long as you get on reasonably well, that's what counts.'

He was pleased to see that his words were having some effect; the anxious look was easing a little from Annie's face. To Ian's surprise and delight she abruptly stood on tip-toes and kissed him on the cheek. 'Thanks, Ian.' she said. 'You're right, I'm worrying about nothing. I'm glad you're old and mature. You can give me advice when I'm being stupid.'

Ian looked at her and grinned, further delighted by the mischievous expression which had replaced the troubled one. She had confided in him and was now making jokes at his expense. Progress indeed! A sure sign that the barriers were coming down, that there was the prospect of a real friendship developing between them.

And more? Could he hope for that? Or was he blundering into this too quickly? Only time would tell. For now, Ian knew simply that he enjoyed Annie's company and that he found her attractive, though admittedly some of that attraction (how much?) was due to her sense of vulnerability, to her aura of little-girl-lost, which she would surely shed within the next few weeks.

'*Boo*!'

They both jumped as they were leaped on from behind. They heard Steph hooting with laughter before they turned and saw her. 'Very amusing, Miss Peele,' said Ian, ruffling her red hair, making her laugh all the more. Neil was grinning, standing a little way off as though disclaiming responsibility for Steph's actions.

'Did you join anything?' Annie asked shyly.

'Steph joined the Drama Society,' said Neil. 'Wound them all round her little finger as usual. I reckon she's assured of all the female leads from now on.' There was a sense of pride to his voice. 'I came to see if Ian wanted to take a look at the squash and tennis clubs. We were talking about playing last night.'

'Yeah, sure,' said Ian. 'How about you two? Annie? Fancy a knock-around on the tennis courts?'

'Way-hey!' cried Steph bawdily. 'That's an offer you can't refuse!'

A bearded man beneath a banner which read: "Join the New Moralists" glared at her. Steph winked at him. Annie blushed.

'Er . . . no,' she murmured. 'You and Neil go. Me and Steph'll wait here.'

'Okay,' said Ian. 'Come on, Neil.' They shouldered their way into the press of bodies and were soon swallowed up.

'Are you going to join anything?' Steph asked.

Annie shrugged. 'I might, if I see anything I fancy.'

'What about Ian Raven?'

'What?'

'Well, you fancy him, don't you?'

Annie's blush, which had barely faded from a moment ago, instantly reappeared. 'I've only just met him,' she protested.

'So? I've only just met Neil but I fancy him like mad. In fact, I've seen quite a few blokes I could go for. Don't tell Neil that.'

Annie said nothing.

'You *do* fancy him, don't you?' Steph coaxed.

'*Steph*!' Annie exclaimed, half-turning away. She was silent for a moment, then she mumbled, 'Well . . . he is nice, isn't he?'

Steph smiled. 'Yeah,' she said, 'he's a nice fella.' She put an arm around Annie's shoulder and gave her a squeeze. 'Come on, let's have a look around. I want to join some more clubs.'

They shuffled along with the crowd, browsing like pensioners at a jumble sale. Annie joined the University branch of Greenpeace and picked up some leaflets at the Anti-Vivisection League table. She would have joined if the softly spoken student with the intense eyes who claimed to be the League's treasurer hadn't made her so uneasy. Steph joined the Dinghy Sailing Club ("something to do on Sunday mornings") and the Cheese and Wine Society ("for a bit of culture").

They were about to head back to where they had parted from Ian and Neil when Steph exclaimed, 'Hey, Annie, this looks interesting.'

Annie turned, a query on her lips, but Steph was already pushing her way through the crowd again. Annie sighed, raised her eyes to Heaven, and followed.

Steph had stopped by a table which was bare save for a neat stack of business cards in the centre. As Annie reached her, Steph was reading one of the cards, a slight squint betraying the fact that she normally wore spectacles. 'I noticed all these and wondered what they were,' she explained. Handing over the card she held she picked up another for herself. 'It's really wacky. Read it.'

Annie did so. These words were on the card:

THE CRACK
MAGIC, MIND-GAMES AND INSIGHTS
COME ALONG! BROADEN YOUR HORIZONS!

'What does it mean?' she asked.

'Dunno,' said Steph. 'Sounds exciting, though, doesn't it?'

Annie shivered. 'Sounds a bit creepy to me.'

Steph shrugged. 'I wonder whether it's –' she began.

Then they both jumped as a voice behind them murmured, 'A very good morning to you, ladies.'

As Annie whirled her long hair swept across her face, obscuring her vision for a second. She tossed it aside with a practised flick of the head, revealing the man who had spoken. He was tall and slim with a gleaming bristle of hair, and skin that seemed to glow from within with a weird alabaster light. He was immaculately dressed. His brown eyes glittered like gemstones.

For once thrown out of her stride, Steph stammered, 'Who ... who are you?'

Annie took an involuntary step back as the man smiled, revealing teeth which flashed like cat's-eyes.

He shot out a long pale hand which Steph automatically took.

'Dan Latcher,' he replied in a honey-sweet voice. 'Welcome to The Crack.'

14

There was an argument that the older one became, the swifter time sped on; that life was comparable to a downhill journey in a vehicle without brakes. As a child a day could seem a week, a week a month, a month a year, whereas with the encroaching spectres of age and infirmity the opposite became true.

Jayne Trent had never subscribed to that viewpoint. In her experience each year seemed longer than the one before. She had a fear that one day time would simply stop, trapping her in an endless hovering moment. That for her would be Hell; to be snagged in eternity, to have no hope of escape from the mediocre shell of her life.

Life. Ha! The word was a cruel joke. Jayne Trent did not live, she merely existed. She had no real idea why this should be the case, why Fate had cast her in the role of Lonely Old Spinster. There were many, of course, who chose this role, who treasured their solitude, who made a conscious decision to remain independent of the bonds of family. But Jayne Trent had never done so. There was nothing in her life precious enough that she would resist sharing it.

So what had happened? Where had she gone wrong? These were questions that bewildered Jayne as much as anyone. The seeds of one's growth were often to be found in childhood, but Jayne's childhood had been happy, normal; religious, yes, but not overly so. She had had friends, she had been denied nothing. Sex, of course, had been a taboo subject, but this was before the swinging sixties, the age of enlightenment, and talk of sex was taboo in almost every household. Boyfriends had been neither encouraged nor discouraged; her parents had stated a desire to meet any prospective suitor but this again was neither uncommon nor unreasonable.

No, the problem (if problem it could be termed; she herself saw it as such) lay in Jayne herself. Sometimes she believed she had been born with a sense of morality that was a century behind the times. But awareness of this fact did not eradicate it. It was like being born with a harelip; it was something one had to accept and come to terms with.

She had found – and invariably still did – the vast majority of the male population to be shallow, brutish and immature. As a teenager she had begun to grow away from her friends the instant they began to giggle and simper over half the boys in school. She had found puberty more distressing and embarrassing than most, had been certain she would die of shame each week when she was forced to undress for gym in the company of her peers, and had felt an almost physical disgust whenever she was confronted with foul language and sexual innuendo.

These attitudes had been natural and instinctive. Reflecting on them later, Jayne wondered whether there was something wrong with her. Classmates began to whisper names behind her back, names like "prude" and "Old Maid Trent" and "Jayne the Pain", names which cut deeply, sent her scuttling for solace, for somewhere to hide.

She found her hiding-place in study, and history in particular. To be embroiled in past centuries, in a way of life that time had reduced to dust and memories − there was something comforting in that, something secure. Jayne had moved through the rest of her school life with her head down, invariably buried in some book or other. She sailed easily through every examination she ever took, applied for and was immediately accepted by Nottingham University.

She entered University in 1963, eager and hopeful. Things will be different here, she thought. There will be people I can talk to, people whose opinions and outlooks I'll share. She was wrong. If anything, she found University even more intimidating than school. She was faced with Beatlemania, the Pill, talk of revolution and a fashion culture that she was neither able nor had any desire to understand.

She graduated in 1966, but it was a further two years before she had her first real boyfriend. She was a twenty-three-year-old infants' teacher, Roger a thirty-year-old archeologist whose wife had been killed in a car accident two years earlier. Roger's four-year-old daughter, Petra, was one of Jayne's pupils. They met at a Parents' Evening and found, to their delight, that they shared a passion for the past. Unfortunately this was the only passion that they did share. Ninety per cent of their relationship was spent in muddy holes digging for slivers of pottery with numbed fingers. Beyond this, their involvement was awkward, directionless. It came to a head one evening when, after dinner at Roger's house, he began without warning to kiss her ear and to paw at her breasts through the high-necked blouse that she wore. So shocked had she been that all she could think of to say was, 'Petra's upstairs.'

'She's asleep,' he'd answered, his fingers fumbling with her buttons.

She'd batted his hand away, shot to her feet and glared at him. 'I don't want this!' she had cried.

He'd said something then, something she couldn't now remember, something belittling and hurtful and crude. And she'd known in

64

that moment that he was exactly like all the rest. She'd grabbed her handbag and her jacket and had stormed out of the house, walked the four miles to her home in the dark. He hadn't followed her, though he'd phoned her three times during the following week in an attempt to make amends. She had never seen him again.

She'd joined Maybury University in 1982 at the age of thirty-seven. She'd been out with four men by this time, but had become serious with none of them. Her instinct had always been to hold back, to keep a cool distance, not to reveal too much about herself, which in each case had incapacitated an always limping relationship. One of the men, a dentist called James, had told her she was a "prick teaser". Jayne had been astounded and shocked, physically repelled by the notion. When James had finally left her house on that awful evening, Jayne had rushed to the bathroom and had scrubbed herself thoroughly beneath the suds of a hot bath. She'd felt dirtied by his language, tainted by his gutter-filth mind.

Now, at the age of forty-four, she was still single, still a virgin, and still, she had to admit, searching for Mr Right. Sometimes she felt proud of her abstinence and dogged resolve not to make do with second best, but not often. Most of the time she felt desperate, angry, and a self-loathing so acute that twice she had sought medical advice. There were times when she felt on the verge of erupting, when she felt all the poison inside her would come bubbling out like pus from a boil.

But it never did. She had conditioned herself so rigidly over the years that she was now finding it increasingly difficult to express even the most basic of emotions. She had caged herself, concealed her impulses beneath an unyielding crust of restraint, just as she concealed her body beneath the heavy voluminous dresses which she locked tightly with buttons and buckles and clasps.

She sighed. Whenever she was alone, which was often, her mind swirled constantly with these thoughts. It seemed there were a hundred flies trapped inside her head, forever buzzing, forever rebounding against the inside wall of her skull in a desperate bid for freedom. But however much self-analysis she engaged in, it never seemed to make any difference. She could never be happy until she could shed the cloying skin which surrounded her, but to do that would be to cast off, to disown, everything that she was.

Still, she thought, as she turned her head to focus on the empty classroom, at least there were some things to be thankful for. At least the endless unbearable summer was over and a new term had begun. No more spending long hot days in the library, working on personal projects which she tried to convince herself were important and fulfilling but which in truth were merely desperate time-fillers.

She stood up slowly, circled her desk, and approached the walk-in storeroom at the back of the class. Her sensible flat-heeled shoes tapped loudly on the polished wood floor. To her right, milky light spilled through a row of tall windows through which she could see the flat grey roof of the gymnasium and a huddle of prefabricated huts. She extracted a key from the pouch-like pocket on the front of her dress and opened the door.

She stepped inside. The storeroom was gloomy and dusty. It smelled of chalk and paper and wood. It was nothing but a narrow corridor stretching back twelve feet, the walls on either side lined with heavily stacked shelves. Jayne looked around for the large box of slides she knew were kept in here somewhere and one of the plastic circular slide-drums. At half-past one her third years would be coming in to begin a course on Victorian England, and Jayne liked to give them a feel of the period before she began to bombard them with names and dates and events. Not that she believed for one moment that her students would actually learn anything new from these slides – watching an episode of *Sherlock Holmes* or a dramatisation of *Jack the Ripper* would probably have proved just as useful. But experience had taught Jayne that the first few days of any new term were an academic washout. For students this was a time for renewing acquaintances, of throwing themselves back into the social swing. Academia took a back seat to all this: groundwork and gentle introductions were the order of the day, not a full-blooded leap on to the treadmill.

She saw the box of slides on the topmost shelf to her right and reached up on tip-toes to lift it down. Looking into the box she frowned in annoyance; the slides were all higgledy-piggledy. Mr Keating must have had them last. He was the most slovenly man Jayne knew. It would take her the rest of the morning and most of her lunch-hour to sort out the ones she wanted. Sighing, she looked around for a slide-drum just as a dark shadow filled the storeroom doorway.

At first she thought the door must be swinging closed on her and turned, irritated. She gasped and almost dropped the box of slides when she realised the light was being blocked by the silhouette of a man. He was plump, dressed in a drab suit, his bald pink head like a planet in shadow. He took a purposeful, almost mincing step forward. His eyes were green and predatory as a cat's.

'Who are you?' said Jayne. She was surprised by the coolness of her voice, and all too aware of the claustrophobic confines of the storeroom.

66

A fat pink tongue oozed out to moisten fleshy lips. 'I am your Destiny,' he crooned.

Jayne struggled for speech. She backed up against the wall as the man advanced. She held up the box of slides as though it were a bomb she was all too willing to detonate.

'Get away from me,' she whispered at last, 'get away from me or ...'

'Yes?'

'Or I'll scream.'

The man halted, tilted his head coquettishly. 'Try,' he said. 'Try to scream. I'd like to hear that.'

The invitation was worse than a hand smothering her mouth. Suddenly she was certain that she would be unable to make a sound.

'I mean it,' she whispered ineffectually. 'You just ... look ... just leave. Let me out. Please. I have work to do.'

She was aware of the ridiculous futility of her plea. The man grinned, unsheathing teeth which had been filed to cannibal points. In the gloom, Jayne could clearly see the flickers of yellow light which danced around and between the teeth like St Elmo's Fire. She dropped the slide box which made a sound like a hammer cracking a skull. Slides spilled everywhere.

'I'll help you to scream, shall I?' said the man. 'I'll give you something to scream about.'

Jayne tried to scream. She tried and tried. But she remained silent even when his hands came up and began to remove his face.

15

Annie and Steph ascended three flights of stairs and walked up and down the same corridor four times before they finally found the room they were looking for. It was Steph who noticed the sign "G7 leading to G8".

'Here, Annie,' she said, pointing, and pushed the door open without hesitation, 'come on.'

Annie pulled a face and followed. She'd been secretly hoping that they wouldn't find the room at all. The last time they had walked up this corridor she'd said, 'I'm fed up of this, Steph. Let's give up and go to the bar.'

'Just once more,' said Steph. 'I'm sure we'll find it this time.'

And they had.

The room they entered, G7, was an empty dusty classroom. Mathematics equations had been scrawled on the blackboard and partially erased. Outside it was dusk, the darkening sky filled with blue-black clouds which reminded Annie of a school of whales sliding majestically through the ocean. The classroom seemed drained of light — desks, chairs, cupboards, walls and floor slowly blending into a coagulation of gauzy shadow. At the back of the room was another door, a rectangle of black imprinted on the greying wall. 'That must be it,' said Steph and led the way across.

She turned the handle without knocking and pushed the door open. She peeked round. 'Wow!' she exclaimed.

'What is it?' hissed Annie, feeling a sudden urge to lower her voice, uncertain whether this was prompted by trepidation or reverence.

'Have a look,' said Steph, grinning, moving further into the room, 'it's really brilliant.'

Annie's mouth was dry, her heart pounding: she wondered why she felt so nervous. She shuffled into the room behind Steph, instinctively staying close to her friend's shoulder. When she had a clear view of the room her eyes widened; she exhaled deeply, too awed to make any sound.

The room was like a sanctum, a holy of holies. Red drapes covered the walls; thick white candles in tall brass holders provided the only illumination. At the end of the room a stage had been set up, heavy red curtains waiting to rise on some mysterious first act. Four rows of chairs faced the stage, two dozen chairs in all, around half of which were occupied.

'Isn't it *fantastic*!' enthused Steph, loud enough for a few members of the audience to turn and stare at them.

Annie swallowed. 'It's ... it's different,' she admitted.

At the back of the room, to their left, a trolley held glasses of red liquid, twinkling in the candle-light. 'Free booze too!' exclaimed Steph. She strode across and picked up two glasses. 'Here you go,' she said to Annie, handing her one.

'Thanks,' said Annie. She felt too apprehensive to drink, but it seemed easier to keep hold of the glass than to put it back. She had an urge to remain as unobtrusive as possible. Not so Steph.

'Let's sit down,' the red-haired girl said, loud enough to make Annie cringe. Steph stomped up the aisle, grinning at people who looked at them, as though they were all children awaiting the start of a Punch and Judy show on the beach. Annie would have liked to have sat on the third or fourth row, out of the way, but Steph sat down on the front row, beside a couple who were smoking a reefer. The man had straggly hair and a beard, blackened teeth, fingers stained with nicotine. He was wearing a filthy green army jacket, a sweater that seemed to have been knitted for an elephant out of barbed wire, and ragged jeans covered with simple flower designs drawn in faded blue biro. The woman had hair so long and straight and black that it seemed like a bad wig, round John Lennon spectacles and a red kaftan covered with a riotous Paisley print. To Annie's dismay, Steph leaned over to them and said, 'Hi. Isn't this weird?'

The man turned slowly and looked at her. Annie saw that he had bad skin and eyes the colour of pond water. He grinned suddenly. Wrinkles creased his face like cracks in dry clay.

'Sure is,' he said. 'You have any idea what's supposed to be happening here?'

'We just saw these cards on a table,' said the woman. 'It sounded like fun so we thought we'd come along.'

'Us too,' said Steph. She sipped her wine; Annie hadn't touched hers. 'What are your names? I'm Steph, this is Annie.'

'Pleased to meetcha,' said the man. 'I'm Carl, this is Meryl.'

'What year are you two in?' asked Steph.

'Fourth years – like Dan Latcher,' said the woman. 'Y'know, it's funny. I never knew Latcher was into all this stuff.'

'What stuff?' asked Annie. It was the first time she had spoken to the couple. Carl's bleary eyes turned towards her. Meryl's head dipped to look past Steph; the images of candle-flames were reflected in the glass of her spectacles.

'Magic, mysticism,' said Meryl, shrugging. 'Whatever it said on the card.'

'So you've known Dan for a while?' said Steph.

'Seen him around,' growled Carl, 'never spoken to him. Always thought he was a posey little bastard.'

'Really?' said Steph, surprised. 'I thought he was kind of dreamy.'

'Yeah, you know it's funny,' said Meryl. 'I always agreed with Carl here, thought the guy was a prick. But the minute he started talking to us after we'd picked up the card, he was just ... I dunno ... impressive somehow. *Persuasive.* He didn't tell us what would be happening here tonight, but he made us *want* to come, y'know?'

'Yeah,' said Steph as though they had voiced some detail she'd overlooked. 'Yeah, that's just how it was for us, wasn't it, Annie?' She glanced at Annie, who shrugged. Undeterred, Steph went on. 'He just took my hand and looked into my eyes and I just ... I just felt I *had* to come.'

The couple nodded their understanding.

Steph said, 'How about these other people here tonight? Do you know any of them?'

The four of them swivelled to look at the rest of the audience. They were a mixed bag which included a scowling guy with dyed black hair and a leather jacket; a boyish-looking girl in a university sweatshirt; two athletic-looking guys in designer clothes; a tall girl who appeared Nordic with a mass of blonde ringlets and dungarees striped in bright colours.

'Seen a few of them around,' Carl said, 'but that's about all. Keep ourselves to ourselves, Meryl and me. We're not fashion victims like most of the prats round here.'

Oh no? thought Annie. In her opinion deliberately dressing down was just as much of a pose as adopting every transient fashion. "Greenham Common chic" she'd heard it referred to as. She smiled secretly to herself though said nothing. As was often the case she had neither the confidence nor the gall to express her opinion. Instead she wondered why *she* hadn't fallen prey to Dan Latcher's charisma, why in fact she had been almost physically repelled by his oily charm and surface glamour.

All at once the candles dimmed, inducing a general intake of breath. Annie felt apprehensive; the candles had not been snuffed out, nor disturbed by a breeze, they had merely *dimmed*, a simultaneous waning, as though someone had turned a dial to a lower setting. She licked lips which felt suddenly dry. A spotlight blinked on from somewhere – she couldn't see where – illuminating the thin strip of blackness which was the parting in the red curtains concealing the stage. Marijuana smoke drifted over her, sweet and cloying; she

70

suppressed a cough. Looking around she saw expressions that were eager, anticipatory, and she felt uneasy. This is silly, she thought. Why is everyone so excited? It's only a slimey fourth year and his stupid magic show for God's sake!

With a dying hiss every candle in the red-draped room suddenly guttered out completely. Someone gave a small excited shriek. Someone else giggled. Annie gripped her knees with clammy hands. She wished again that they hadn't sat on the front row. She stared at the white disc of light illuminating the red curtains, holding her breath when the curtains began to peel slowly back like wrinkled flaps of raw skin.

The spotlight pierced the darkness between the curtains. Annie saw it flash on stripes of metal, a cage within which something prowled. As the curtains rose fully, taking their shadows with them, the full splendour of the caged beast was revealed. There was a murmur of awe. The tiger's eyes flashed as it growled softly. Its huge paws were like muffled drumbeats on the bare wood of the makeshift stage.

A tiger? How the hell had Latcher got hold of a tiger? Annie realised her hands were now rigid on the edges of her seat. She no longer felt nervous − she felt scared. The tiger, the excited faces around her, the red room with its guttering candles, all this contributed to her fear. But it was more than that − it was the aura of the place, the sense that something was wrong here, fractured, almost nightmarish. She would have got up and walked out if she hadn't wanted to draw attention to herself. The small audience was beginning to clap, the applause building up rapidly, accompanied by whistles of approval which made the tiger flinch. Annie looked to her left: Steph was clapping too, the rapt expression on her face so fixed it appeared mask-like.

Then ... something happened. There was some kind of lighting effect, a stroboscopic fluttering, that made Annie blink. On stage the tiger moved like a jerky black-and-white film, and then, incredibly, seemed somehow to *invert*, to flip inside-out, as though it had been an enormous glove puppet which had been peeled swiftly from a gigantic hand. Annie caught a confused and unpleasant impression of a rib-cage, a skull, an oily red-grey mass of innards. Then the stroboscope ceased, was replaced abruptly by the harsh static cone of the spotlight, and Dan Latcher was standing, arms outspread and grinning cadaverously, within the outwardly collapsing walls of the cage.

There were only a dozen or so people in the room but the place seemed to erupt around Annie. Hands slapped together, feet stamped, whistles and shouts echoed off the ceiling. Dan milked the

71

applause, his head moving slowly, reptile-like, from side to side. His eyes glittered like shards of black glass in his grinning face.

Annie joined in the applause so that her antipathy would not appear conspicuous. Dan was dressed in a baggy blue- and white-checked suit, pale pink shirt, blue bow tie, white shoes and white kid-gloves. The effect was that of a sinister *jongleur*, or some outlandish adversary from a comic book. He waited until the audience was completely silent before he began to speak.

'Ladies and gentlemen,' he intoned then, grinning all the while, 'welcome to The Crack.'

Another foot-stamping ovation. Latcher waited this one out too. He had no intention of damping his audience's ardour.

'My name,' he continued at last, 'is Daniel Latcher. I am a friend, a guide and a brother to each and every one of you. I am your Destiny, your Truth. Together, hand in hand, we shall explore Epiphany. I will show you wonders beyond your comprehension. I am your Way Forward, your Life. With my tutelage you shall view the blackest depths, scale the most glorious heights. My friends, I offer you challenge. I offer you absolution. I offer you the world. I offer you love ...'

He paused here, his arms upheld, palms stretched towards the Heavens. This is ridiculous, thought Annie incredulously. I don't believe this! Why isn't this prat being laughed off the stage? But she for one didn't feel like laughing. She glanced at Steph to see how she had reacted to Latcher's banal senseless rant. She was shocked to see tears glistening in her friend's eyes as she joined in the latest outbreak of applause.

What was going on here? How was Latcher doing this? Mass hypnotism? If only Steph wasn't a part of this mindless adulation Annie could maybe appreciate the ludicrousness of the situation, perhaps even laugh about it in the bar later on. But instead she felt frightened, and physically sick, her stomach cramping though it didn't usually this far into her period, her head throbbing with pain.

She gave up any pretence of being a part of Dan's admiring flock and laid her hands in her lap. She closed her eyes and breathed slowly to quell her nausea, but it was a difficult thing to do. She couldn't shake the unpleasant (and surely illogical?) impression that Latcher would single her out, point an accusing finger, condemn her as an imposter. But why should he do that? She didn't *have* to enjoy herself here, did she? She didn't *have* to take part in the acclamation; she was entitled to her own opinion.

She opened her eyes as a gasp of admiration came from the

audience. An instant later she was gasping herself, though fortunately the sound was drowned out by yet more applause.

Latcher was floating in mid-air, hovering above the stage like a giant grinning insect. Annie looked hard for the glint of the wires that were holding him up there, for the upraised tweak of material on his back or shoulders where the wires would be connected: she could see neither.

'For my next trick,' Latcher said, 'I need a volunteer from the audience.'

He began to float out above them, his feet clearing heads by no more than a couple of metres. Hands reached up to caress him as he floated by; a gentle touch of a trouser leg, a shy fingering of his jacket, or his outstretched arm, or the dangling laces of his white shoes.

Annie crushed herself back into her seat, certain that he was going to choose her as his "volunteer". But he did not. He floated above her head like a sinister Peter Pan. Heads swivelled to watch as he drifted beyond the back row, alighted daintily, turned and placed a slim-fingered hand on the shoulder of the guy in the leather jacket. The guy looked like an excited puppy. Annie would not have been surprised had he turned his head and begun to lap lovingly at Latcher's hand. 'Come with me,' Latcher said, leading him to the stage as a mother would lead a child across a busy road. Annie's stomach clenched as Latcher and his apostle passed by a few inches from her. There was a sickening expression of adoration on leather-jacket's face. She pressed a hand against her nose and mouth, her throat stinging. Latcher reeked of perfume. For a few moments she couldn't draw breath, so overwhelmed was she by his stench.

Latcher motioned to leather-jacket to stand in the middle of the stage, beneath the full glare of the spotlight. 'Tell the audience your name,' he ordered.

'Eric,' said the boy shyly. 'Eric Temple.'

'And what year are you in, Eric.'

'Second year.'

'And your subject?'

'Communication Studies.'

Latcher turned to the audience, teeth flashing as though polished, and then back to his stooge. 'This next trick is very dangerous, Eric. Many men in your position have died during its execution. I need your unflinching trust. I need your love. Do I have that, Eric? Do I?'

'Yes,' the crowd whispered, 'yes.'

'Yes,' echoed Eric.

73

Latcher beamed.

'Thank you,' he said, his voice dripping with sincerity. 'Then let us commence.'

He reached behind his back and produced a large square can, painted white, the word "Petrol" printed on it in bold black capitals. He was like a character in a cartoon, thought Annie, Wile E. Coyote or Bugs Bunny, producing a prop from nowhere.

Slowly, drawing out the moment, Latcher unscrewed the cap of the petrol can, placed it on the stage, and turned to flash a secret grin at the audience. Then he began to shake the can over the uncomplaining student, dousing him with liquid. The audience murmured. Annie felt her fear pressing back inside her, trying to squeeze itself into invisibility, to find a warm quiet secure place far removed from what was about to happen. Latcher held up a hand, fingers outstretched. He blew on the fingers and from the tip of each one burst a thin white flicker of flame.

He extended the hand slowly towards Temple, who waited demurely, his body relaxed. It's only a trick, Annie tried to convince herself desperately, just an illusion, that's all. Yet fear writhed inside her like a foetus struggling for life. Latcher's hand hovered before Temple's face, so close that its reflection flashed like gold in the teenager's blank eyes. Annie wanted to stand up, to scream for this to stop. She remained seated. The room was hushed as a chapel of rest.

'Now, Eric,' said Latcher, 'I want you to take my hand.'

No, Annie screamed silently, no, don't!

Unflinchingly Temple reached out and clasped Latcher's lethal hand with his own.

A jagged line of flame leaped instantly up Temple's arm, across his shoulders and down his chest. It obliterated his face, reduced his hair to an orange crown. As though awakening from a trance, he snatched his hand from Latcher's grasp and began to stagger, screaming, about the stage. Arms like black bones beneath a shifting heat-white skin beat at himself in a desperate attempt to put out the fire. Unable to do so, he spiralled to the centre of the stage and fell to his knees, still screaming.

Annie sat in the front row, shaking her head, unable to believe her eyes. Huge sickening waves were rising up through her body, making her teeth chatter, her limbs shake uncontrollably. This isn't happening, she thought desperately. This can't be happening, it can't! She looked around. There were stunned looks on almost every face, but there was also admiration there — no shock, no disbelief, no horror.

74

She touched her friend's sleeve, whispered, 'Steph,' surprised at how hard it was to make her throat work. Steph's head turned slowly to look at her. Annie couldn't help but recoil. This wasn't the exuberant self-willed Steph she knew. It wasn't even the Steph who had entered this room with her, bubbling with excitement at the 'weird night' they were about to have. This was a Steph who seemed ... empty. Drugged or hypnotised, her eyes round and staring, her facial expressions unconvincing, lacking warmth, like the stiff muscular jerks of bad animatronics.

'What's the matter, Annie?' Steph said. Even her voice sounded wrong. A sudden impression that this was Dan Latcher speaking to her through Steph's mouth swept over Annie and she shuddered.

'All this, Steph, it's ... it's ...' The words wouldn't come. Finally she blurted, 'What's wrong with you?'

'Wrong?' repeated Steph, puzzled. 'Nothing's wrong. What do you mean? Everything's great.'

'But look what's happening,' said Annie, gesturing at the stage, trying to prevent hysteria from making her voice rise. '*Look what's happening.*'

Steph looked. 'It's a trick, that's all,' she said. 'A conjuring trick. Dan's a magician.'

'How can you be so stupid?' Annie sobbed. 'It's murder, it's sick. What's going on here?'

Steph looked at her as though *she* was the crazy one. Annie sagged, pressing her hands over her face as she was overcome with sobs, shudders, cramping pains in her stomach and limbs. She needed to think, to sort this out. It was all so disjointed, the perverse abrupt logic of nightmare. When had the line been crossed? What had turned Steph and the others into mindless adoring zombies? All afternoon Steph had been full of Latcher and The Crack, but she had still been Steph; it had all been a great mysterious joke to her, something fun and exciting and different. So what had happened? Had the wine been drugged? Had Latcher silently implanted some subliminal message into the minds of everyone he'd spoken to, to be activated when the curtain came up on his depraved magic show? No, it was crazy, far-fetched, but then so was this entire situation. Up on stage, Temple's screams had dwindled to nothing, though Annie could still feel the heat of his death swarming up her exposed shins, over the backs of her hands which were still pressed against her face.

There was a flap and a dark flicker across Annie's closed eyelids. Fearfully she opened one eye, half-expecting to see Latcher transforming into a giant vampire bat. He was not; he was shaking out a large black cloth, as though in preparation for some grotesque picnic. With a flourish he flung the cloth into the air. It settled gently over Temple's blackened and smoking remains.

'*Voilà*!' Latcher cried then, and plucked the cloth immediately into the air again. The audience gasped as the cloth came away to reveal bare unblemished boards where Temple had burned and died. Latcher flung out an arm. 'Eric, if you please!' Annie twisted her head, as did the rest of the audience. Temple was standing quietly at the back of the room. He smiled and bowed.

Plaudits rained down upon Latcher, who accepted them with smug modesty. Annie laughed and clapped too, though more from relief than approbation.

'The world is an illusion!' roared Latcher. 'I will show you the true reality!' He threw up his hands, laughing like a madman. A tumult of fluttering shapes − hawks, parakeets, wasps, confetti − filled the air above his head before sparking out of existence.

A succession of illusions followed, interspersed with Latcher's demented pontifications and absurd promises, each of which was met with hysterical applause. Some of the illusions − a book which flew solemnly about the room like a bird; a frog which swelled to the size of a man and then exploded, scattering tiny silver stars over the audience − had even Annie gasping in wonder. But however amazed she was, she could not shake off her feeling of dread. She expected at any moment the axe to fall, waited in terror for the advent of some apocalyptic finale.

The climax, when it came, was impressive. Dan set a tub on the stage, produced a glittering red seed − that flashed under the spotlight like a droplet of blood − from his ear, and conjured a watering can out of mid-air. He dropped the seed into the tub, watered it, and hurled the watering can towards the audience: it vanished even as Annie was throwing up a defensive arm. Almost immediately vines began to writhe from the tub, to thicken into branches, to sprout leaves and blossom, to strain towards the ceiling. The tub bulged and cracked and then burst apart as roots squirmed like thick brown tentacles across the stage, seeking the cracks between the boards, niches in which to anchor themselves. Within moments a fully-grown tree stood in the centre of the stage, its topmost branches lost in the shadows. To prove that this was no projection, no phantasm conjured by mirrors, Latcher reached up, grasped a thick branch and swung himself athletically into the lower limbs.

He began to scale the tree like a chimpanzee, leaping from one branch to the next. High above the stage he turned and screamed,

'I am the Father! I love you as my own children!' The response was so pandemonious, so passionate, that Annie was certain the echoes must be reverberating throughout the University. Then the cheers broke into gasps, the audience lunged forward, many stretching out their arms, as Latcher twisted in the tree, let go of the branch he was clinging to, and plunged towards the stage.

Annie braced herself for the sound of his impact. It didn't come. Instead the stage yielded like water; Latcher gave a final grin before being submerged. Before anyone could react, the tree began to blaze with a spontaneous and brilliant light, a pure effulgence that scorched the eyes. For the second time in a matter of minutes, Annie pressed both hands to her face, felt tears squeezing down her cheeks. The light attempted to pierce even this barrier of flesh and bone, imbuing the darkness behind her eyelids with a fiery orange glow. Annie kept her eyes squeezed tight for what seemed minutes, until at last the glow began to fade and die.

Cautiously she removed her hands from her face and squinted at the stage. The performance was over. The red curtains had fallen; the candles lining the walls were burning softly again. People were rising and heading towards the door. Annie was exuberant: she had survived! She turned to Steph who was blinking confusedly, looking around like an awakening sleepwalker.

'Steph . . . are you all right?' Annie asked. Despite her relief, physically she felt dreadful, as though 'flu, period pains and migraine had coalesced to claim her body.

Steph looked blearily at her. 'Yes, I'm fine. Why shouldn't I be?' A sickly smile appeared on her face. 'Isn't Dan just wonderful?'

Annie passed on that one. 'I think I'm going straight to bed,' she said. 'I don't feel too good. Do you mind?'

'Mind? No, of course not. You do what you think is best.'

The girls began to follow the rest of the audience from the room. Each and every face Annie looked at was radiant but blank, idiot children happy in their ignorance. She wondered again what Latcher had done and why she hadn't been affected except adversely. Spectacular and bizzare as Latcher's performance had been, it alone could surely not have had such an effect on his audience. There he was now, at the door, gushing goodbyes and handing out flowers, accepting the adulation of his audience with the slick platitudes of a tinpot Svengali. As he turned to the girls, brandishing his grin like a weapon, Annie tried not to flinch back for fear she would jeopardise her repatriation into the "real" world.

'Oh, Dan, that was *wonderful*!' Steph exclaimed, and flung her arms around Latcher's shoulders in what seemed to Annie a distressing parody of her uninhibited manner. As Steph kissed Latcher on the mouth, Annie tried to sidle past. Latcher gently disengaged Steph, still grinning.

'Thank you,' he murmured modestly. 'I hope you'll both return.'

'Oh, yes!' confirmed Steph. 'We will, definitely. Won't we, Annie?'

'Yes,' Annie lied, forcing herself to smile. She tried to edge past but Latcher's long fingers reached out and touched her lightly on the hand. It was like coming into contact with a live electric cable. Annie gasped as she felt a gout of fire rip through her groin and stomach. She pulled herself out of his reach, remaining upright and even smiling only through sheer willpower.

'Splendid,' Latched cooed. 'Until next time then, a small token of my love for you both.'

From nowhere he produced two red roses, one of which he handed to Steph, the other to Annie.

'Oh, wow!' Steph said. She sniffed the rose deeply. Tears filled her eyes. 'Thank you, Dan. I'll treasure this.'

Her exaggerated reaction would have been risible had the genuineness of her gratitude not been so chilling.

'Yeah ... thanks,' Annie managed to mutter through her pain.

'Think nothing of it,' said Dan. 'Remember, The Crack is always with you.'

Annie nodded – it was all she could manage – and then she and Steph moved from G8 into the adjoining classroom. Dan closed the door behind them. The instant he had done so, Annie staggered to the nearest chair, put her head between her knees and threw up. She felt no better with her stomach voided. She had a craving to crawl beneath the jets of a hot shower, let it wash away the filth of that evening, and then to sleep until her dreams were her own, until her mind was free of Latcher's insidious probings. She looked at her hand, noticed she was still holding the rose Latcher had given her, and threw it to the floor. Steph had not waited for her, had shown not even the slightest concern over her condition. Sobbing, Annie ground down her heel on the rose, reducing it to a red and perfumed pulp.

16

For the second time in two nights he came awake with a jolt. This time it *must* be the rain which had woken him — it was clattering against his window like handfuls of nails. Despite this his room was muggy; the pillow beneath his head was damp with sweat. His eyes felt gritty; his mouth tasted sour. The flavour of a dream bobbed in his head, but dissolved before he could grasp any of its images.

He lay motionless, his eyes gradually adjusting to the dark. As a child he'd believed that if you remained completely still, blending with the night, the monsters couldn't get you. How wrong he'd been. Since his tenth summer he'd come to realise that nowhere in the world was safe. The monsters could get you anywhere, anytime. It was all just a game to them.

He sat up. This was stupid. There were no monsters. There was nothing except his imagination. He was restless, that was all. He had too much energy to sleep for more than a few hours at a time. He would make himself some hot milk and read for a while. If he was tired in the morning, too bad. He could always catch up on his sleep tomorrow.

He threw aside his bedclothes and swung his legs out of bed — and there he stopped. Something gleamed on the carpet in front of him. In the darkness it resembled a fan made of metal. Quickly he drew back his feet, suddenly and illogically fearful that the thing might be alive. What could he do now? He didn't want to get out of bed until he knew what the object was, but unless he switched on his light he wouldn't know.

He considered throwing something at the lightswitch, hoping for a lucky strike, and looked around for something appropriate. There was his alarm clock — no, it would only get damaged. Then how about his Reeboks on the floor at the bottom of his bed? He bundled his bedclothes around his body and shuffled the length of the bed on his knees. He was leaning over the end of the bed, reaching down cautiously, when his curtains glided open of their own accord.

His heart thudding like an alarm, he jerked upright. Fear tightened his throat, drained the moisture from his mouth. How had they opened? It was impossible. Light shattered by rain gave the room a murky definition.

He looked round at the metal fan on the carpet and a squeal of fear escaped him. It wasn't a fan at all; it was a display of vicious cutlery, a

79

semi-circular arrangement of knives and hatchets, cut-throat razors, skewers, machetes and cleavers. He began to shake. Sweat sprang like heat blisters from his pores and began to roll down his chest and his forehead. No, not knives. *Please*. He hated knives. Ever since that summer when he had ... he shook his head. He confronted a blade's work each morning and he could take that, he could accept it. But to see them arrayed like this, a savage grin of steel ... No, it was too much. Too much. He began to weep.

'Still, my child.'

He shrieked, though the voice was soft, placatory. Where had it come from? His question was answered by the wardrobe door which was yawning slowly open. No, he thought, no. Could this really be happening? Had Corcoran returned after all these years? He should arm himself. He recoiled from the thought. No, all of this was over a long time ago. Go away, he implored, go away.

Hello, Larry. Want some fun?

'No!' he screamed, though he suspected the voice was in his head. Still, the weapons were real, flaunted like a butcher's boast, as was the bald porcine figure stepping from his wardrobe, dusting himself down.

He tried to calm himself, to reel in the panic that was threatening to drag him away, but he couldn't stop shaking. 'Wh-who are you?' he said, barely able to get the words past his trembling lips.

'I am Destiny,' said the man. 'I am the rest of your life.'

'Get out or I'll call the police.'

'I think not, my friend. I think not.'

The man approached the array of weapons, reached down and selected a scalpel. He held it aloft, allowing the light to play over it, to flash on the blade.

'Please,' he whispered, crushing himself back against the head-board, 'please don't hurt me.'

The man chuckled. 'I've come to release you, my friend, not to hurt you. Hence my little gift.'

He gestured with a flourish at the myriad cutting edges.

'What do you mean?' he whispered. 'I don't understand.'

'Oh, you will, my friend. Don't worry about that.'

Smiling, the man circled the half-moon and perched on the edge of the bed. For all his bulk, his movements were dainty, almost balletic. He tilted his head and his eyes flashed green. His pointed teeth glowed softly like a mouthful of fireflies.

'Please,' he wept, eyes rivetted on the scalpel that the men held. 'Please, go away.'

'You have needs,' said the man. 'You have desires. I'm here to help you realise them.'

'No,' he whispered, 'no,' denying not only the man's words but the fact that he felt himself dwindling. He fought against the spinning faintness, the flecks of black behind his eyes.

'Yes,' countered the man. He drew the scalpel blade swiftly across the pad of his thumb; blood welled from the cut. 'Yes. Oh yes. Oh yes.'

The sight of the blood sent him tumbling towards darkness. He grabbed at his sheets, his bed, his pillow, anything he could use as an anchor to drag himself back to the surface. It was no use; his flailing hand caught his alarm clock which fell to the floor and began to emit a high-pitched bleep-bleep, bleep-bleep. As he drifted away he was vaguely aware of the man's face looming closer. But surely it was only the onset of dreams that made him think the face was a mask, and that beneath the mask something was struggling for release, like a litter of puppies squirming to break free from a sack.

17

What a life, thought Kelly Black, shrinking against a wall to avoid the rain, what a bloody life.

She consulted her watch and made a snap decision. It was almost three and she had the sniffles; she would treat herself, knock off early, call it a night. She felt a momentary pang of guilt − Michaela's fifth birthday was only ten days away and Paul needed a new sports bag for school − but she quickly and indignantly overrode her conscience. Better to get home to bed now, nip her cold in the bud, than to be off the streets for a week nursing the 'flu. *She* didn't get sickness pay; *she* didn't have a sugar daddy to fall back on like Little Miss Innocent Fiona; *she* didn't have thousands stashed away and plans of the high-life in Spain which one or two of the other girls bragged they had.

She stepped from the semi-shelter of the wall and began walking. The rain was not heavy but it was incessant; it chilled her skin, made her imitation fur coat resemble a drowned yak. There was a wind too which whistled in and out of the raindrops, encircling her stocking-clad legs like gossamer snakes let loose from a freezer. She shivered and clutched her coat tightly around her, wished she was wearing something warmer than a mini-skirt below her waist, wished she wasn't still two miles from home. None of the other girls seemed to be about tonight. They all had more sense than she did, or maybe they weren't so desperate. A car engine rumbled behind her; the reflection of its headlights lay like scattered stars on the wet tarmac. Kelly drew away from the kerb to prevent getting splashed, but the car slowed, then eased to a stop by her side.

She looked round. The man in the car was half watching her, half watching the road, his face expressionless as though he didn't know the form and was waiting for her to take the initiative. Kelly considered telling him to fuck off but then thought better of it.

Aw, what the hell? One more punter wouldn't make much difference. It was money in the bank and maybe he would even give her a lift home afterwards. Not to her door, of course – she was smarter than that – but at least to within a couple of streets. Out of habit she glanced up and down the road, then sauntered over to the car and leaned in.

'Looking for business?' she asked.

The potential punter didn't look at her. His eyes were fixed on the road ahead as though he were negotiating busy traffic; Kelly could see how tightly his hands gripped the steering wheel and realised he was scared to death.

A virgin, she thought. How sweet.

The man's eyes flickered towards her, rested a moment, then skidded away. He gave a quick hesitant nod and unlocked the passenger door.

Kelly strolled round the front of the car. She was dying to get into the dry warmth but made herself take her time. She had learnt a few things over the years: not to appear too eager was one, for that put the ball in the punter's court, made him feel stronger, more confident, than was wise. Another was: don't rush things. A timid punter, such as this, was apt to feel intimidated and inadequate if you tried to hurry events along.

She waited by the door until he had opened it for her, then climbed in, allowing him a good view of her long legs, a glimpse of a stocking-top. She smiled warmly, said, 'Ooh, it's lovely to get in out of the rain. I hope I don't drip too much on your upholstery,'

The punter threw her another quick glance. 'S'okay,' he murmured. He let the car idle along the kerb for a few moments as though he wasn't sure he wanted to go through with this, then he pulled out into the road.

Kelly looked through the windscreen, watched the rain scutter in the headlights like a shower of sparks. Sometimes the punter wanted to speak first, express his preferences, and she always allowed sufficient pause for him to pluck up the courage to do so. She waited until the car had reached the end of the road and turned left. Thirty seconds passed and still the punter remained silent. Okay, she thought, it was time for a few gentle words. A little coaxing and cajoling would soon pry him out of his shell.

'Do you have anywhere in mind you'd like to go?' she asked, keeping her voice casual, friendly.

The punter said nothing. She sighed inwardly.

'Would you prefer to find a hotel room or to stay in the car?' she prompted.

The punter cleared his throat. Kelly could tell by the subtle messages his body transmitted that he was preparing to speak, building himself up, attempting to relax. They stopped at a red light which was a slither of blood in the rain. The red light became a tiny orange sun, then a glowing green Martian face. As the car eased forward he said, 'Hotel.'

Hallelujah, she thought. She smiled warmly. 'Okay. Do you have a particular one in mind or would you like me to choose?'

The punter shrugged. Kelly continued, 'Shall I choose one? I know a place not far from here that's very discreet.'

Another long pause. Kelly was beginning to regret this, beginning to wish she'd told him to fuck off and walked home as she'd originally intended.

Then he muttered, 'Okay.'

She breathed a sigh of relief and gave him directions, which saved her from having to chatter mindlessly to keep the silence from growing awkward between them. The place she chose was laughingly called The Mansion. It was a place that many of the girls used. The woman who owned it, a hatchet-faced battleaxe named Millie Macau, had, it was rumoured, bought The Mansion from the proceeds of her own stint on the game. Elaine had told her that Millie used to be a whips 'n leather specialist, that some of the beatings she had administered had put her buyers in hospital. Looking at her, Kelly was quite prepared to believe it. Millie Macau was not a large woman but she had arms like knotted bars of iron.

They pulled into The Mansion's modest car park between weathered stone gateposts, each surmounted by a snarling lion with its paw atop a sphere. This neighbourhood, quiet and residential, had seen more affluent times. The houses were large, set well apart, Victorian edifices which reflected all the grandeur and austerity of that period. Trees and bushes, grown thick and old and gnarled, contributed to each house's privacy, and indeed the buildings themselves seemed to hide beneath beards of ivy, whiskers of wistaria.

The punter eased his car into a space where the overhanging shadows of trees enfolded it, and cut the engine. The rain pattered down, hissing in the foliage, slithering across the windscreen. Still the punter didn't look at her directly. Kelly could see that his hands, balled in his lap, were trembling. Now came the most crucial and delicate moment, the one where they talked of requirements and, more importantly, money. With some punters she could simply reel off the services she performed and the price she charged to perform them. But others, especially first-timers like this one, needed more subtle, less direct handling.

'Well,' she said brightly, 'we're here. What do you think?'

He turned and gave the building an obligatory once-over, but with the trees and the rain and the darkness there was little to admire.

'S'okay,' he said.

'You sure? We can go somewhere else if you like.'

Kelly suggested this knowing he would refuse, and sure enough the punter shook his head. 'No, this . . . this is fine.'

Kelly smiled encouragingly, turned and draped an arm across the back of his seat, barely touching his shoulder. She felt the skin and muscle beneath the material of his clothes flinch from her touch like a snail recoiling into its shell.

'The lady who owns this place is an old friend of mine,' she lied.

The punter nodded, not the slightest bit interested, and said, 'Oh.'

'She charges very reasonable rates. Five pounds an hour for a room. That's good isn't it?'

She'd phrased it so that the punter would agree, which he did. 'Mmm,' he said.

She leaned closer, allowing her hand to settle delicately on his shoulder, and applied gentle pressure with her fingers. He was like stone beneath his clothes, but she guessed this was the result not of callisthenics but of fear.

She put her mouth close to his ear, smelled a clean, almost baby fragrance which was refreshing − so many of her punters thought BO was a cologne, week-old sweat a deodorant. In a practised tone, one that was seductive without being intimidating, demure without being submissive, she said, 'What is it you'd like, exactly?'

84

Firebrands of embarrassment flared across the punter's cheeks. He began to swallow convulsively. Kelly kneaded his shoulder, not least because she wouldn't have been surprised if he had thrown the car door open and bolted into the night.

'Okay,' she said gently, 'just relax. Would you like me to tell you what's on offer?'

There was silence for a moment, then almost miserably the punter muttered, 'Just ... just ... just normal.'

'Okay,' smiled Kelly, 'that's fine. I ... um ... don't suppose you'd pay in advance, would you? Twenty pounds? I mean, it's not that I don't trust you or anything, it's a policy of mine, that's all.'

The punter cleared his throat and gave a sharp nod, reached into his jacket pocket and took out a wallet. All the time he kept his eyes on the blurred tangle of trees through the windscreen, as though his intellect was detached from the sordid deal that would gratify his physical demands. He extracted two ten-pound notes, hesitated a moment, then snatched out a blue five. He closed the wallet, replaced it in his pocket and held out the money for Kelly to take. She did so, allowing her fingers to briefly touch his. She felt him shudder.

'Okay,' she said. 'Shall we go inside?'

He nodded again and they got out of the car, Kelly pulling her collar up against the rain. A few lights burned in the windows of The Mansion, though not many. The only people awake at this hour were ladies such as herself, policemen, villains and insomniacs. He hovered uncertainly until she was by his side, then they splatted across the rain-pocked tarmac to the welcoming canopy of the hotel lobby. Strands of carefully crimped hair started sticking to Kelly's face like old bootlaces; she tried not to sniff as her nose ran in imitation of the water trickling down her neck. She rooted in her pocket for a handkerchief but pulled out only a pair of white lace crotchless panties. Oh, what the hell, she thought, buried her face in the panties and blew.

The hotel staff were just as she'd promised, discreet and incurious. Kelly approached the reception desk, asked a blonde with a stud through her nose if room twenty-two was available and placed the five-pound note on the desk. The blonde picked up the money, took a key from a hook on the board behind her and handed it over. Kelly thanked her and crossed to where the punter was making a pitiful attempt to appear inconspicuous. She alarmed him by slipping an arm through his, and bearing him gently but firmly towards the lifts. The punter was sweating, fidgeting, trembling. When the lights above the lift read G, the doors opened and they stepped inside.

'You okay?' Kelly asked as the lift ascended. The punter swallowed, grimaced, wiped a trickle of sweat from his face, and finally nodded. Kelly squeezed his arm and smiled, attempting to relax him. This was not entirely for his benefit; she had spent many a frustrating hour trying to coax a terrified penis to life, lying beneath nervous punters whose tension manifested itself in flaccidity.

The lift doors opened. They stepped out onto a richly patterned carpet whose threadbare patches were carefully concealed beneath pot plants and rugs. 'This way,' Kelly said and turned right, tugging the punter along with her.

They stopped outside door 22. The punter's eyes flickered this way and that as Kelly took the key from her coat pocket and fitted it into the lock. His stance implored her silently: hurry, hurry, hurry. Kelly ignored it; she knew how uncomfortable things could get, both physically and in establishing a rapport (however bogus) with the punter, if she allowed his agitation to rub off on her.

The moment the door was open the punter lunged inside, almost barging her out of the way as he did so. Kelly's first reaction was one of anger. The scornful tease: 'My, my, aren't we eager?' rose to her lips but she managed to repress it. Unerringly she reached for the light-switch, the cord dangling by her right hand. She had been here so often before that as the light came on she already knew what she would see.

The room was small, almost entirely dominated by a large double bed. The walls were a pastelly pink, the carpet and furnishings scarlet, colours both passionate and soothing. The punter stood with his back against the wall, looking down at the bed as though it were some large and carnivorous beast. Kelly crossed casually to the bedside table, switched on the lamp there, and walked back across the room to douse the main light.

'There,' she said, 'isn't that better?'

The light now was gentle, the contours of the room marshmallow soft.

The punter jerked his head in a nod though he appeared unconvinced.

Kelly went through to a tiny bathroom, grabbed a hand-towel off the rail, dried her hair, then passed the towel to him. He dried himself dutifully, then carefully folded the towel and draped it back over the rail in the bathroom. When he emerged, Kelly was perched daintily on the edge of the bed, patting the coverlet.

'Won't you come and sit beside me?' she said.

86

Jerking like a puppet, behaving as though this was very much against his will, the punter did as she suggested.

'It's a lovely comfortable bed,' Kelly murmured, stroking it almost affectionately. 'Is there anything else you'd like? Something to drink perhaps?'

'N-no,' the punter stammered. 'No, I . . . no. Thanks.' He blushed again, his cheeks looking as if he were altering, chameleon-like, to suit his surroundings.

'Okay,' Kelly said. She leaned over, kissed him on the cheek, allowed her hand to rest lightly on his thigh for a moment. The side of her thumb brushed against his crotch with enough contact to tell her that his penis was already stiffening.

Thank God, she thought. Her sinuses were beginning to throb, making her head feel stuffed with dough. The sooner she could get home to bed the better. She kissed him again on the cheek and then on the mouth. After a couple more kisses he responded.

He tasted nice, which again was something Kelly appreciated. Though it was hard work, she could take timidity if it was accompanied by personal hygiene. A hand clamped on her right breast and squeezed; the punter's lust was getting the better of his trepidation now. Kelly kissed him once more, then pulled gently away. In her profession foreplay had to be moderated, used purely as the briefest of curtain raisers.

'Shall we get undressed?' she said breathily, knowing that her cheeks were flushed, her eyes sparkling in convincing but spurious excitement. The punter licked his lips, gave an almost imperceptible nod. Kelly smiled seductively, stood up and let her fake fur slide to the floor. With slow steady fingers she began undoing the buttons on her blouse.

The punter watched her, eyes both hungry and fearful. Five buttons and a zip later, Kelly was standing in black lace bra and panties, black stockings, suspenders, and high-heeled shoes.

'Now,' she said with a smile, 'it's your turn.' She knelt in front of him, lifted his right foot and quickly untied his Reebok running shoe. She eased it off, peeled down his right sock, then started on the left foot. He sat there, breathing heavily, his palms flat on the bed by his side.

Kelly removed his shoes, socks, jacket and shirt, then started to unbuckle the belt of his trousers. He pulled away from her, placed a hand over hers. 'No,' he said thickly. She looked up, surprised. He cleared his throat. 'No.'

For a moment they faced each other in silence, Kelly's eyes looking coolly into his, never wavering, not even blinking. Up to now she had

87

goaded him along, taken gentle charge of each situation. Now he had gone against the grain, initiated this latest turn. It was up to him to continue.

'I'll do it,' he said after a moment. 'I'll ... I'll do it.'

'Okay,' Kelly said. She removed her hands slowly, carefully, let them fall to her sides.

He unbuckled his belt with clumsy fingers, popped open the button on his waistband, pulled down his fly, a metal rip. With an expression of excruciating embarrassment, almost of wretchedness, he dug in his thumbs and pulled both trousers and underpants down to his ankles.

He straightened up. Kelly leaned forward to take him in hand, then froze and let out a gasp. 'Oh my ...' she whispered, then checked herself before she could complete the oath.

But it was too late. The damage was done. His face crumpled. He bared his teeth. He looked as though he were fighting back tears. Kelly leaned forward again to make amends.

'I'm sorry, I didn't mean — '

'*Get away from me*!'

His out-thrust hand caught her shoulder hard enough to jar it, to send her sprawling. Kelly groped for her coat, clawed desperately through the pockets in search of the aerosol she had only had cause to use twice before. She found the metal cylinder and closed her hand around it, though didn't draw it from the damp folds of the imitation fur for fear it would antagonise him. She would use it only if needed. Rule One in a predicament like this was to make every effort to prevent the situation from escalating.

'I'm sorry,' she said in a low even voice. 'I'm sorry. I'll make it up to you. I shouldn't have acted like I did.'

He ignored her, which was fine by Kelly. She clammed up and pulled herself slowly out of his range, coming to a stop only when the wall prevented her from going any further.

She watched him as he pulled up his trousers, zipped them, buckled his belt. She was only too aware of punters who used women like herself as scapegoats for their own marital inadequacies. Fuck, one or two women she knew of were even willing to be used as punchbags for the right price, charging men as little as fifty pounds for the privilege of using their fists rather than their dicks. But Kelly had never been into that scene, had never worked out whether the women who allowed it were courageous, desperate, masochistic or all three.

She stiffened as he bent towards her, but he was merely picking up his shirt. As he buttoned it, still looking as though he were trying not to cry, Kelly relaxed a little.

His violence had been spontaneous, a one-off. He had lashed out like a child; he wasn't about to follow it up. It was cold sitting here on the floor. She dragged her coat across her knees for warmth and watched him pull on his socks, lace up his shoes.

When he had done so he grabbed his jacket, shrugged it on and stomped across to the door. Kelly was relieved to see him exit, to see the door click closed behind him.

She stood up, retrieved her clothes and dressed slowly. Delayed reaction was making her tremble, causing her heart to pound, her mouth to dry up. Christ, the sight of his prick! It had been a mass of scar tissue, criss-crossed with white healed-over flesh. The thought of having that thing inside her! Like being fucked by a lumpy mis-shapen candle.

She felt suddenly ill and staggered to the bathroom, leaned over the sink to be sick. After a moment the feeling passed, and raising her head she was startled by her reflection in the mirror. Her hair was a mess of rat-tails, her mascara had run, she looked washed-out, in need of a hot drink and a warm bed. She thought of the punter again, of the moment he had straightened up after pulling down his trousers, and she felt an overwhelming rush of relief, pity, horror and a kind of perverse humour. As she snatched toilet paper from the dispenser and blew her nose, she pictured his face, the way it had twisted in shame and fury. Then she stumbled back into the bedroom and slumped on the barely-rumpled coverlet, suddenly overcome by a bout of giggles which she thought would never stop.

18

It was action-replay time: second morning, second hangover. And despite setting the alarm on his watch for eight-thirty, Ian found himself opening his eyes at seven-fifteen again.

Bloody body-clock, he thought. He rolled onto his back, groaning. The inside of his stomach seemed to be swelling and bursting apart. Never again, he thought, never again will I allow alcohol to pass my lips.

He needed a piss. Badly. He pushed the duvet away from him and found he was still wearing his jeans and one sock. Shit, it must have been a good night last night. For the moment he couldn't remember quite what had happened and he didn't want to try. His head hurt so much that each little thought, each nugget of memory, was like a separate shard of glass being scraped against the inside of his skull.

He sat up, very slowly and very carefully. Despite this the room still tilted like the inside of a funhouse, causing great queasy waves to slosh inside him. He squeezed his eyes shut. Little gleeful sparks of sickness danced in his vision. His head was the drum to which they danced.

'Oh God,' he groaned.

He stood gingerly and tottered to the door, certain from the motion of the floor that the university had set sail overnight. Out in the corridor he could hear someone snoring, someone else playing a radio – the dj sounded so cheerful that Ian would gladly have strangled him. He stumbled into the toilet, unzipped himself and pissed for what seemed like minutes.

Back in bed he slept for two more hours. When he awoke it was nine-thirty, which meant he'd missed breakfast (big deal), but was still okay for his first lecture which wasn't until eleven. He felt a little better. His stomach was still tender but controllable, his mind able to construct coherent thoughts without it feeling as though someone were hammering tent pegs into his brain.

He remembered yesterday, last night, and tried to tell himself he was silly for being disappointed that Annie and Steph hadn't turned up in the bar at nine-thirty as Annie had promised they would. This weird society they had joined, The Crack, must have gone on for longer than they'd expected it to. Or maybe they had met someone there and had gone for coffee or something – a likely possibility, knowing Steph. Ian found himself hoping it wasn't men they had met. He derided himself for his jealousy but he couldn't stop the emotion persisting.

He and Neil had got pissed with some of the lads from Phys Ed, the course that Neil was doing. Ian had been taking it easy at first, but after it became obvious that the girls were not going to turn up he had thrown as much down his neck as he could in a rather childish attempt to mask his disappointment. How the hell Neil's mob drank as much as they did and still managed to leap around a gymnasium the following day was anyone's guess. Ian could barely crawl, let alone run. He was surprised the additives in the alcohol had not triggered off an asthma attack.

He got up, brushed his teeth, showered, dressed slowly. Movement made him feel worse – his stomach grumbled, his head felt like a cavity inside which a hedgehog was trapped. He looked in the mirror and groaned. What a ladykiller, he thought. Red-rimmed eyes, blotchy skin. All he needed were two holes in his neck and he could pass for Dracula's last meal.

He went to his lecture looking forward to seeing Annie. She was not there. He was disappointed and puzzled. He kept looking round the room as though half-believing that she would mysteriously appear or that he had somehow missed seeing her. So distracted was he by her absence that at one point Paul Carmichael asked casually, 'Mr Raven, are you with us this morning?' making Ian blush and nod.

After the lecture, at twelve-thirty, Ian hurried towards the coffee bar, wanting to know what had happened to Annie that morning and hoping Steph would be there to enlighten him. To his frustration she wasn't, and neither was Neil, though some of Steph's drama group were gathered in their clique in the corner. He hurried across. The ponytailed student with the stripey trousers – Simon or whatever his name was – looked up at Ian but showed no sign of recognising him.

'Hi,' Ian said, mustering a smile. 'Remember me? I'm a friend of Steph Peele's. You haven't seen her around have you?'

Ponytail squinted through cigarette smoke. 'Er . . . no, sorry. Not recently anyway.'

'Did you have a lecture this morning?'

'Yeah.'

'And was she there?'

'Er . . . yeah. Yeah, she was. But she was acting a bit kinda . . . weird.'

Ian felt a thread of unease worm through him. 'How do you mean, "weird"?'

'Well, just kinda ... withdrawn. Quiet. Like she didn't wanta speak to anyone. Just like ... weird, y'know?'

'Okay,' Ian said, 'thanks.' He moved away, wondering what to do. Annie not turning up for her lecture, Steph acting "weird" – what was going on?

He looked at his watch. It was almost 12:40. He had another lecture in fifty minutes – an introduction to teaching. Before that he had to have something to eat – now that his hangover had abated his stomach was muttering a relentless request for food. Also he had to go to the bookshop to buy a couple of books Carmichael had mentioned in the lecture, and to the library to photocopy some notes that Carmichael had requested they read for tomorrow. Well, if he was quick he ought to be able to do all those things *and* still have time to see if Annie was in her room before 1:30. He could even buy the books and photocopy the notes for her. She'd appreciate that.

He considered buying a snack from the coffee bar but then decided he needed something a little more substantial. Besides, the queue at the food counter was too long – not only would it be healthier buying a decent meal but probably quicker too. Unfortunately he was wrong. He reached the dining room only to discover that the queue was twice as long here. He cursed but tagged on to the end of it. By the time he had finished his chicken salad and baked potato it was almost 1:15.

He rushed to the bookshop, clutching his side as though that would prevent him from getting stitch, and purchased two copies of each of the two books that Carmichael had mentioned, the outlay taking a £49.80 bite out of his bank balance. Then it was to the library, a frustrated five-minute search for the enormously heavy out-of-print reference book that Carmichael had insisted was imperative to their future success, and another few minutes waiting for a gangly beak-nosed lecturer to run off twenty-four copies of a three-page newspaper article.

By the time Ian had finally copied the notes he wanted and returned the book to the shelf it was 1:28. Shit, he thought. Now he'd have to wait until 3:30 before he could see Annie.

His next lecture passed so slowly, and was concluded with such an interminable question-answer session, that Ian began to believe there was a conspiracy against him. At last, however, they were allowed to leave, whereupon Ian followed the signs to Merlin Hall, which was where Annie and Steph's room was. In his eagerness he became lost twice and had to double-back. By the time he finally pushed open the swing doors and stepped into the cramped but thankfully air-conditioned lobby he was sweating and irritable and his breath was rasping in his chest. Normally he made himself rest, take a few deep breaths, when he got into this state, but on this occasion he simply had two long blasts on his inhaler and made for the stairs. Steph and Annie lived in room 34. With six rooms on each floor this meant that Ian had to climb countless stairs, weighed down with a bagful of writing pads and hardback books, before he finally reached his destination.

He arrived sweaty and exhausted, and knocked on the girls' door, staring at the plastic sheet tacked below the room number, which was so obviously 'Steph'ian that it made him smile despite his discomfort. The sheet depicted a slyly grinning Garfield in the top left-hand corner beside which was a space on to which Steph had scrawled in pink felt-tip pen: Steph and Annie are ... Below this a sliding red arrow pointed to one of three options: In, Out, Shaking it all about. At this moment the arrow was pointing to none of these options. Indeed, it had sunk right off the scale as though afflicted with apathy.

Ian knocked again. 'Annie?' he called. 'Steph? Are you in there?' He had resigned himself to the fact that they were not, which would have caused the mystery to become deeper and even more frustrating, when a small tremulous voice said, 'Who is it?'

Ian felt something jump in his stomach. 'Annie?' he said. 'Is that you?'

'Who is it?' came the voice again.

'It's me − Ian. Are you all right?'

He heard movement, the soft creak of furniture as it was relieved of weight. 'Hang on,' called Annie, and Ian was certain he detected relief, even joy, in those two small tired syllables.

Footsteps padded towards him, muffled by the rectangle of dark wood. The door inched open. Annie's face peeked out. 'Ian,' she said as though she hadn't really believed it was him. She held the door wider and retreated into the room. 'I'm so glad to see you. Come in.'

He followed her into the room, looking around with both caution and interest. The closed curtains made the place seem dingy; it was a far more cluttered room than his, and not much bigger considering that two of them shared it. Everywhere Ian looked Steph's influence seemed prevalent, as though the red head's personality had overwhelmed Annie's. Books and posters reflected Steph's interest in stage and screen. The personal items on show − the knick-knacks and ornaments − were trivial, amusing, bawdy: it was immediately obvious to whom they belonged. The clothes draped over chair-backs, spilling on to the floor, were a crumpled pile of purples, reds, vivid greens, mustard yellows – the colours that Steph wore. Her toiletries and cosmetics outnumbered Annie's at the sink by at least four to one. Ian would even have laid money on the fact that the state-of-the-art radio cassette that gleamed majestically on the desk, and the haphazard stack of tapes beside it, belonged to one Stephanie Peele.

Annie, clad in a filmy but not at all revealing night-dress, crawled back on to her rumpled bed and looked at Ian through miserable bloodshot eyes. Her hair was a mess, her skin even paler and more blotchy than his had been that morning, her naked feet tiny and white, one laid over the other like new-born piglets seeking warmth.

She looked so confused, so exhausted, so defenceless, that Ian felt a catch in his throat. Not for the first time he felt an urge to put his arms around her, but if she took it the wrong way it would only add to her obvious distress. He pulled a chair from beneath one of the twin desks and perched on the edge of it. Clasping his hands between his knees, he asked pointlessly, 'Are you all right?'

Annie looked at him. Her bottom lip quivered. Then suddenly, shockingly, she burst into tears.

That did it. Ian was up off the chair, across the room, sitting down on the bunk beside her, embracing her, pulling her to him. There was no resistance on her part. She snuggled into his chest, her tears soaking his shirt-front.

'Shh,' Ian said, 'shh.' He felt weird: a little awkward, dismayed by her tears, but also happy to be holding her, strangely content that it was in his arms she had chosen to cry.

'Hey,' he said, 'shh, it's okay, Annie.' He patted her on the shoulder, still trying to shake off his feeling of awkwardness.

'Sorry,' she said in a voice so small it tugged at his heart. As though suddenly realising what she was doing, she pulled gently away from him, groping under her pillow for a handkerchief.

She blew her nose, wiped her eyes. Smiling what he hoped was a sympathetic and reassuring smile, Ian said, 'Do you want to tell me what's wrong? Have you and Steph fallen out or something?'

Annie shook her head, then winced in pain. 'No,' she said. 'Well . . . no, not exactly. It's more than that.' Haltingly she told him about their nightmarish visit to The Crack and its aftermath.

'Steph's just been acting really strange since we came back from that meeting. She's been kind of cold, withdrawn, spaced-out like she's on drugs or something. When she does talk, it's about Dan Latcher or The Crack. That's the only time there's any kind of spark in her eyes. I don't know . . . something happened last night . . . something . . . He *did* something to those people, I don't know

94

what. It's ... it's hard to explain, Ian. You've got to see Steph to know what I'm talking about. I .... I just don't know what to do about it.'

Her voice faded off. She looked scared, sickly-pale. Ian didn't know what to think. His instinct was to seek a rational explanation and yet he didn't want to do Annie a disservice by expressing doubts, reeling off glib theories, undermining her fears. Trying not to sound disparaging he asked, 'But what about you? How come you weren't affected?'

'I was,' Annie responded tiredly, 'but not in the same way.' She wafted a hand at herself. 'I mean, look at me. I look dreadful, don't I?'

Ian shrugged. He didn't want to say "yes", but to say "no" would be a lie. Realising his dilemma, Annie gave a strained smile.

'I look dreadful,' she confirmed. 'And I feel dreadful. Ever since last night I've had headaches, pains in my limbs, stomach cramps, a runny nose. Every time I eat or drink something I bring it straight back up again. And there's ...' She suddenly blushed, tailed off. 'No, it doesn't matter.'

'What, Annie?' Ian asked. He reached for her hand, which lay in his like a limp fish. But when he squeezed it, it squeezed back. 'What?' he persisted.

'It's ... it's a bit embarrassing.' She wouldn't look him in the eye.

'I don't mind,' Ian said. 'You can tell me.' I'm probably going to regret this, he thought.

There was a pause as Annie considered. Then she said, 'Well, it's just that ... well ... I'm having my period at the moment ... and ... well ... God, this *is* embarrassing ... well, you see, since yesterday ... well ... my flow has been like ... really heavy ... y'know ... which is unusual for me.'

She pulled her hand from his grasp and used it to half-shield her face as though suddenly fearful of their intimacy. 'I'm sorry,' she said. 'I shouldn't have told you that.'

'No, no, that's all right,' Ian mumbled. He tried to project an air of maturity but his cheeks were blazing. 'Have you ... er ... have you seen the doctor or anything? About your ... er ... all your symptoms, I mean?'

'No,' said Annie. 'I've just spent the day in bed ... well, running between bed and toilet to be precise. When Steph went out this morning I asked her if she'd get me some paracetamol and stuff from the shop and she kind of vaguely promised she would, but I haven't seen her since. Actually, though, I don't feel quite so bad now. Everything seems to have calmed down a bit.'

'Would you like me to go and get you the stuff?' Ian asked. 'The shop shuts at five and it's twenty past four now.'

'Would you?' Annie said. 'Oh, thanks, Ian, that'd be really nice.'

She wrote down what she needed and gave him some money. He was back eight minutes later. Annie directed him to the cupboard above the sink, which contained glasses, mugs, teaspoons, coffee, tea, powdered milk, sugar, a kettle, a teapot and biscuits.

'You're certainly well stocked,' he said, handing her two para-cetamols and a glass of water.

'It's all Steph's stuff,' Annie admitted. 'To tell you the truth, I hardly brought anything with me except for clothes and toiletries. I didn't really want to come here, you see. I wanted to stay at home with my family and friends. I suppose by not bringing much I thought I could sort of keep a link with home, do you know what I mean?' She shrugged. 'I've never really been away from home before and the thought of cutting myself free was terrifying ... God, you must think I sound pathetic.'

'No,' he said, moving across to sit beside her again, 'not at all. Leaving home is a big step. I remember when I got my job in Leeds, I almost felt like turning it down because I didn't fancy the thought of fending for myself after living with my mum in Huddersfield for the last eight years. I even said as much to her and she nearly bit my head off about it.' He smiled affectionately. 'She's a strong-willed lady, my mother.'

'So you're not actually *from* Leeds then?'

'Oh yes, I was born there. I lived there till I was ten. My dad was from Leeds, you see, and my mum was from Huddersfield, which is about twenty miles away. They met at somebody's wedding. Actually I think my mum was a bridesmaid and my dad was best man – you know, real romantic stuff. Anyway, they got married and we all lived in Leeds, and then they split up and me and mum moved back to Huddersfield where all her relatives were. My dad got a job in London, and then eventually moved out to Indonesia. I haven't seen him for about six years now.' He looked down at Annie and smiled wistfully. 'But you don't want to hear my life story. The boredom'll send you to sleep.'

She drew up her knees and pulled the edge of a rumpled blanket over them. 'Don't be silly,' she said, 'it's not boring at all. It's *my* life story that's boring. I was born in Preston. I've lived there all my life. I've got two brothers and a dog called Roxy. My mum and dad are still happily married after twenty-nine years. The end.'

Ian shrugged. 'I wish I had that sort of life. I wouldn't say my parents splitting up was exactly an *interesting* time. More like traumatic. It wasn't an easy divorce.'

'Oh, no, I didn't mean it like that,' Annie said, a little flustered. She touched Ian's arm. 'I'm sorry, I didn't mean to sound insensitive.'

'Nah, it's all right. It all happened a long time ago. It doesn't really bother me any more. I still get letters from my dad. He's always saying I'll have to go over to see him but nothing ever comes of it. Maybe one day I will, though.'

'I'm sure you will,' said Annie. 'Do you ... do you miss your dad?'

Ian thought for a moment. 'I suppose so, yeah. Sometimes. I don't really think about it too much. I regret that he wasn't there when I was growing up, or not much anyway. We never really got the chance to become close. I'd like to have played football with him and gone fishing and ... I don't know ... just talked. I'd have just liked to have been his *friend*, you know?'

'Maybe you still will,' said Annie. 'There's still time.'

'Yeah, I suppose.' Ian blinked, seemed to rouse himself. 'God, I haven't spoken to anyone like this for a long time. It's strange talking about yourself. I suppose I had a fairly insular existence in Leeds.'

'Sorry,' said Annie, 'I didn't mean to pry.'

'Oh no,' said Ian, 'that's okay. It's quite nice really. Nice that someone's taking an interest.'

Annie smiled. Ian smiled back. An awkward silence followed, a temporary hiatus. 'I'll make some coffee, shall I?' Ian said, standing up.

Annie nodded. 'That'd be nice. If my stomach allows me to keep it down, that is.'

'How are you feeling now?'

'Physically, a bit better. Mentally – scared, worried, confused.' She paused for just a second then blurted out, 'It's really nice to have you here though, Ian. Thanks for listening to me.'

'That's okay,' he mumbled. He could think of little else to say. For the next few minutes he busied himself making the coffee while Annie stared into space, hugging her knees. When the coffee was ready, Ian handed her a mug and sat on the edge of the bunk again. He sipped, grimaced at the heat, then said thoughtfully, 'What I still don't understand is why Dan Latcher should have had a different effect on you than on everybody else. I mean, how come everyone else thought he was Superman, whereas he just made you – literally – sick?'

97

Annie cupped her mug in both hands as though it were something live and delicate. 'I've been thinking about that a lot too,' she said. She was silent for a moment as she sipped her coffee, collected her thoughts. Then she said, 'Maybe it's because I was the only one in that room who didn't *want* to join his stupid society. All the others were open to it, but I resisted. I mean, it was Steph who dragged me along. She was the one who spoke to Latcher at the ECA meeting. I just hung back, I didn't like him from the start. His eyes and his smile and his voice − ' she shuddered ' − urgh! It was like ...' she searched for a comparison ' ... like the wolf in Red Riding Hood, all dressed up in Grandma's clothes. Trying to be friendly and alluring and charming, whereas all he really wanted to do was gobble us up.'

She looked at Ian. There must have been scepticism on his face, though he wasn't aware of it, for her next words were defensive.

'Oh, I don't mean literally, of course. But there was something ... ugly ... nasty ... something voracious about him.' She shuddered again, more violently this time. 'And stuck in that room, watching him do his magic act; seeing that guy burn up on stage and thinking he was dead ... I was so scared. Not just because of what was happening, but of *him*. Of Latcher. There's something *awful* about him. Something dangerous.' Her face was screwed up with the effort of trying to express the extent of her revulsion and fear.

Ian said gently, 'So you were the only one who reacted in the way you did? The only one who was sick?'

Annie paused. It was obvious from her expression that she hadn't considered this.

'I think so,' she said guardedly. 'At least, I didn't see anyone else. But then all I wanted to do was get away. I didn't pay much attention to what the others were doing.'

'Hmm.' Ian tapped his lip thoughtfully. He stared blankly at a poster that Steph had pinned above her desk: *The Taming Of The Shrew* starring Burton and Taylor. 'If Dan Latcher is as dangerous as you say he is, then something's obviously got to be done, someone needs telling − the Union President or even the Chancellor. We have to find Steph and anyone else who went to this meeting and talk to them, find out what sort of hold Latcher's got over them. I mean, is there any chance that he was using some kind of drug? In the candle smoke or the wine maybe?'

Annie pulled a face. 'I thought of that but it doesn't really gel, does it? I mean, drugs wear off. And I've never known a drug have that sort of mass reaction before. And not everybody drank the wine. And if it was the smoke, why wasn't I affected in the same way? No. Something else that I wondered about was whether Latcher used some kind of hypnotism or something, but that doesn't really ring true either. Nobody can hypnotise somebody into doing something they don't want to do, can they?'

'I don't know,' Ian said. 'I don't think so.' He stood up, paced the room for a moment. 'Okay, we'll talk to Steph when she turns up, see what we can get out of her. And after that, if needs be, we'll confront Latcher. Maybe we could even infiltrate a Crack meeting.'

Annie reared back as though confronted with a venomous snake. She shook her head vehemently.

'No way. I'm not going back to that place again. And you shouldn't either, Ian. You might end up like Steph.'

He raised a hand to placate her. 'Okay, maybe that isn't such a good idea. But when you're well we can at least take a nosey into the room where the meeting took place, see what we can find.'

Annie nodded reluctantly. 'Okay, but only on the condition that we go there during daylight and that we make sure Latcher is somewhere else at the time.'

'You talk as though he's a vampire or something,' Ian said half jokingly.

'Maybe he is,' Annie replied, then she leavened her comment by smiling a little. 'Oh, I know it all sounds far-fetched, but you weren't there, Ian. You didn't see it happen.'

He shrugged, took a gulp of coffee. 'I wonder if Neil's seen Steph today. I'll be playing squash with him later. Is it okay if I tell him what you've told me?'

'Yes, course. It isn't a secret. The more people that know about this, the better.'

'I reckon if anyone can get through to Steph, Neil can. They get on really well together, don't they?'

Annie nodded, unconvinced. Since yesterday's fateful meeting with Latcher at the ECA Fair there had been only one man in Stephanie Peele's life. She thought of the way her room-mate's eyes shone whenever she spoke of Dan. It was a flat, somehow desperate shine, the hungry glee of a heroin addict who manages to score after going for too long without a fix. She thought of the way Steph was before: bubbly, full of opinions and *joie de vivre*. In many ways, she supposed, Steph − despite her strong-willed self-confidence − was like a little girl. Naive, trusting, wide open to the corrupting influences of parasites such as Dan Latcher. She felt the anger and dismay welling up inside her all over again. Suddenly she wanted to change the subject, felt a need to talk of mundane things, to regain a handhold in normality.

'How did the lecture go today?' she asked. 'Did I miss anything vital?'

That reminded Ian about the books he had bought and the notes he had photocopied for her. Annie was touched by the gesture and leaned forward to kiss him on the cheek. They talked a little more — at first about the course, about the lecture that morning, but eventually, inevitably, they returned to the subject of Steph, to Dan Latcher and to The Crack.

'Look,' Ian said, 'I'll speak to Neil tonight, and tomorrow we'll come round and all confront Steph, make her talk to us. What time would be best? I was thinking early morning. Around eight-thirty?'

Annie nodded. 'Yes, before she has time to go out. I hope we have better luck with her as a group than I've had on my own. I've tried talking to her till I'm blue in the face but it's hopeless. It's like talking to an answering machine.'

'Don't worry,' Ian said, narrowing his eyes. 'Ve haf vays of making her tok. Or at least,' he amended, 'we'll try and think of some before tomorrow. She surely can't be evasive with all three of us getting at her.'

'Can't she?' said Annie. 'We'll see.' She snuggled down into her bunk, pulling the blankets up to her waist. Delighted as she had been to see Ian, their conversation was beginning to take its toll on her. Her head was throbbing again, and the coffee she had drunk was coiling and burbling in her stomach, deciding whether to allow itself to be digested or whether to follow the example of everything else she had swallowed that day. Ian, bless him, seemed to get the hint immediately. He looked at his watch, stood up.

'Well, I'd better get going,' he said. 'I want something to eat before I play squash. Something to line the stomach in case I'm bullied into consuming vast amounts of alcohol again.'

Annie smiled tightly. 'Enjoy yourself,' she said. 'Good luck with Neil.'

'Thanks,' said Ian. 'Take care. I'll see you tomorrow.' She nodded. He left.

After he had eaten and changed and thought about what Annie had told him, Ian went to call on Neil. They had arranged to meet at the squash courts, but Ian wanted a chance to talk before the rubber balls started to fly. He heard the Fine Young Cannibals blasting out of Neil's open door as soon as he stepped on to his landing. He walked up to the door, knocked perfunctorily, and stuck his head round. Neil, scowling and bare-chested, was peeling the plastic packet away from a brand-new Fred Perry sports shirt.

Under cover of the music, Ian sneaked up behind him and tapped him on the shoulder. Neil dropped the shirt, leaped approximately two feet into the air, and spun round, eyes and mouth wide open.

Ian started laughing. After a moment Neil relaxed and grinned ruefully. 'You bugger,' he said, punching Ian on the arm. He bent down to retrieve his shirt, then crossed the room to turn the music down.

'Where's Bobo?' Ian said, looking around. Bobo was Neil's room-mate who Ian was yet to meet. According to Neil he was a Yeti-proportioned heavy metal freak with a repertoire of around thirty million jokes, ninety-five per cent of which were unrepeatable in polite company. Despite their differences, Ian gathered that so far the two of them were getting along pretty well.

'In the bar as usual, I suppose,' replied Neil. 'I haven't seen him since breakfast. What brings you here anyway? I thought we were meeting at the courts?'

'We were,' said Ian, 'but there's been a change of plan. I wanted to talk to you first.'

'What about?'

'Steph.'

Neil scowled. 'Oh, yeah? What about her?'

'You don't seem too pleased to hear her name. I thought you two were hunky dory.'

Neil pulled his shirt over his head. 'So did I, until today.'

'Until today? What do you mean?'

Neil sat down, pulled his trainers on and began to lace them up. 'Oh, I dunno,' he said, shrugging his muscular shoulders. 'She's been ... really off with me today. As though she doesn't want to know me any more. She avoided me in the coffee bar this morning, and when I was finally able to catch up with her she just acted really cool. I mean, you know what she's like, Ian − all smiles and hugs and jumping around, saying exactly what she thinks and everything. Well, today when I reached out to touch her, she just kind of flinched back, wouldn't let me near her. And when I asked her what the matter was, she just said, "Nothing", and started walking away. I mean, she wouldn't even look me in the eye. I asked if I'd be seeing her later and she said she didn't think so, she had things to do.' He looked up at Ian, waved a hand in frustration. 'What the hell have I done, eh? I just don't understand women. You think everything's going okay and then they just turn round and smack you in the face. It's just ...' He struggled for adequate vocabulary. 'It's just bloody annoying,' he finished lamely.

Ian leaned against the top bunk, swinging his squash racket in his

101

hand like a pendulum. 'That's what I wanted to talk to you about,' he said. 'I know why Steph's acting weird.'

'Do you?' Neil said, surprised. 'Why?'

Ian told Neil what he had heard from Annie a couple of hours before.

Neil glared into space, the muscles in his arms tightening as he clenched his fists. 'I'll mash this Latcher's fucking brains in,' he muttered.

'That is one solution,' agreed Ian. 'However, Annie and I thought that subtler tactics were called for − at least at first.'

'Such as?' said Neil.

Ian repeated what he and Annie had decided − confronting Steph in the morning, and if possible, investigating The Crack.

'Yeah, count me in,' said Neil, 'especially if you tackle this Latcher guy.' He shook his head. 'I mean, who the hell does he think he is, eh? What sort of hold has he got over them, do you reckon?'

Ian shrugged. 'We wondered about drugs or hypnotism, but, well, I can't really see that, can you?'

Neil considered. 'I dunno. I suppose it must be something like that. Like some sort of brainwashing or whatever. I mean, you know Steph − she does her own thing, she doesn't let anyone push her around. She's not acting like she was today because she's fallen for this Latcher guy's charm. She just wasn't the same person. Something was missing −' he tapped his head '− up here.' His bewilderment was superceded by anger again. He looked around the room as though for something to tear apart. 'If I could get my hands on that bastard, I'd soon shake it out of him.'

'Bottle it till tomorrow,' advised Ian. 'Come on, let's go and play squash.'

Neil glared at him. 'How can you be so calm? Steph might be with this Latcher guy now.'

'Yeah,' replied Ian, 'but there's nothing we can do about it, is there? We don't know where they are. It's pointless running around like headless chickens.'

Neil sat and glowered. Then he said, 'How about this room where the first meeting was held? We could just go and check that out.'

Ian looked doubtful. 'I dunno, Neil. I promised Annie we'd leave all that till tomorrow.'

'So?' said Neil. 'They might be there now. We could be doing something to stop it.'

Ian said nothing.

Neil jumped up. 'I don't believe this,' he exclaimed. 'What's the matter with you?'

102

Ian squirmed inwardly but remained silent. Instinct told him that what Neil was proposing was inadvisable, but he could think of no concrete reasons to back up his qualms. In the end he murmured feebly, 'It's just that ... well ... Annie told me that Latcher was ... was dangerous. She said there was something ... bad about him. I just think it would be better to get more information before we do anything rash.'

'Bollocks!' replied Neil, shaking his head in disgust. 'Well, I'm going, even if you're not. I'll see you at the courts.'

He stormed out, clutching his squash racket as though it were a spiked club he intended to hunt dinosaurs with. Ian hovered for a second, then went after him, muttering, 'Shit,' under his breath. 'Hang on, Neil,' he called, pulling his friend's door shut, leaving the Fine Young Cannibals to amuse themselves. Neil, about to crash through the fire door that led onto the stairwell, turned with a scowl.

'What?'

Ian caught up with him. 'You didn't really think I'd let you go on your own, did you?' he said.

The frown remained on Neil's face for two seconds longer, then was replaced by a grateful smile. 'Come on.'

The two of them marched down the steps, across to the main University building, and along the largely deserted corridors. A chorus of drunken and sarcastic wolf-whistles filtered through the open door of the bar as they walked past in their shorts. Ian's heart began to pound as they came to the first staircase and began to ascend. He licked his lips. The higher they climbed the deeper the silence that enveloped them. Neil's face was set and determined; concern for Steph was giving him a tunnel-vision fury that deflected fear and doubt. Ian clutched the metal hand-rail to stop himself from trembling. His breath was coming too quickly. He realised with a sudden shock that he had left his inhaler in the bag which contained his clothes back in Neil's room.

He considered bringing the fact to Neil's attention but then decided against it. He doubted he would receive much sympathy; Neil was so hyped-up that Ian didn't think he would be prepared to wait while it was fetched. They continued to ascend. Floor F came into sight; only one more floor to go. Some of the floors were in twilight darkness, some flooded with light, depending on whether or not the rooms were in use this evening.

Floor G was one of the dark ones. Ian was not sure whether to feel relieved or apprehensive. His breathing was under control, but only just. Without a pause Neil pushed open the fire door, stepped forward and ran his hand down the bank of light switches on his left.

Panels of strip lighting flickered erratically to life. As a result the twilight outside the steel-framed windows abruptly deepened to near-black. Neil marched down the corridor, Ian in tow, checking off the door numbers. Eventually he came to the door beneath the sign: "G7 leading to G8". 'This is the one, isn't it?' he asked Ian.

Ian nodded silently. He was too busy regulating his breathing to speak. Neil's jawbone clenched; he reached out and curled his fist around the door handle. He jerked it down and shoved. Nothing happened. The door was locked.

'Can I help you, *gentlemen*?'

The two of them whirled round at the voice, Ian desperately sucking in air. The voice's owner was a barrel-shaped man in his sixties, wisps of white hair straggling over his wrinkled scalp. A pair of black-framed spectacles perched on his pug nose; his jaw jutted aggressively. He wore a blue overall and carried a tool box. There was a distinct look of suspicion in his piggy eyes.

'We ... er ... thought there was a meeting up here tonight. For ... er ... a club we've joined,' stammered Neil. Ian was breathing deeply, in and out, like an expectant mother.

The man eyed the pair's attire sceptically. 'I think it's the gym you'll be wanting,' he said. 'First years, are you?'

'Yes, sir,' managed Ian, adopting his best "We're-new-we-don't-know-anything" smile.

The man didn't smile back but he jerked his head towards the staircase. 'Aye, well, there's no meeting up here tonight. I'd go down to the bottom and start again if I were you.'

'Thanks, sir, we will. Come on, Neil,' Ian said tightly. Neil gave the locked door a final scowl and followed.

'I'll get that bastard,' he muttered as they descended the stairs.

Ian's breathing was easing enough for him to joke. 'The caretaker?'

There was no answering smile from Neil. 'Latcher,' he muttered. 'I'll fucking find him, I mean it.'

'We'll all find him,' Ian said, 'but tomorrow. For now I'm going to have a blast of Ventolin then I'll thrash you at squash. Loser buys the drinks. Agreed?'

'Agreed,' said Neil grimly, 'but you'll regret it.'

Ian did regret it. And the next morning, when he woke up, he also regretted getting reeling drunk for the third night in a row.

19

It was filled with vicious, sentient life. It forced its way between his lips and prised his teeth apart. Unwillingly his jaws yawned wide to receive it, his mouth providing a soft haven, a warm dark feeding-ground. He felt its fat sliding, tasted it — like a salty slug — and wanted to gag but could not. It seemed as though his body was numbed, as though he were alive solely from the neck up. It pushed against the roof of his mouth, suddenly engorged, and a moment later was spitting its slimy offspring deep into his throat . . .

His teeth clamped like a sprung trap. He flung himself upright as though motion could shake off his disgust. He was wheezing and sobbing; the memory of his trauma chilled his stomach, trampled down the barrier that the years had erected. He was ten years old and he lived in a terror that his parents only knew the half of. He heard his father's voice: 'You'd better buck your ideas up, my lad,' and he looked across the room and saw him standing there, massive and scowling in the darkness, his face — his *man's* face — full of scorn and disgust and shame at his miserable excuse for a son.

Then he remembered where he was, who he had become. His past slipped back down the years where it belonged. The figure standing at the far side of the room was not his father. His father was large and dark and muscled, not bald and squat and paunchy. His father did not have eyes that flashed in the darkness, teeth that glowed like phosphorous. His father was — had been — a hard man, sometimes a brutal man, but he was not a nightmare wearing a human face.

'No,' he moaned and pulled his blankets over his head, 'no, you're not real, you're a bad dream, go away.' He imagined his blankets were a womb, a deep soft place where nothing could touch him. He squeezed his eyes shut, sealing himself in. Almost subconsciously he began to whisper, 'Our Father, Which Art In Heaven . . .'

When the prayer was over, he peeled his blankets slowly down from his face and looked across the room. The nightmare-man was gone. He felt a surge of unalloyed triumph that he had managed to banish his fear. Last night, which he could remember only as a buzzing confused set of memory-flashes, must have been a dream after all. Certainly he had awoken in his bed, disoriented, sobbing, his damp blankets plastered to his body. But, like all nightmares, the shock-waves had quickly died. A hot shower, a good breakfast, and the equilibrium had been restored.

But now ... this. He was back in the night-world again. His mind felt pulled out of shape by something larger than he was. Thoughts long suppressed were being sucked like abortions through wounds in his psyche which had all but healed many years ago. He remembered his dream and shuddered; but the fat alien thing sitting in the hollow of his mouth was simply his tongue, dry and stale with nightmare. He hawked up a ball of phlegm; the unpleasantness of it against the back of his teeth encouraged him to get out of bed. Shaking his head, shivering slightly, he padded barefoot until he came to a lightswitch and a sink.

He spat out the debris of his dream, twisted the taps full on so he would not have to look at it. Water swirled round the sink, splashed up off the sides like breakers against a sea wall, wetting him. He altered the faucet, reducing the flow of water, and cupped his hands under the cold tap. Bubbles sparkled in his open palm; his hands looked blurred beneath. Lowering his head, he splashed needle-cold water into his face.

He watched his reflection in the mirror as he dried himself off. He was looking for the emergence of a ten year old but saw only the he that was now. By the side of the sink sat a glass that contained a blue toothbrush and a tube of toothpaste carefully squeezed from the bottom. He took these items from the glass and placed them on the shelf of the sink. The bottom of the glass contained a few smears of dried toothpaste and a film of cloudy water. He rinsed out the glass twice, then filled it almost to the brim and drank.

The coldness sprang to his temples and made him wince. When the pain began to ebb he switched off the tap, dried his hands, put everything back in its place and returned to bed. He lay in the darkness, open-eyed, his blanket pulled up to his chin, the fingers of both hands overlapping the top like a "Wot No" cartoon.

Gradually, muscle by muscle, he felt himself relaxing. He turned onto his side, eyes drifting closed − and then sleep fled like a fox into the darkness. The scream inside him seemed to ignite every nerve in his body but emerged from his throat as a tiny incoherent sound. He sat up, staring at what had torn all hope of sleep away from him.

It was the smile of the butcher. The grinning arc of steel was back, like a lethal slice of moon, on the carpet. *No*, he breathed, but the glint of the blades silently contradicted him. It was impossible. Unreal. It was a dream ...

It was no dream.

A hand curled from the silence behind him and closed over his mouth. An arm slithered round his body like a snake, clamping his

106

arms to his sides. He began to struggle desperately, the scream that could not be released making his eyes bulge, his temples pound. He was helpless as a child in the grip of an abuser. A whispering voice spoke directly into his ear, hurting the delicate inner mechanisms; freezing them, burning them, he couldn't tell which.

'Look,' the voice said. 'Look and remember.'

He looked. The silent scream lurched up another notch, causing an almost unbearable pressure to build in his head. The blades were beginning to *move* on the carpet, to collide one against the next, with a series of sharp sly metallic clinks and scrapes. And within the movement there were flashes and sparks as light danced on polished steel. Sparks that resolved themselves into pictures, patterns.

And he saw . . .

Himself.

He was ten years old. It was summer. Though what happened lasted for only two months it seemed to fill his childhood, to be all that growing up consisted of. He saw himself that fateful day as clearly as a photograph. He wore blue shorts, grey socks concertina-ed round his ankles, black scuffed shoes and a white shirt with thin brown diagonal stripes. He was lightly tanned and the sun had bleached his hair the colour of corn. The skin was peeling from his nose and his arms. He had a grubby plaster on his right knee and a graze on his elbow where his bike had skidded as it took a corner and spilled him on to tarmac. He was singing some song as he walked, humming where he didn't know the words, now and then breaking into short sprints, kicking imaginary footballs between imaginary goalposts.

Summer sounds, summer smells, summer colours. His friend, Mike Greenland, had wavy hair like tiny brown serpents, a square heavy-fleshed face that would never be thin. He opened the door wearing a white t-shirt whose arm-holes looked tight as tourniquets. The baggy blue trousers that he wore were stiff and shiny with grass stains.

'Hi,' Mike said.

'You coming out?'

'Yeah, just a minute. My mum's writing out a list of stuff she wants from the shops.'

They waited on the doorstep, lazy as lizards. Watching the heat haze flowing across the road at the end of the street, they debated whether to buy sherbet bombs or a *Captain Magnificent* comic with the change that Mike's mother would let them spend. At last Mrs Greenland emerged from the house and gave Mike the list and the money. The boys moved slothfully away, feeling the heat of the pavement even through the soles of their shoes.

'Oi, Mally, watch this,' Mike said, and suddenly went down on all fours. With a grunt he kicked up his legs, took two unsteady steps on his hands before the coins his mother had given him cascaded from his pocket. 'Aw, shit,' he moaned. The money bounced and rolled over the pavement. The two boys scampered about, retrieving it, saving the coins from slipping into drainage grilles and the cracks between paving slabs.

Mally. The nickname rose in his mind, a jolt of nostalgia, though without disrupting the story that the knives were unfolding. The name conjured a feeling in him, too vague to be termed a memory, of a time before Bad Things. He and Mike and two other boys in their class − Doug Stoughton and Graham Warwick − had once had a spate of calling each other by their middle names. For what reason he couldn't now recall; he simply remembered that as ten year olds they had found the whole thing quite pointlessly funny. Mike's middle name had been Nicholas (hilariously stupid); his own had been − of course, still was − Martin, later modified to Mally. In time the craze wore off but his nickname stuck. Strangely, however, after that summer no one ever called him Mally again. It was almost as though the nickname had been a charm against evil, which events proved didn't work and which was thus discarded. Or perhaps it was simpler, more brutal than that; perhaps it was that owning a nickname was primarily a child's right, and after that summer, after what happened, he could never again claim to be a child.

Four streets from Mike's house was The Edge. This was little more than a dirt-track which ran behind the grounds of the grammar school. The point where the sports fields ended and The Edge began was marked by a tall wire-mesh fence which was slowly falling prey to entwining weeds and wild grasses. On the other side of The Edge the ground sloped gently down to a valley floor rough with heather and bracken and stark malnourished trees. The Edge continued uphill for about a mile until it reached a peak which afforded a magnificent view of the valley below, a few houses shining white as sugar cubes on the opposite side, and away to the left a squat cluster of red-brick buildings which made up the grammar school.

The view, the isolation, the wild freedom of the landscape were all reasons why Mally and Mike liked The Edge. But the main reason, what really drew them, was that standing right on top of the hill, jutting from the earth as if it grew there, was a bleak decrepit monument to a violent past: the Tower.

It could be seen for miles yet it was somehow solitary and secret, a place where they knew they couldn't be observed. Not that they did anything to be ashamed of, but sometimes it simply felt good to be immune from jurisdiction. They would sit among the heather at the base of the Tower, ingesting the view like gods overlooking their territory. Or they would go inside the Tower, climb the winding broken steps to its summit, and bask there unseen, shielded from the breeze by the crenellated wall that encircled them.

The decision to go to the Tower that day was silent and mutual. Mike's mother did not need the shopping urgently so they could afford to take their time. In the streets that led to the slope where The Edge began, people were languishing on lawns, many in clothes whose skimpiness would normally have embarrassed them. The path along The Edge was circuitous, but neither boy questioned the logic of the other as their feet began to follow that route.

That walk to the Tower stood out sharp and clear, as though the events to come had thrown out some precursive energy that had attuned Mally's senses but failed to provide a warning. The knives showed him a ladybird landing on his hand, tickling his skin, before flying away; a dead hedgehog in the undergrowth, deflated and eyeless and baked dry by the sun; Mike juggling with rocks, then jumping away as he lost control, and the rocks thudding to the earth like enormous hailstones; the two of them picking blackberries and eating them, and then spitting them out because they tasted so sour.

The day seemed to snooze, to drift by languidly. It was a day when nothing should have happened; a day whose only purpose was to fulfil its duty as a minuscule chip of time in the life of the planet.

'God, it's hot,' Mike said, flapping at the midges that hovered around his face.

Mally watched them scatter then reform into a tight, darting, spherical formation.

'Yeah,' he said. He was thinking about the hedgehog they'd found, wondering how something so dry and still, like a curled-up piece of old leather, could ever have lived and moved and breathed.

'I know what we'll get with my mum's money,' said Mike. 'Icepops. We'll sit up in the Tower and eat them.'

'Yeah,' enthused Mally. 'Fab idea. Maybe you'll have enough to get some icepops *and* a comic.'

Mike looked doubtful but he nodded. 'Yeah,' he said, 'maybe.'

They fell silent as they began to trudge uphill. It was so humid they felt as though the air were pressing them down, as though their breath struggled in their lungs because the close atmosphere had no spaces into which it could escape. Mally looked up and saw the Tower, grey-black and brooding. It pointed at the sky, dusty and old and somehow scaly, like a mummified finger.

The sun was so bright that walking into the Tower's shadow was like stepping into a dark room. The boys stopped and blinked, momentarily disoriented. Here, on the sheltered side, the stone of the Tower was deliciously cool. Mike said, 'Right, I'll go get the stuff. Do you want to come or are you staying here?'

'I'll stay,' said Mally. 'I'll be up at the top.'

'Okay. I'll see you back here in twenty minutes.'

Mally nodded, and Mike began to trudge down the opposite side of the hill, back into the full heat of the sun. Mally watched him until his head dipped below the line of heather, then he stepped into the Tower.

After being outside it was like a fridge. Mally shivered as the cold worked on his skin, chilling it. He began to ascend the winding stone steps, his left arm held out, hand skimming gently over the rough brick of the wall. At intervals slits were set into the stonework, admitting golden rods of light.

By the time he reached the top his legs were aching. He stepped into the daylight and stood motionless for a few seconds, blinded and dizzied by the sun. The heather which coated the valley was a rich purple-brown, the grammar school playing fields a brilliant, almost luminous green. The sky was so blue it hurt his eyes. He felt breathless, dazzled; felt as though he were perched on top of the world.

He sat down, resting his back against the Tower's crenellated rim. A slight breeze riffled his hair; whatever the weather there was always wind up here. Clouds inched ponderously overhead. Far off in the distance a car was a flicker of red steel. An ant-woman stretched to hang up sheets that were snippets of tissue paper.

He smiled, murmured as contentment slipped through him. Sitting here felt somehow like being at the centre of all things, like being in perfect tune with his surroundings. His body and soul seemed snug and perfect. He was filled with such well-being he felt sure he could levitate. An insect droned overhead, then drifted away. He closed his eyes, let his thoughts wander; his mind was a warm sea and he flotsam, riding the gentle swells.

He was jarred from his doze by scraping sounds, by the hollow rise and fall of voices. For a moment, confused, he looked around him, even peered into the sky, then he realised that the sounds were echoing up from the Tower's stair-well. Mike was back, he thought, and it sounded as though he had someone with him. Peering into the stair-well he saw a head appear, a white arm, heard a buzz of conversation and a snickering laugh.

He opened his mouth to say something, then the head jerked up and an unfamiliar face looked at him. Mally closed his mouth and retreated nervously back from the stair-well. The boy who had looked up, older than Mally by at least five years, pulled himself into the sunlight. He was followed moments later by his companion, a skinny boy with a sharp sly face. Mally felt dry-mouthed, jittery; he remained silent. He had seen neither of these boys before, yet he could sense the menace in them.

'Well, well, who's this?' said the boy who had been first up, and turned to say something to his companion that Mally didn't catch. The other boy laughed harshly and gave Mally a sidelong look. Mally was suddenly and uncomfortably aware of how high off the ground he was.

'What's your name, son?' said the boy who had spoken, jerking his head at Mally. He was square-set with flat slow features. Flecks of saliva sprayed from his mouth when he talked.

'Er ... Mally,' he said, unwilling to give his real name. He looked at his wrist but he wasn't wearing a watch. Unconvincingly he said, 'I'd better go. I'm supposed to be meeting my friend.'

He tried to sidle round the boys, but Sly-face moved between Mally and the stair-well. Flat-face said, 'You'll go when we say so. We've got some stuff to show you first, haven't we, Simmsy?'

'Yeah,' said Simmsy with a nasty snigger. 'Fuckin' right we have.' He pulled up his black t-shirt, and Mally saw that tucked into the front of his jeans, flat against his thin white stomach, were two magazines which he pulled out and handed to Flat-face.

'Ta,' Flat-face said, and lowering himself on to his knees beckoned Mally over. He approached nervously, though jumped back when Flat-face lunged for him, but too late. Flat-face's large thick sweaty hand closed over his wrist.

Mally struggled but the older boy's grip was clamped tight. 'Please let go,' he said. 'I've got to meet my friend. Honest I have.'

Flat-face smiled, and Mally saw a brown pulp of compressed food lining the gap between each of his teeth like cement.

'Calm down, son,' Flat-face said. 'We won't keep you long. We're gonna give you a bit of an education, that's all.'

Slouched against the wall, Simmsy chuckled. Mally looked nervously at him, then back at Flat-face who leaned forward conspiratorially.

'You ever seen a naked woman, son?' he asked.

Suddenly Mally's stomach was full of ping-pong balls dancing on

111

fountains of air. He remembered last Christmas when Aunt Lillie and Cousin Rachel had come to stay. He had had to share a room with Rachel, who was seventeen years old. One night he had still been awake when she'd come to bed, and had feigned sleep as she undressed in the semi-darkness. So awed had he been by her naked beauty he had almost cried out. He had remained awake long after Rachel was asleep, staring at the dark mass of her hair on the pillow of the camp bed, feeling enraptured and breathless and sick.

However this was his secret, something he carried with him, precious as his crab's claw, his shark's tooth, the coin his grandfather had given him commemorating VE Day. He wasn't about to cheapen the wonder of his experience by voicing it here. His gaze flickered between the two teenagers again and he shook his head.

'No.'

Flat-face grinned, again displaying his pulp-clogged teeth. 'You wanna see some?' he said quietly.

Mally did — but not here, not now. There was danger in this situation. He shrugged, scratched his leg nervously with his free hand. 'Dunno,' he mumbled.

'Course you do,' Flat-face informed him. He tugged on Mally's wrist, almost pulling him over. 'Come here and have a look at this.'

Mally watched as Flat-face spread the magazines on the dusty roof of the Tower. One of the magazines was titled *Naturist*, the other *Playboy*. One cover depicted a bronzed bare-breasted woman emerging from an impossibly blue sea on to an impossibly white beach, holding a large conch shell in her hands; the other showed two naked women playing with a red-and-white striped ball as they smiled demurely into the camera.

Mally's stomach was churning. He felt faint and fearful and excited. Looking at the photographs, at the warm inviting smiles on the faces of the women, made him almost embarrassed, as though the magazine covers were merely windows, as though the women beyond those windows were aware of his emotions, knew his thoughts exactly. He glanced at Flat-face. The look of scrutiny on the older boy's face became a slow gunge-toothed smile. Flat-face glanced at Simmsy, who, unseen by Mally, had moved closer. Almost lovingly Flat-face began to turn the pages of one of the magazines.

Silence fell over the group for what seemed an endless thread of time. The pages turned, each bringing new enchantments, fresh delights. Mally felt strange: he had a frog in his belly, he wanted to flee. And yet at the same time he felt that intense, almost divine rapture he had felt in that darkened room watching Rachel, felt as though he wanted this to go on for ever.

The first magazine came to an end, the second began. The pages made a wet sensual "flip" sound as Flat-face turned them over. It seemed the photographers had captured Heaven, frozen it there for all time. Sun gleamed on breasts and buttocks and partly concealed vaginas. Mally found the vaginas almost overwhelmingly exciting, though elusive, mysterious. They resembled, he thought, small animals — shrews, mice, peeking out from the junction of silky golden thighs.

'You see?' Flat-face said. His voice was husky; sweat glossed his forehead.

Mally nodded. He wasn't sure what Flat-face meant. But he saw, all right. He saw.

'You know what we do to this?' Flat-face went on. There was a peculiar timbre to his voice, something furtive, suppressed.

Mally felt uncomfortable, out of his depth. *You know what we do to this*? What did *that* mean?

'No,' he said.

Flat-face looked at Simmsy, who was standing immobile, breathing loudly through his nose. Simmsy looked back at him, inscrutable. Flat-face picked up *Naturist* and gave it to him.

'Show him, Simmsy,' he said.

Simmsy took the magazine and retreated to the far side of the Tower's roof. He sat down, his back against the stone rim, and placed the magazine beside him. Mally tensed, felt Flat-face's hand tighten on his wrist, as Simmsy unbuckled his belt, unbuttoned his trousers, unzipped his fly. Simmsy hooked his thumbs into his waistband, raised himself a little from the stone floor, and pulled his jeans and underpants down to his knees.

The frog in Mally's belly leapt frenziedly; his heart juddered against his breast bone. Simmsy's cock was sticking straight up, pointing at him like a thin white club, surrounded by a curly tangle of hair. Mally felt his throat becoming tight as he watched Simmsy fondling himself, pulling his organ, cupping and squeezing his balls.

Apart from Simmsy, everything else seemed motionless. The air around them had become still; the sun's heat was thick and hard and bright as metal. Mally felt as though the whole morning, the whole day, was passing; hours were sliding by. Where was Mike? Simmsy began flipping over the pages of the magazine, still playing with himself. After a while he encircled his cock with his left hand and began pumping it slowly up and down.

Sweat trickled down the back of Mally's neck. He watched what

113

Simmsy was doing in a state of appalled fascination. Little by little Simmsy's pumping action became faster, more frantic. He started to gasp and pant; sweat gleamed on his face; red blotches stood out on his cheeks and forehead. Mally was barely aware of Flat-face's hand still clamped around his wrist. Simmsy flipped pages over with feverish intensity. His eyes were rolling and unfocussed, his lips curling around gritted teeth. Why doesn't he stop?, Mally was thinking. Why doesn't he stop if it's hurting so much?

Then, suddenly, something happened. Simmsy let out a strangled cry, dug in his heels and half-raised his buttocks from the ground. Mally flashed a fearful glance at Flat-face, but the teenager was watching his friend, smiling, nodding. When Mally looked back he was shocked to see white stuff spurting from Simmsy's cock, across his thighs and on to the ground.

What's he done to himself? Mally thought. Oh God, what's happened to him? The white stuff stopped coming out, and Simmsy sank back on to the dusty cement, his eyes half closed, his breathing ragged and heavy.

Mally felt sick. He didn't know what to do or say. Then he was almost jerked off his feet, heard Flat-face's rough voice growl, 'Come on, now it's your turn.' He stumbled and cried out at the pain in his arm. Flat-face's words didn't register until he felt a hand fumbling with his shorts.

'No!' he screamed, suddenly panic-stricken. 'No, get off!' The hand was dragging down his shorts and his underpants, and Mally clutched at them in a desperate attempt to keep them up. Another hand closed over his mouth and pushed him to the ground. He heard deep breathing that was a series of grunts, smelt sweaty stale flesh.

What happened next was a nightmare. He was pinned to the ground, the sun glaring into his face, while he was stripped from the waist down. He was half-aware of hands groping and grasping at him, pulling him, hurting him, and then he saw Flat-face stand up and pull down his own jeans and underpants.

'Get him on his knees,' he heard Flat-face mutter and felt himself being dragged upright by thin cruel fingers that dug into his armpits. Flat-face's cock wavered hugely in front of him, thick and fat and greasy-looking, veins curling round its length like thin blue piping under the skin.

Mally heard another muttered command, and then his jaws were forced open. Flat-face stepped towards him, blocking out the sun. There was a smell, like a public toilet, and then something was crammed into his mouth, pushing against the back of his throat. He

114

panicked, felt sure he would choke to death, but could do nothing. A hand clutched the back of his head, impaling him deeper. The thing in his mouth began to pound, jerking his head, suffocating him in stink and sweat. At some stage he blacked out.

When he came to they were gone. He sat up, crying and shaking, his jaws feeling bruised, his tongue and throat coated in something slimy, repellent. He gagged and spat, and some of the white stuff like that which had come out of Simmsy's cock hit the Tower's dusty roof, mingled with his saliva. He felt real panic grip him. What was that stuff? Was it poisonous? Was it the product of some hideous disease? He tried to make himself vomit but couldn't. He spat until he could spit no more, until the inside of his mouth felt rough and dry as his father's stubble.

Unsteadily he got to his feet. His shorts and underpants had been stamped into the ground, resembling small blue animals squashed flat by a car. Mally picked them up and shook them, coughing at the dust which billowed up. Still shaking he got dressed.

He felt ill and exhausted and terribly afraid. He peered over the rim of the Tower to see if Flat-face and Simmsy were still around. He was both relieved and alarmed to see Mike struggling up the hill, laden down with shopping, his lips stained green from the icepop he was eating.

When Mike reached the top of the Tower, Mally frightened him by breaking down, becoming hysterical. He couldn't believe Mike had been gone less than half an hour; it seemed that hours had passed since the start of his ordeal. He wouldn't tell Mike what had happened, except to say that some older boys had beaten him up. His clothes were dusty and torn, his hair dirty, his knees and elbows bleeding, and there was a bruise on his left cheekbone and a cut on his top lip. With Mike's help he got home, and told his mother the same story he had told Mike. He had a bath, brushed his teeth and went to bed, and stayed there for the rest of the day, pretending to sleep whenever someone came near him.

For the next two days Mally lived in fear, certain that the stuff he had been made to swallow would poison him to death. In the deep silence of night he was certain he could feel it moving and growing inside him, just like that thing, *The Blob*, that he and Mike had climbed through the Odeon's toilet window to see. On the third day he began to think that maybe he wouldn't be poisoned after all, but that didn't help his appetite. His stomach was empty but the thought of eating repelled him. On the fourth day Mike came to see him and asked him when he would be coming out, but Mally said he didn't know. By the fifth day the pity and concern shown him after the incident was beginning to wear a little thin, especially where his father was concerned.

'What's wrong with that boy? He's been in bed five days now. You'd think he had something terminal the way he's been carrying on,' Mally heard his father muttering outside his bedroom door.

He pictured the scene: his father, grumpy and dishevelled from work, sweaty and scowling, covered in grease and oil; his mother, fluttering like a nervous butterfly, trying to be placatory without daring outright contradiction.

Sure enough his mother's reply was just as he expected, her voice a little shrill, a little fearful, trying desperately to be soothing – the kind of voice you might adopt if confronted with a large and savage dog.

'He had a bad shock, Geoff. I think it's best if we leave him to get over it in his own way.'

Mally heard his father snort disgustedly. 'For God's sake, woman, he only got roughed up a bit, that's all. That was happening to me all the time when I was a lad, but I didn't lie around in bed, snivelling. If he had any sort of backbone he'd round up a few of his pals, give them buggers a good hiding.'

'Now, Geoff, that's not the answer, is it? There's nothing to be gained in pitting violence against violence.'

Mally heard his father snort again. 'Bloody hell, don't be so soft, woman. There's no wonder we've got a pansy for a son the way you mollycoddle him. Sometimes violence is the only way. It's certainly the only thing these buggers understand. I've a good mind to enrol the lad in boxing lessons down at Barney's gym. Maybe when he's been knocked around a bit he'll learn to stand up for himself.'

Mally dragged his blankets over his head, blocking out the rest of the conversation. He felt empty and worthless, felt as though his father was right, as though he deserved all that had been done to him. Maybe he did ought to round up some of his friends, hunt his attackers down and give them a pasting. But it wasn't as simple as that; the older boys' advantage over him was not merely one of violence, it was a sexual thing, and that was something whose intimacy terrified Mally. In a way, what they had done to him was like a spell, like black magic – something pervasive, something that had got inside him, something whose boundaries he could not fully comprehend. He didn't like violence but at least it was simple: first one to cry is the loser. Mally didn't know why, but he had the impression that if he told his father what had really happened, he would be treated as a leper, an outcast, something tainted and vile and weak.

He spent the rest of the day in bed, and then on the sixth day he

116

forced himself to get up and walk to Mike's house. His skin and eyes seemed sensitive to the sun; out in the wide streets he felt prickled by agoraphobia. That morning he had eaten some Weetabix and it was now sitting uncomfortably in his stomach, like the white stuff he sometimes still imagined was growing inside him. He and Mike played World Cup Kick-Off for two absorbing hours, and then in the afternoon, after Mike's mum had made them cheese salad sandwiches which Mally was surprised to find he actually enjoyed eating, they played with Mike's soldiers, a bunker of British survivors scoring an astounding victory over thousands of invisible Nazi storm-troopers and Japanese fighter pilots.

When Mally arrived home that evening he felt proud of himself, happier than he had all week, but his father deflated him somewhat by simply muttering, 'About time too.' On the seventh day, exactly a week after the assault, Mally played outside, kicking a football about with Mike on the playground behind Mike's house. On the eighth day he strayed a little further afield, and on the ninth day further still. He still felt threatened whenever he saw boys older than himself, and he didn't think he would ever set foot near The Edge and the Tower again, but the special resilience of childhood was slowly but surely working inside him, healing his wounds, curing his neurosis.

He might well have come through this ordeal unscathed if, on the tenth day, fate had not brought Flat-face and Simmsy back into his life.

It was his father's fault. Mally was upstairs reading when he heard his father's footfalls approaching his room. He wondered why his father always clomped everywhere instead of simply walking, why he always seemed so full of anger. Mally groaned inwardly as his door was shoved open and his father's blunt scowling head poked through the gap.

'Pop down the shop for me, son. Get me some fags and a paper.'

Before Mally had time to say anything, his father had tossed a handful of coins on to the bed and pulled the door closed with a bang.

Mally sat up slowly, his book forgotten. He collected the coins together and let them drop into the pockets of his jeans. The heatwave was entering its fifteenth day and through his window Mally could see paving stones baked to chalk, his mother watering her meagre wilting garden. The newsagent's was in a territory he hadn't dared venture into since his assault; it involved using a subway to cross a main road that was a ceaseless blare of traffic.

117

He dragged on his shoes and laced them painstakingly, as though half believing that if he was slow enough night would fall before he could carry out his errand. It was no use telling his father he didn't want to go; the thought of what his reaction would be made Mally shudder. He trudged downstairs, out the front door, the money tinking gently in his pocket. His mother, her hands clumsy in gardening gloves, was trimming some thorny bush with a pair of secateurs, and beamed up at Mally as he approached her.

'Going out?' she trilled. It struck Mally that gardening was the only activity his mother was decisive about, perhaps the only one that really made her happy.

'Dad wants me to go to the newsagent's,' he explained, instilling as much reluctance as he could into his voice.

His mother, however, didn't rise to his bait. She simply nodded and bent to her task again. Mally sighed and plodded away, feeling as though he were swimming out from shore into shark-infested waters.

The sun was so hot it seemed to scour the sky. A layer of heat was poised on the earth, shimmering. Mally half-expected gardens he passed to crumple noiselessly into flame. Bees wavered between flowers like drunks on a pub crawl.

At the top of his street he turned left. Past a church, past a row of terraced houses with dark glottal openings that led to back yards, and there was the junction and the main road. Mally approached it slowly. Cars and lorries were snarling as they raced one another, the sun glinting on chrome and glass. Immediately before the main road, by a bus stop, was an opening in the railings, stone steps leading below pavement level to a mouth beneath the ground. Already Mally knew what would be waiting for him inside that mouth: litter, graffiti, the stink of urine.

He started down the steps. The hand-rail was viciously hot and he let his palm skim over it, hissing in air in short sucks that were not quite sounds of pain. Engines bellowed by his head, then muted as they rose above him. Mally's thudding heart was oppressive as the heat. He reached the subway entrance and peered down its dark length. He smiled in heartfelt relief. The subway was empty.

He tried to hold his breath as he entered, but the sharp sourness of the air seemed to infiltrate his pores. In the centre of the subway, at its lowest point, was a dark puddle − of water, beer or urine, or perhaps all three − and Mally's feet made a tight echoing splat as he jogged through.

Brightness sprang on him when he came out the other side, jabbing at his eyes, raising dots of sweat on his skin. In front of him Mally

118

could see a butcher's, a baker's, a newsagent's and greengrocer's. Two women were talking outside the butcher's while a toddler circled them frantically on a tricycle.

Mally looked left and right, then began to cross the paved area in front of the shops. As he did so he glimpsed movement out of the corner of his eye and looked round. Two figures had appeared at the end of the row of shops, to his right. He looked more closely at them, then froze in horror. Flat-face and Simmsy were walking towards him.

They didn't see him at first, and might not have done so at all if he had strolled calmly into the nearest shop and remained there until they'd passed. However the impression of someone frozen in his path, staring at him, made Simmsy look up. At first it was obvious he hadn't recognised Mally, then his eyes widened, his thin lips twisted into a nasty grin. He nudged Flat-face and muttered something. Flat-face looked up too, and was suddenly giving Mally his brown-toothed smile, his doughy features crinkling like an old mattress.

'Well, well, look who's here,' he said. 'If it isn't our old friend, Larry.'

Even now Mally instinctively opened his mouth to correct Flat-face, but his voice had dropped into his belly somewhere and refused to let itself be heard.

'Larry the Lamb,' Simmsy sneered and cackled inanely.

'Come looking for us, have you?' Flat-face said, and cupped the crotch of his jeans. 'Fancy some more fun?'

The invitation unlocked Mally's legs. Without a word he bolted for the subway entrance. More out of instinct than anything, his two assailants began to run after him. Mally was half aware of the two women and the toddler staring at him in astonishment, then the black stinking throat of the subway swallowed him up.

He was so terrified he felt he was flying through the tunnel, felt he was somehow being propelled, like a bullet from a gun. The cries of his pursuers bounced from the walls around him, wordless, bestial, full of echo. The postage stamp of light he was aiming for rushed towards him, engulfed him, and suddenly he was out. He raced for the steps and began to bound up them; moments later Flat-face and Simmsy emerged into the light, looked around for a moment, then followed.

Mally's fear turned him into a blade which sliced a route through the humid air. Simmsy and Flat-face were able to keep up only because their legs were longer. As he reached the church, Mally half-wondered whether he ought to run inside, but he was past before the decision could be made. The row of terraces flickered by on his left. People out hanging washing or reclining on deck-chairs barely gave him a second look.

He turned on to his street, saw his house, his mother still in the garden, weeding. 'Mum!' he yelled. 'Mum!' He saw his mother look up, her face unreadable, her gloved hand clutching a small metal implement.

He flapped a hand in the air and ran towards her. Now he could see her face clearly: her expression was one of surprise.

'Darling, whatever's the matter?' she asked.

'Behind me,' he panted, stopping and turning only when he was by her side.

The street was empty. Either Flat-face and Simmsy had given up the chase at the subway or they had seen his mother and turned back.

Suddenly Mally felt nauseous. He bent double, his hands clutching his knees, and tried to control his breathing which was coming too fast, one breath tripping over another. His mother asked, 'Darling, are you all right?' When Mally looked up, his mother's expression had changed to sympathy and concern.

'Yes,' he said unconvincingly, 'I'm okay.'

'What happened?' she asked.

Briefly he told her.

'Right,' she said firmly, 'we'll tell your father about this.' But when they did so he was less than sympathetic.

He stared at Mally as if it was his fault he had been chased, or as if he should have stood up to the boys, fought them. At last he sighed and used his thick oil-engrained hands to push himself up from his armchair. 'Fetch my shoes,' he muttered.

'Why, Dad?' asked Mally. He had visions of his father kicking him around the house or giving him a hiding.

'I haven't got my bloody fags or paper yet, have I? We'll walk on to the newsagent, see if we can spot these buggers.'

They did so, but Flat-face and Simmsy were nowhere to be seen. Mally was uncomfortably aware of his father scowling down at him, as if he wished to disown him, as if he wished he had a son who was a bully rather than one of the bullied.

When they got home, Mally went up to his room, lay down on his bed and cried.

Two days passed. Mike came round and they played on their bikes. When Mike suggested building a ramp in the park, Mally declined; he was reluctant to stray too far from home. 'Okay,' said Mike, but Mally sensed the resentment in his voice. It was obvious he was growing a little tired of his friend's timidity. Mally almost began to wish the holidays were over and they were back at school.

Once school started again, he told himself, all of this would stop.

That night, round about midnight, Mally was lying in bed when he heard a noise in the garden. It was a stealthy noise, a noise he knew he wasn't supposed to hear, and his hands spasmed into fists, crumpling the blankets under his chin. The noise came again, a dull bumpy sound that Mally instinctively knew was human movement. He stared at the ceiling, his body rigid, darkness swarming over everything like cataract vision.

Go away, he breathed, *go away*. The house seemed to be pulsing in time with his heart. Another sound: a voice, perhaps, and a chuckle. Unable to stand it any longer, Mally pushed back his covers, swung out of bed, stood up, walked to the window and looked out.

He thought he glimpsed a dark shape capering across the lawn but he wasn't sure. It was as if the shape had anticipated his opening the curtain and had dodged behind it. Mally squinted, trying to penetrate the darkness, but black overlay black beneath the hedge, an inchoate mass defying the street lamps. Releasing the breath that had been frozen inside him, he turned from the window to confront his room.

A bulky figure stood by the door, enough light bleeding through the window for Mally to distinguish its identity. It was Flat-face, his eyes and nose triangles of shadow, the teeth in his grinning mouth slick individual gleams of light.

'Hello, Larry,' he said softly. 'Want some fun?'

Mally opened his mouth to scream, but Flat-face held up a finger and suddenly Mally found he was mute.

'That won't help,' Flat-face said. 'I've fixed it so no one will hear you.' He stepped forward, his movements exaggeratedly languid, as though he was relishing the power he held.

Mally found himself sinking to his knees. Realising the implications of this he struggled frantically, tried to remain upright, but his mutinous limbs defied him. He came eye-to-crotch with Flat-face, tried to moan, to scream, to call for help, but his throat would not yield a sound. Flat-face grinned and unzipped himself slowly, a grotesque parody of seduction. Incongruously his open fly in the half-light resembled a vagina edged with glinting teeth.

Terrified, Mally stared into the maw. He felt something awaken inside him, and knew it was the white stuff growing in his belly, stimulated by the creature, the thing, which had birthed it. He saw something move within the black opening of Flat-face's crotch; something moist, grub-white, segmented, that coiled in upon itself, rustling as it did so. Flat-face's grin was now so wide it threatened to

121

meet at the back of his head. The thing in his crotch gave a shudder, a ripple, and suddenly slid out into the light.

Mally opened his mouth wide to scream, but all at once realised how the gesture might be misinterpreted and clamped his lips tight. The worm sliding from Flat-face's crotch was bloodless and clammy-looking, thick as a man's arm and twice as long. It spiralled like a white whip down Flat-face's left leg, reached his foot, and began to edge across the floor towards Mally. Less than a foot away it stopped and reared up, and Mally saw its eyes, black unblinking beads, and its mouth, a ragged opening criss-crossed with stringy white mucus . . .

Pain awoke him. His pillow was wet with tears, and with blood from where he had bitten his tongue.

Mally did not sleep again that night, and the next day felt drained and fragile, felt as though the sun could make him crumble to dust. He sat in his room and looked out of the window. Ate little. Said even less.

Round about five he had a bath, and was just beginning to drift to sleep in the warm water when he heard his father arrive home. He tensed, recognising his father's disgruntled tone, his mother's conciliatory one.

'Leave him, Geoff,' he heard his mother say, then there was a bump or a bang which made Mally want to crawl whimpering down the plughole.

'I've had enough of his whingeing,' he heard his father say angrily. 'It's time this was sorted out.'

Mally heard his father's booted feet approaching; the door was shoved open; his father entered.

'What's this I hear about you cowering in the house all day again? Why don't you pull yourself together? What's the matter with you?'

Faced with his father's anger, Mally felt tears welling up, felt a large painful lump jamming the back of his throat. *Don't cry*, he urged himself, *don't cry*. It was no use. A tear squeezed its way out of one eye and then the other. His bottom lip trembled. Even through his swimming vision he saw his father's disgust.

'For God's sake, boy, what's wrong with you?' his father roared. 'When I was your age, if anyone picked on me I got a bunch of lads together and we went and gave whoever it was a good hiding! Why can't you do that, eh? Why are you behaving like such a bloody pansy? I'll tell you now, lad, this situation had better have changed by the time I get home from work tomorrow or the hiding you got from those lads'll be nothing to the one I'll give you!'

122

He stormed out, slamming the door behind him. His father's words seemed to echo and echo inside the white-tiled bathroom. Mally sat and wept, his tears forming tiny ripples in the rapidly cooling water.

The next day it rained and he was given a reprieve. Mike brought round his World Cup Kick-Off, and they played an entire tournament which lasted all day, Portugal beating Scotland 8 − 5 in the final. Mally shouted and punched the air when his plastic men scored a goal but he was not as abandoned as Mike. There was a sense of fear, of desperation, inside him, like a leash restraining his enjoyment.

Once, when he got up to go to the toilet, he glanced out of his bedroom window and saw Flat-face and Simmsy standing shoulder to shoulder in the rain, their hair and clothes plastered dark with water, smiling up at him.

He froze, let out an involuntary squeak. Mike, the manager of Brazil, looked up in surprise.

'What's the matter?' he said, frowning slightly. Mally was still staring out of the window, trying to work out how he could have mistaken the blurred angle of that wall, that white car, that darkened window for two smiling motionless figures.

'Oh, er . . . nothing,' he said. 'I thought I saw something, that's all.'

Mike gave him a puzzled suspicious look which Mally countered by saying, 'My Wales are gonna slaughter your Brazil in this match. It'll be the biggest upset in World Cup history.'

Mike jeered good-humouredly as Mally headed off down the corridor towards the bathroom.

For the next two weeks Mally played a dangerous game with his father. He stayed indoors as often as he could without his mother thinking it was unnatural, but always remained close to the house, hiding whenever his father appeared for lunch, which he invariably did. Mally was now living in a fear so profound it had settled into a dull solid ache inside him. There was a very good reason for his fear, though his father would not have seen it as such.

The reason was that Flat-face and Simmsy were watching the house.

Oh, they were very discreet, and they had the unnerving ability to dissolve like phantoms whenever Mally focussed upon them, but nevertheless they were there. He had seen them as he had that day in the rain, a quick glimpse of them standing shoulder to shoulder, smiling up at his window. Sometimes they were standing in the road, sometimes in the garden, sometimes on the opposite pavement. They were too clever to be seen clearly; they were never there when Mally was deliberately looking for them. But if he happened to be passing a window they would be there, a dark fleeting image at the edge of his vision. Of course by the time the image had registered and he had gone back to take a closer look, they would have disappeared – probably hiding somewhere, sniggering nastily behind their hands.

This half-seen threat began to wear Mally down, had an even more intrinsic effect than the solid undeniable fact of their physical presence. Nightmares began to rule his sleep; the darkness became as malign and menacing as it had been when he was four and five years old. He felt nervous, skittish during the day, often physically ill, weighed down beneath an all-embracing depression. His thoughts began to drift between light and dark, fiction and reality. Things happened, and then he wasn't sure when they had happened, or even if they had happened at all.

The telephone calls were a case in point. Mally would pick up the receiver and put it to his ear and say, 'Hello, who is this please?' And always silence was the only reply. But it was a silence so dense, so total, that Mally would *know* there was someone there, on the other end of the line, listening to him. Sometimes he was certain he heard breathing; once he was sure he heard a word that sounded like "fun" or "lamb". He was always the first to break the connection. And then he would wonder why he had picked up the phone at all. Had it rung? He couldn't remember it doing so.

And then there was the note. One day Mally found a blank envelope on the doormat which he picked up and carried to his bedroom. He opened it with trembling hands and drew out the sheet of paper which had been neatly folded inside. It was cheap lined notepaper with a row of torn perforations across the top. Heading the sheet was the single word, "You", and beneath it a crude pencil drawing of a boy sucking a penis.

Mally dropped the note and threw up his hands as if the paper had been smeared with excrement. He drew himself back into the centre of the bed, pulled up his knees and stared at the small white rectangle with the impotent fear of a man watching a fin circling his raft on the high seas. Under his gaze the scrap of paper seemed to grow, to adopt an awful significance, to pulse whitely with a life of its own. Mally was lulled into sleep, though later he could not recall the point at which he had closed his eyes and loosed his thoughts, and when he woke up neither the sheet of paper nor its envelope were anywhere to be found.

Magic, he thought. The white stuff was working magic inside him, tormenting him, trying to drive him mad. When Mike came round he casually asked him, 'If, say, you found out a witch or a demon or something was casting evil spells on you, what would you do?'

Mike considered the question carefully. He was not surprised by it; it was the kind of dilemma that ten year olds presented to each other all the time. At length he said, 'I'd get some books on magic from the library and make it so the witch's spells rebounded off me and went back on her.'

An oblique answer to an oblique question, but it set Mally thinking. Three days later, when his mother went to the library, he accompanied her.

'I'd like some books on black magic, please,' he told one of the librarians. The girl, whose gum-chewing ceased whenever the Head Librarian came into view, seemed taken aback but proved more than helpful.

Later that evening Mally poured over the four books he had withdrawn. He discarded two, a book by a man called Aleister Crowley which he couldn't understand and a book called *The Devil Rides Out* by Dennis Wheatley which he realised, after reading a few pages, was a novel. Of the other two books, one – *A History of Folklore* – was interesting, though hardly relevant to his problem, but the other – *Black Magic, Witchcraft and Voodoo* – seemed as if it had been written solely for him.

The next day Mally undertook a heart-pounding expedition to the shops to buy some plasticine. He hadn't seen Flat-face or Simmsy watching the house for almost a week now, but that didn't mean they weren't somewhere nearby, waiting to leap out on him. He took each step as though negotiating a minefield, was alert to every sound, every movement. The worst part was when he saw something dark, knee-high, moving in the shadows of the subway, but it turned out to be nothing more than a dog sniffing the piss-stains on the walls. He bought the plasticine and scuttled home, and in the solitude of his bedroom he set to work.

He made two figures, one large and square-set, the other thin and weaselly. He dressed them as they had been dressed on that day, then he spat into both their faces. He carried the figures to the window and looked out; some little kids were poking sticks down a drain but otherwise the street was deserted. He stood the figures on the windowsill, leaning them against the glass, and sneaked into his mother's bedroom for her sewing box.

'Die, you bastards,' he muttered as he pierced the plasticine bodies. The needles glittered like silver thread; their points slipped easily into the bright pink flesh, into the eyes that were blobs of brown, the mouths that were slits made with a fingernail. By the time he had done, the figures were ragged with holes, their crude faces cut to

125

ribbons. In his frenzy Mally had twice stuck needles into his own flesh, and now the plasticine was smeared thinly with his blood, adding an extra measure of realism.

He cut the figures into small pieces, put them in a plastic bag and buried them in the dustbin. He would have liked to have burned them, but his mother would never have let him set the brazier going on his own, and he couldn't ask her to do it because she would have wanted to know why. As a compromise he muttered some suitably demonic words from the Aleister Crowley book over the bag of dismembered remains before consigning them to the trash. Then he took the books back to the library and waited for something to happen.

Six days later Flat-face was knocked down and killed by a car. It was in all the papers. His real name was Noel Corcoran, and it had happened because he had been drinking cider with his friends to celebrate his sixteenth birthday, and had decided to do a dance in the middle of the road at the very same moment that a black Ford Cortina had appeared round the corner. The driver had refused to stop and the police were now looking for him, though they were finding it difficult because Corcoran's friends had been both too shocked and too drunk to note down the car's registration or to get a look at the driver. Mally read the article in a state of horrified excitement. He had a feeling that, hard as they tried, the police would never find that car, that the sole reason for its existence had been as Noel Corcoran's murder weapon, a weapon which he had conjured out of thin air, and made vanish just as easily.

Mally thought that this would mark an end to his fears but he was wrong. If anything his nightmares intensified; he began to catch fleeting glimpses of thin grey figures in the house, watching him. Simmsy, he knew, was out for revenge — how did he know that? Had he dreamt it? Had Simmsy rung him up and told him? He couldn't remember. But even worse than the threat from Simmsy was the slowly dawning knowledge that Corcoran had risen from his grave and had taken up occupation in the attic.

How had Mally come by this information? Again, he couldn't recall. It had insinuated itself into his mind, curled around his thoughts like a poisonous weed, strangling them, suffocating them, replacing them with its message. Corcoran was in the attic. That much was undeniable. Mally would lie awake in bed at night, listening to the stealthy scrape and tremble of movement from up above, and he would know that it was Corcoran, Flat-face, shifting his unearthly weight, biding his time.

The day before Mally was due to go back to school was muggy,

126

overcast. Bad-tempered clouds trundled moodily across a sky which was the colour of fine dust. Now and then rain-spots hit the pavement like darkness blossoming. The air seemed fat and hungry, greedily gulping any resonant sound, giving it a flat dense thudding quality.

'Here's your uniform, cleaned and pressed,' his mother said, bustling into his room. The clothes draped neatly over her arm were grey as his depression. She placed them carefully on the bed, then went across to the wardrobe and opened it. 'Now, where's that blazer with the torn pocket?' she asked, rummaging. Mally was about to tell her when he suddenly found he couldn't respond. Something was floating dimly in the shadows of the wardrobe by his mother's left shoulder. It was blurred, indistinct, a curdled yellowish light, and then suddenly it surged into focus. Mally suppressed a scream.

Corcoran's pale slack face, the flesh puckered and drooping, was hovering in the wardrobe's musty interior, its shrunken staring eyes drilling into his own.

'Ah, here it is,' his mother said. She slipped the blazer off its hanger and closed the wardrobe door. It seemed to Mally that the inside of his body was tightening, collapsing, dragging him inwards. His mother glanced at him as she exited, but she didn't seem to notice anything strange about her son.

Mally sat on his bed for a long time after she had gone and stared at the closed wardrobe doors. It was an old wardrobe, of filigreed walnut, that had used to belong to his grandparents. It stood tall and imposing, somehow stern, patriarchal. Should he look inside it or sneak past, out of his room?

He decided on the latter. Hardly breathing he put a tentative foot to the floor. He had just begun to unfold his other leg from beneath him with infinite slowness when there was the tiniest creak and the right-hand door of the wardrobe inched ever so slightly open.

Mally felt a scream jolt up his body at the same moment that his throat squeezed closed, locking the sound inside. He stared at the thin black line that had appeared between the doors, expecting at any moment for that line to widen, for the door to come crashing back, and for Corcoran's flabby stinking form to come lurching out. But nothing happened. The door stayed as it was, minutely ajar. All at once the air seemed dead, stuffy with silence, as though motion and sound were being sucked into that narrow voidal gap.

Mally's breath was frozen, a plate of ice lodged in the base of his throat. The tip of one foot still rested on the floor, and now he put his weight on it, brought his other leg round as though he were Daniel afraid of waking the lions. With both feet on the floor he used his arms to lever himself up. He felt weightless but un-coordinated; it seemed he was floating towards his door, the held breath beginning to spread fingers of pain into his chest, threatening to lay a veil across his mind.

And then he was out of his room and breathing again. He staggered downstairs, each lurching step making him feel he was on the verge of tumbling headlong. His ears seemed to pop. His heart was a fist thumping for release. He heard his mother humming in the lounge; the faint squeals of little kids; the grinding chomp of a lawnmower.

What should he do now? Tell his mother what he had seen? Go outside? But what would that achieve? Corcoran would still be there in his wardrobe, waiting for him when he came back. So, what *was* the answer? Perhaps he should take his father's advice — stop running, face his fear. He turned towards the kitchen. As he did so, Simmsy rose from beneath the sill of the window beside the front door and pressed his face to the glass.

Mally whirled round. Simmsy was gone again, had obviously ducked down out of sight. Mally felt a familiar pang of fear, and then, suddenly, this was swept aside by a black, almost electric rage that seemed as though it were making the short hairs at the back of his head sizzle to attention.

'Right,' he said, and grabbing the door handle jerked it towards him. A giant slab of warm light fell across him, made him wince, but he plunged out, turned towards the place where Simmsy would be crouched.

He saw only chalk-white paving stones and a brick wall the colour of dried meat. Even here, this close to the house, Simmsy had somehow managed to perform his magic disappearing act once again. Mally let loose a sigh that was like a sob, felt an urge to pound and kick the wall as if Simmsy might be crouching there, invisible. He sunk on to his knees and stared at the cracks in the paving stones. There were tiny flickers of movement between them. Woodlice. Beetles.

He stood up slowly, walked back into the house and closed the door. Okay, he was thinking, okay you bastards, okay. Listening to ensure his mother was still in the lounge, he sneaked into the kitchen. Slowly, so as not to make a noise, he opened the cutlery drawer and took out the carving knife — the large one with the gleaming blade that looked as though tiny half-moons had been snipped from the metal.

He turned from the room and walked upstairs, the arm holding the knife hanging limply by his side, the knife-blade only inches from the floor. His heart was really hammering now; paradoxically, being armed made him feel even more terrified than ever. He kept imagining his mother emerging from the lounge, seeing him, and demanding to know what he was doing, and that was part of his fear. But the main part was that having the knife seemed to commit him somehow, seemed to compromise him into going all the way with this, no matter what the danger.

Reaching the top of the stairs, he turned and walked towards his open bedroom door, went inside. The wardrobe was still cracked teasingly open, wooden lips parted, threatening to yawn. Mally strolled across to it, though with each falsely casual step he felt the pull of his own fear, felt it wanting to drag him back, out of harm's way. He stretched out his left hand. His right fist tightened on the knife blade. His fingers curled around the elaborate brass handle of the wardrobe and he plucked the door fearfully open.

Coat hangers rippled like skeletal laughter. Jackets, shirts and trousers were soft hollows waiting to be filled. There was a faint smell of mothballs and age-old varnish. That was all. Corcoran, or whatever was left of him, had gone.

Mally felt a mixture of both relief and frustration. He hadn't really relished the prospect of facing Corcoran, but neither did he want to go through life catching glimpses of things he would rather not see, living with a perpetual unspoken threat. He sighed. Suddenly he felt ridiculous holding the knife. He began to close the wardrobe door . . .

. . . when a voice from inside whispered, 'Larry.'

Mally dropped the knife. Almost immediately he bent and snatched it up again. The wardrobe door swung slowly, ominously, open. And now when Mally looked it seemed dark and depthless, seemed like a black tunnel that stretched on and on, down and down. Endlessly. Into nowhere.

A rustle of movement from behind the clothes made Mally flinch back. The darkness seemed to follow him, thin writhing tendrils reaching towards him like tentacles of grey-black smoke. Before his eyes, Mally saw his clothes begin to bleed together, to merge, one item into the next, until they became a pulpy wet curtain of grey. From behind the curtain a voice drifted, a single terrifying word, barely audible.

'Larry.'

'It's Mally,' Mally heard himself saying. '*Mally*. Not bloody Larry.' He raised the knife and stepped forward, licked his lips and tasted salt tears on his tongue.

'Larrry,' the voice murmured again, gently mocking.

Mally let out a sound, half shriek of fear, half war cry, and slashed down with the knife.

He saw the blade sink into the stodgy grey curtain that moments before had been his clothes. The blade cut through the curtain easily, as though it were composed of wet newspaper packed together, or of something long-drowned, the flesh saturated and rotten. He withdrew the blade, saw it was clogged with a filthy grey gunge that made him think of the slugs in his mother's garden after she had poured salt over them. From the cut he had made a colourless gluey liquid dribbled, pattered to the floor, pooled there.

'Larrry,' hissed the voice. It was way back now, retreating into the shadows. 'Larrry, want some fun?'

'Mally. It's Mally. It's Mally.' His words became a chant as he arced down, again and again, with the knife.

It took only moments to destroy the flimsy barrier of oozing grey. It lay about him in hacked strips, like an octopus ripped to shreds by a shark. Mally stepped through, into a dark pit-shaft tunnel which could not exist. As cold fetid air swarmed over him, he could not help thinking that this was like a book he'd read, a gateway to a nightmare Narnia.

He walked forward, footsteps tapping nervously. The tunnel was square as the inside of a box. Thick wooden supports held back a mass of grey-brown clay, glistening with moisture. Here and there oily pools of water were like mirrors dappled with mould, white blades of light sidling across them. Mally was aware of a smell, like rotting vegetation sealed for too long in an enclosed space. He moved to his left to skirt one of the pools of water – and a hand and arm formed from the clay wall beside him and wound coldly around his neck.

Mally screamed, but this time had the presence of mind to keep hold of the knife. He brought it up and slashed at the clay hand, saw a severed finger fall to the floor where it wriggled like a blind grey worm. The sense of triumph he felt was all too brief. Immediately the digit had been lopped off, another grew in its place.

Mally went beserk with panic. He slashed and cut and hacked at the body that was now prying itself from the wall, a man moulded of clay like the original Adam. It soon became apparent, however, that his attack was futile. He opened wounds only to see them close a second later, pared and severed portions of the clay man's strange anatomy only to witness a miraculous and near-simultaneous re-construction.

'Larry,' the clay man whispered, and a second arm pulled free from the wall, closed cold fingers around Mally's right wrist. Mally broke

130

down, could only stand, weeping. Through his tears he saw the clay man's hand turn to rot-damp flesh, felt a freezing week-dead breath crawl over the back of his neck, around the side of his face, prickle his nostrils with its stench.

'Larry,' the voice whispered again. 'Larry, want some fun?'

Mally felt the ice-damp hands slither up to his shoulders, turn him implacably around.

He stared into Corcoran's dead face, the flesh white and puckered, the eyes deep in their sockets, the lips curled back, furry black mould growing between the teeth.

'Want some fun?' the corpse said again, releasing a breath like stagnant swamp-water. 'Want some fun?'

Mally felt movement around his belly. He looked down. Corcoran's jeans were stained dark with the discharge of decay, soiled with grave-dirt. Mally saw that Corcoran's fly was open, that something moved in there, coiled and uncoiled with a slick wet sound. He knew what it was. He moaned in fear. And then, as the creature nosed into the light, he leaped back, ripping himself free of Corcoran's grip with a scream.

This time the worm had Simmsy's face. It was a ghastly fish-belly white, scaly like a reptile's, with black beads for eyes and fangs instead of teeth, but doubtless it was Simmsy. The worm reared up from Corcoran's crotch, wavered in front of him like a cobra. It opened its mouth wide and Mally saw a long deep gullet, pale grey, smooth as coffin silk. The worm, Simmsy, wavered from side to side like a lazy metronome, beating a time that drifted, dream-like. Like an idiot child, Corcoran began to sway too, in sync with the grotesquerie that served as his pudenda.

And then, incredibly, both worm and corpse began to sing.

It was a strange song, ugly, composed of words that had no meaning, of sharp spiteful vowels whispered in the manner of a lullaby. The tune to it was both beautiful and sinister; Mally found himself weeping, absurdly moved, but beneath this emotion was another: terror. He instinctively knew that the song conjured not only a chimera of sentimentality but also of something much darker. It was a song devoted to suffering, a veneration of pain. Its subtle barbs caught in the depths of his soul, performed delicate surgery on his heart. Opened his eyes to the Glory of Anguish, the sweet harmonies of Grief.

'No,' he whined, and raised the knife which suddenly seemed heavy as an anvil. His voice strengthened. 'No.'

He staggered forward, slashed at the worm. He saw its flesh

131

open neatly. It screamed. He screamed. He could feel its pain. He slashed again.

'Nooo! Stop!' He was not sure where the voice came from. He slashed again. Again. Again. His vision swarmed with blood. His body sang with such exquisite pain it was like a revelation. He felt himself weakening, his energy seeping away. A large black eye opened somewhere beneath him and he dropped into it, spinning ...

They had not called him Mally in a long, long time. Crazy people do not have nicknames. Like the abrupt ceasing of conversation, the knives became still, insensate, their patterns fading like mist. The past slowly gave him back to the present, and the memories, uncaged now, scampered through his mind. His mother had followed his screams upstairs, had found him lying amid his tattered clothes, covered with his own blood. He'd mutilated himself badly, tried to castrate himself. He was rushed to hospital where the doctors managed — just — to save his life. When he woke and felt the hurt he knew that it was over, that the game was up. Sobbing uncontrollably, he had told his mother everything that had happened.

For many months he was under the auspices of a psychiatrist, and after that he had his own counsellor, a nice lady called Ruth to whom he talked about his problems. But Ruth was not here now. There were only the knives and their memory-dance, the man with the lantern-eyes and the stinging voice. The voice was speaking now, filling his ears with a cleansing fire, with truths he had never considered, revelations which took his breath away.

'Do not fight what you have inside you,' the man told him. 'It is beauty. It is Art. You are the Unmaker. You have the power to change people. This gift should be cherished and nurtured. I have come to help you do that, to set you on the true path. You must grow, you must thrive, you must work at your Craft.'

Yes, it all sounded so good. So right. Why hadn't he seen it before?

He clenched his fist, and suddenly felt something hard in his grip. The scales fell from his eyes; the arms, which had been tight around his body, no longer incapacitated him. He saw himself reflected in the cleaver's blade, the light of Epiphany creating a halo of fire around his head. And he whispered, 'I am the Unmaker. Yes,' and 'Yes,' and 'Yes.'

'Destiny,' the voice sighed behind him. 'You were born for this moment.'

'Yes,' he said, his voice stronger now. 'Yes!'

He threw back his head. Held the blade aloft.

Brought it to his lips.

Kissed it.

The voice came again. 'It is inside you, yours for the taking. Your reward.'

He understood.

The cleaver sliced down.

And the blood oozed and pooled into his open palm.

Part Two

The Thousand-Mile Stare

*'I am your thinker, I am your brain.
Have no give and take with negative
thoughts.'*

Sun Myung Moon

20

Rupert Lascombe, editor of political fiction magazine, *Wargasm Words*, leaned back in his chair. His hands were trembling and clammy, his brow tight from concentration. His eyes felt pierced as though all too suddenly aware of the bleached September light pouring into his office. He expelled a breath he didn't realise he'd been holding, which seemed to act as the cue for his heart to begin thumping uncomfortably. When he looked around, his office depressed him as never before; it seemed grey, confining, weary with dust. It was like waking with a jolt from a wish-fulfilment dream, being thrust from the sublime to the mundane in an eyelid-fluttering instant.

He reached out to his desk with both hands, placing his fingertips on the rim as though testing for vibrations. Outside his third-floor window Soho teemed. The repartee of the market-traders was coarse, grating. The flow of humanity – tourists, commuters, thrill-seekers, pickpockets – sickened him to the core. He stared again at the innocuous buff envelope, the fifteen-page story, black type on plain white paper, and felt an almost superstitious chill squirm through him. He'd been excited by fiction before, thrilled by it, even awed by it. But never had he been elevated to such a level; never had his spirit been touched so intimately; never had the simple procedure of reading become what could quite seriously be termed a religious experience.

No, he thought, and shuddered again. He was aware of the absurdity of his reaction even as the final ripple of it ebbed through his system. Reading the story before him had been like a spiritual orgasm; every comma, every verb, every adjective had caressed him, lulled him, stimulated his soul to the brink and held it there.

It's impossible, he told himself, but he knew it was not; the evidence was here in black and white. For fiction, words, to have such power ... He trembled. It was terrifying.

He brought his hands to his head, massaged his temples slowly. He thought about the story, the nuts and bolts of it, forced himself to consider such devices as narrative drive, sentence structure, plot, grammar, characterisation. But if he hoped to unravel the secret of the story's magic by such methods he was disappointed; analysis killed it, dissection stopped its heart. No, the answer was simply to open one's mind and allow it access; to give thought, feeling, imagination over to its tender artifices.

He leaned forward and picked up the story almost reverently. Its plot was unremarkable and oblique: a nameless man walking a deserted town, drawing light from his surroundings until eventually he *was* light whilst all around him lay darkness. Such a stark synopsis seemed to hint at a theme of birth and re-birth, or perhaps a nuclear allegory. But this story, taken as a whole, was about *life*; indeed, it *was* life. It was the miracle of creation captured in prose. It was the one single story mankind had been striving to tell for millennia.

No, what was he saying? He dropped the manuscript, stretched an open palm across his forehead as though to negate the revelations that threatened to swell his mind like a melon. Dare he publish the story? He snorted. Dare he *not*? He stretched out a hand, grabbed his telephone and dragged it across the desk towards him. There was a phone number on the title page together with a name and address. With clumsy fingers he dialled the number. He listened to the soft trilling at the other end and tried to calm himself.

Clunk. The trilling stopped. Someone had picked up the receiver. Rupert waited for a greeting, some phrase of acknowledgement, but only a cold silence rushed at him, seeming to block his ear like a pressure-change.

Eventually he stammered, 'H-hello, is Dan Latcher – '

'Speaking,' came a voice.

'Oh.' Rupert, normally so self-assured, felt himself floundering. 'Er ... I ... I'm – '

'Rupert Lascombe,' the voice finished for him. 'I've been expecting your call.'

'You've been ...?' Unease strangled the rest of the sentence. He gripped the receiver tighter, drew a deep breath to regain his composure. 'That's rather egotistical of you, isn't it?' he joked feebly.

'It was preordained,' said Latcher without even a hint of badinage. 'We're all just instruments of destiny.'

'Yes, I suppose we are,' said Lascombe faintly. Suddenly he wanted to put the phone down, cut this creep off, drop his story into the wastebin and burn it.

But he didn't. He couldn't.

Destiny, he thought, and shivered.

'I'd like to publish your story,' he heard himself saying. 'I'd like to put it in next week's issue.'

'This week's,' Latcher corrected him.

'This week's? Well ... no, look, I'm afraid that's impossible. This week's issue is already pasted up. It's Thursday now and the magazine has to be on the stands by Tuesday. It will be going to the printer's tomorrow morning, ready for Monday evening. It's a very tight schedule we work to here, Mr Latcher.'

'This week's,' Latcher repeated. 'You know you can do it. You know you *must*.'

Rupert clenched his teeth. Something seemed to be raging inside him, an electrical storm of thoughts and emotions, hanging just out of sight behind muggy clouds. Every instinct told him *he* should be calling the shots, *he* was the boss here, Latcher had pushed him too far already. But something greater than instinct, something intangible yet terrifying, was overriding his natural reactions, threatening to bend his will. He heard himself muttering, 'I suppose ... if I work on it today ... rearrange a few items ... I can maybe just slot your story in.'

'Oh, I *know* you can,' Latcher said. 'I know you can do it, Mr Lascombe. It's been a pleasure speaking to you. Goodbye.'

And that was that. The connection was severed. Rupert dropped the receiver, which hit his desk and was pulled up short of the floor by its cord. It swayed to and fro like a hanged man dropped through a trapdoor. The dialling tone was an incessant, barely perceptible scream.

Rupert stood up, staggered to the window. His office was cloying, oppressive, as though sticky dust was coating his throat and nostrils. He threw open the window and the city-smell filled the room: sweat, sleaze, pollutants.

He breathed it in. It smelled so sweet, so ... normal. Not once had Latcher mentioned money, a factor which seemed to Lascombe to hold sinister implications. He held up his arm, stared at his watch until the blur of numbers on the dial became meaningful. 8:20 a.m., still forty minutes before the first of his editorial staff began drifting in, yet already he felt the need for a break. He simply had to get out, had to become part of the ever-increasing flow of people which minutes before had disgusted him. A McDonald's breakfast: bacon, egg, waffles, coffee, surrounded by gaudy decor, plastic plants. He held on to this image as he grabbed his jacket and hurried from the office. He fled down the stairs and into the street like a man in fear for his life.

21

Silly old Howard, thought Frances Duffy affectionately. He was a sweet boy but he worried too much. Treated her like bone china, carried her here, there and everywhere as if she didn't have legs, fluttered round her like a broody mother-hen. She appreciated his concern but it all got a bit claustrophobic sometimes. She was a tough old bird, was Frances Duffy, liked to do as much as she could by herself. All right, so she wasn't as strong as she used to be, and sometimes she became a little confused, but that didn't make her an invalid, did it? She could still get about, even if she did have to rely on that wretched walking-frame. If it wasn't for the fact that her friend, Miriam Atkins, agreed with her, she'd probably waste away in no time.

But fortunately Miriam did agree. Miriam understood. Miriam was of an age where her own body was beginning to turn against her. Unlike Howard, Miriam was an ally in her battle against age. Frances' philosophy was simple and logical: if the body was only half as effective as it used to be, then that half had to be kept moving and active, had to be pushed to its limits to stop it from seizing up. She didn't hold with this nonsense of Howard's: that she should conserve energy, wrap herself in cotton wool like some rare and precious egg. For goodness' sake, if that was his attitude then why didn't he just pickle her and have done with it?

She thought these thoughts as she climbed the stairs to the bathroom. Well, perhaps climbed was too mild a word to describe her ascent; *scaled* was probably more appropriate. She shuffled on all fours like a toddler, bony hands reaching up for each step, wasted legs providing what little leverage they could. She resembled an awkward slow-moving insect, or a mountaineer attempting a precipitous rock-face.

She did this every day, two or three times, *and* came down again; Howard would have kittens if he knew. Miriam had never offered to help her and Frances had never asked for help. Afterwards she would be exhausted, her limbs jittery, but she would feel as if she had achieved something.

Reaching the top step she hauled herself on to the landing and lay for a moment, eyes half-closed, arms and legs aching with effort. From down below she could hear Miriam chuckling at the man on Breakfast TV who wore the silly hats, her knitting needles clicking like morse. Frances gave a small groan and pushed herself up by her elbows. Sharp pains shot through her upper arms but she gritted her teeth, willpower overriding her discomfort. Moments later she was sitting upright. Wrapping her arms around the banister, she hauled herself painstakingly to her feet.

Her breath struggled in her reedy chest, yet despite this Frances felt triumphant. She had defied the odds yet again, or she had defied Howard at least. She shuffled towards the toilet, hands outstretched to the walls in case she should fall, thigh muscles singing with pain at each step.

It was a relief to sit down after her exertions. She remained there until long after her bowels were empty, gathering her strength for the descent. Miriam was conversant with Frances' toiletary habits and the time she took to perform them — twenty minutes was the norm, even thirty minutes not uncommon. Frances was therefore undisturbed, left to her own devices, which was just as she liked it. Howard, like most young people, was too impatient, rushing her from one thing to another as if she had appointments to keep.

Her head was just beginning to nod forward in a light doze when she heard the whispering. She jerked awake so violently that she cricked her neck. A dull ache floated across the back of her skull like a drop of blood in water. By the time the pain had faded the whispering had stopped.

She cocked her head to one side.

Nothing.

A dream then, she thought. Or the television. Or a bird outside the window. Maybe even the wind as yet another summer slipped by, darkening to chilly autumn. She shivered at the thought, felt a sudden urge to be sitting with Miriam in the lounge, warming herself by the fire, draping their chatter and the mindless patterns of the television around her like a shawl. Time just raced by when she allowed herself to think about it. Soon autumn would slip into winter, then spring, and then it would be summer again. As a young girl the seasons had fascinated and delighted her, but now they were merely inexorable, a grinding ever-turning wheel on to which she clung literally for her life.

Melancholy washed over her, at its heart a fear that was cold and bitter to the taste. She tried to assuage it by shoving herself almost angrily to her feet, wiping herself, pushing down hard on the lever that flushed the toilet. Beneath the rush of water was whispering — incessant, wordless. No, she was imagining it. She tried to cheer herself with the thought that a healthy imagination denoted an active, inquiring mind.

She blundered out of the toilet, pulling the door closed behind her. They made doors heavier these days, locks and handles stiffer. British craftsmanship, she thought, wasn't like it used to be. She muttered and grumbled to herself. This time the whispering was right beside her ear.

She spun round. There was no one there. They're coming for me, she thought before she could stop herself. Then she demanded out loud, 'Who? Who is? You stupid old woman.' She turned towards the head of the stairs, which lay eight feet away. 'Nobody,' she said in a determined voice. 'Mr Nobody, that's who.'

Reaching the top step, she lowered herself into a sitting position. This was how she descended, step by step on her bony backside. Undignified, perhaps, but not as undignified as sitting on that dreadful commode behind the curtain that Howard had erected in the lounge, making noises and smells in the company of her dearest friend.

Pride, she thought. Pride was important, though everyone else seemed to be of the opinion that it didn't matter when you were old. But Frances had never subscribed to that viewpoint. Age was no excuse. Her pride –

'Pride comes before a fall.'

The voice came from right behind her, the words hissed but intelligible. Frances twisted her head, and immediately the pain jumped back into her spinal column and fanned out across her skull, this time with enough force to cause tiny black dots to jitterbug in her vision. Through the dots she saw a pale teenager with spikey white hair, red-rimmed eyes and a cluster of sores around his mouth and chin. He was kneeling behind her. He looked ill and crazy. He stank of glue and piss and sweat, a rank musk which made her want to heave.

For seconds the two of them stared at each other, gazed into each other's eyes like grotesque lovers.

Then Frances stammered, 'Who ... who are you?'

'Mr Nobody,' said the boy.

And pushed.

22

It was getting monotonous. Yet again Ian found himself waking up with a thick head, a dry mouth and a hyperactive bowel. He showered, dressed, and dragged himself to the dining hall. The sight and smell of fried eggs laid out on the hotplate like giant amoebas made his stomach roil, but a few rounds of lightly buttered toast and two cups of black coffee quickly doused his nausea. By seven forty-five he was out walking, breathing in the smell of the fields that encircled the University, letting the fresh clean air fill his lungs.

At eight o'clock he trudged almost reluctantly to Mordred Hall to call on Neil. He was not looking forward to this confrontation with Steph. He was already envisaging a heated round of accusations and histrionics. He himself had not seen Steph since the ECA Fair a couple of days ago, but he had garnered enough from Annie and Neil to know how she was behaving. He wondered for the thousandth time what had happened to her, indeed what exactly had occurred at the initial meeting of The Crack. Annie had described the evening to him in detail, but still Ian could not get a grip on the perspective between emotions and actual events, could not understand what had so enamoured Steph and terrified Annie. This guy, Dan Latcher, sounded pretty strange all right, but could he really be as bad as Annie had depicted? And the nature of the evening – a magic show, for God's sake! Ian had heard of people 'seeing the light', being 'born again' in an instant of divine revelation, but for such a conversion to occur to almost an entire audience whilst watching a conjuring act? It just didn't make sense.

Neil was waiting for him when he reached Mordred Hall, sitting on the low wall outside the entrance doors. He was dressed in a tracksuit and jumped up as soon as he saw Ian, obviously eager to get started.

'Hi,' he said. 'All ready?' He began striding determinedly towards Merlin Hall, Ian having to jog to catch up.

'I suppose so,' said Ian. 'I'm not looking forward to this much, though.'

'I am,' replied Neil. 'I'm determined to get to the bottom of what's going on.'

They said little else as they entered Merlin Hall and climbed the stairs to the sixth floor. Though Ian had his inhaler tucked into the inside pocket of his jacket, he was grateful that his asthma was not playing him up today. Usually, after a night on the booze, his chest was tight the following morning. Today, however, he felt okay; either last night's brew had been particularly wholesome or his immune system had been working overtime, producing antibodies to counteract the huge volume of alcohol he had been pouring down his throat.

Neil rapped on the door of room 34 and called, 'Annie, it's us.'

They waited a moment and then the door was opened – though surprisingly not by Annie but by Steph. Despite what he had been told, Ian was shocked by her appearance. She looked so ... cold, her face an inanimate mask, her eyes devoid of any flicker of spontaneity. She seemed to be staring not only at them, but through them, as though there were no barriers to her sight.

She looks blind, thought Ian, and shuddered convulsively.

'What do you want?' Steph demanded. Aside from a trace of hostility, her voice was flat, dispassionate.

'We want to talk to you,' Neil said. 'Let us in, Steph.'

'I've got nothing to say,' she replied and started to shut the door. Neil jammed his foot in it.

'But *we* want to talk to *you*,' he reiterated.

She pulled the door back, though only in order to slam it harder on his intruding foot. Before she could do so, Neil shot out his arm, ramrod-straight, hitting the door with the heel of his hand. The door handle was jerked from Steph's grasp as the door crashed against the side of the wardrobe that stood behind it. Steph accepted her defeat with indifference. As the two of them entered the room, she crossed unhurriedly to the armchair and sat in it, her freckled face still chillingly bland.

Annie was standing by the sink, staring at the boys with round eyes. She looked better than yesterday, though still frail enough that it seemed a strong wind could blow her away.

'Hi,' she said in a soft voice. She was holding a pink toothbrush at chest height like a crucifix in a vampire film.

'Hi,' returned Ian, hoping his smile would ease the tension in the room; it didn't. 'How are you feeling today?'

'Better,' replied Annie. 'Not a hundred per cent, but ... better.' She turned to Steph. 'I asked Neil and Ian to come by this morning, Steph. They want to talk to you.'

Steph's implacable eyes shifted to focus on her room-mate. Her head moved slowly, minutely. Ian was reminded of some stone carving coming to life.

'I don't want to talk,' she said. 'There's nothing to say.'

'Yes, there is, Steph,' said Neil, stepping forward, 'there's plenty to say.'

Steph simply stared at him but made no comment. Neil walked across to where she was sitting, hunkered down so he could confront her eye to eye. He placed his hands one on each chair arm as though caging her. Ian saw him swallow, saw him tighten his grip to keep himself from trembling. He realised that all this was affecting Neil more deeply than he was letting on. He'd only known Steph for a few days, but he was genuinely concerned about her, bewildered and upset by her actions. In a voice that was surprisingly gentle he said, 'Come on, Steph. Tell us what's wrong.'

There was silence for what seemed an unbearably long time, but was probably no more than ten or fifteen seconds. Only one curtain in the room was open, light spilling through the window and across the twin desks, though encroaching no further. Neil and Steph were in semi-shadow, Steph's rust-red hair drained to a lacklustre brown. Ian had all but forgotten's Neil question, and was holding his breath, when Steph replied, 'There's nothing wrong. Everything's fine.'

Neil's hunched back rose and fell with a sigh. There was restrained anger in his voice, a manifestation of his anxiety.

'Of course something's wrong. Why are you behaving like this towards us? We're your friends, Steph, remember?'

Another pause. Then: 'He warned me about the spirits.'

Annie and Ian looked at each other, both frowning at the unexpected reply. Neil spluttered, 'Spirits? What do you ... I don't understand what you mean. Who warned ... Oh, you mean Latcher?'

At the mention of the name there was a subtle change in the air, a heightened though almost intangible charge of atmosphere. Annie stiffened; Steph's body seemed to become somehow *tighter*, in a way almost regal. There was a hungry shine in her eyes, an expression on her face too tenuous to be termed longing but was nevertheless the faintest shadow of same. Ian could sense impatience building inside Neil and touched him on the shoulder, indicating that he wished to speak. Neil tensed, then nodded. Ian was relieved. He could understand Neil's desire for haste, but bluster would lead them nowhere.

'Steph,' he said, kneeling beside Neil. The dead, hungry eyes swivelled slowly to regard him. 'Steph ... who is Dan Latcher?'

Steph's lips curled back − in contempt, Ian thought at first; but no − what appeared on her face was the parody of a rapturous grin. Her answer shocked everyone, Annie included.

'He is the Messiah,' she said simply.

145

'The *what*?' Neil exploded, his face full of rage and scorn. Ian waved him furiously to silence.

'What do you mean, Steph?' he urged. 'Do you mean he's God?'

Steph stared at him. Her head tilted forward. 'He is the Messiah,' she repeated.

'How do you know this, Steph? Who told you?'

'Dan told me,' she replied.

Ian rubbed a hand across his mouth. His throat felt dry. He was scared, profoundly scared. Somewhere deep inside.

'And you believed him?' he asked.

'Yes.'

'Why?'

'Because he speaks the truth.'

'How do you know he speaks the truth?'

'I know.'

Ian paused again. This was like a game of logic where you had to ask the right question to advance a further step into the maze.

'If I told you I was the Messiah, Steph, would you believe me?'

'No.'

'But why not? What can Dan do that I can't?'

'He can perform miracles.'

Ian sighed, leaned back, glanced at the others. Now his chest was beginning to tighten up, as though the air was thickening around them.

'What miracles, Steph?' he asked quietly. 'Tell us about the miracles.'

Steph's head moved slowly until she was looking at Annie. 'She knows,' she said accusingly.

Neil and Ian turned to regard Annie. She was still standing by the sink, still unconsciously clutching her toothbrush. Her eyes were wide and fearful. She looked guilty, though it was obvious Steph's words had taken her by surprise.

'*Do* you know, Annie?' Ian asked softly.

Annie swallowed, gave a darting shake of the head. 'No,' she whispered.

'She knows,' Steph insisted. 'She was there.'

Annie opened her mouth in a further denial, then realisation crossed her face. 'You mean the magic-show?' she said. 'Those weren't miracles, Steph, they were just tricks, illusions. You said so yourself.'

'They were miracles,' Steph said simply. 'They were proof of his deity. You were the one who was tricked. You were tricked by the spirits.'

Ian turned back to Steph. 'The spirits?' he repeated. 'What spirits, Steph? Tell us about them.'

Steph sighed, but her face remained deadpan. 'You know as well as she does,' she said. 'You try to trick us because we know all about you, because you're scared that we'll destroy you. Well, we will. You won't break us up. We'll reach Epiphany and we'll wipe you out. Your days are finished. We'll grow stronger. We'll take back the world, we'll purify it, we'll eradicate your sickness.'

She had been growing steadily more animated throughout the discourse, her voice rising in pitch. Now she slumped back as though unplugged, her muscles relaxing into impassivity once more, her eyes glazing over, turning inward.

Ian was trembling badly. He took his inhaler from his inside pocket and sucked the bitter air into his throat. Not too much, he thought, keep calm, keep in control. He clenched his fist. His fear ran deep; it seemed to stem from his marrow, as though the molecules there were in a state of agitation. He touched Steph's hand and it was cold. She did not react to his touch.

'Steph,' he said, 'who is it you want to wipe out? And why? Tell us. We don't understand.'

A fleeting look of cunning crossed Steph's face. 'You understand,' she said, 'and you're scared, I know that much. You're full of them, aren't you? You're full of the spirits, they control your every move. They're killing you from the inside. They're working through you to create Hell on Earth. They're trying to make you turn me against Dan. But it won't work. My love is too strong. All you can do is join us. It's the only way you'll be saved.'

She allowed her eyes to linger first on Neil and then Ian, and then she slowly raised a hand and pointed at Annie.

'She's black with them. Corrupt. They're so rife in her that not even Dan could drive them out. But he will. He weakened them, made them sick, but now they're growing stronger again. But it's not too late. There's still time, there's still hope. Dan will help you. It's easy if you want it to be. Disconnect all thoughts. Pain equals purification.'

She began to murmur to herself, whispering the words that Dan had yelled from his pulpit a couple of days before.

'I am a friend, a guide and a brother ... I am your Destiny, your Truth ... your way Forward, your Life ... You shall view the blackest depths, scale the most glorious heights ...' Then a rictus grin split her face and she began to chant, deep and low:

'Disconnect all thoughts, pain equals purification. Disconnect all thoughts, pain equals purification ...'

'Steph!' Neil shouted. He gripped her arms and shook her. She lolled like a rag doll, but, aside from increasing the volume of her chant, failed to respond to him. 'Steph!' he shouted again, and this time his voice was shot through with a vicious, barely restrained rage.

She ceased her chanting, raised her head slowly and looked into his eyes.

Neil's face was twisted with misery. He began to speak to her, making each word count, foam collecting at the corners of his mouth, his hands tight as manacles around her upper arms.

'Steph, listen to me. You've got to stop all this now, do you hear? You're sick, Steph. Latcher's filled your head full of lies and shit. There are no evil spirits. We're your friends, Steph. We want to help you.'

Silence followed his outburst. Annie and Ian stood immobile, both holding their breath. Steph's intense stare seemed to absorb Neil, to suck him into itself. Then in a low, deliberate voice, which gradually increased in both speed and volume, she said, 'Disconnect all thoughts. Disconnect all thoughts. Disconnect all thoughts. Disconnect all thoughts.'

'*No!*' yelled Neil, and lunged at her. For one awful second Ian and Annie thought he was about to strike Steph. Ian stepped forward, shooting out a hand to drag Neil away. But his intentions were not violent.

He attempted to clamp a hand over Steph's mouth, cutting off her mindless exhortation. With a quickness that belied her earlier sloth, Steph twisted from his oncoming hand, then incredibly drew back her arm and pistoned it forward. Her clenched fist crunched sickeningly into Neil's face and he toppled backward.

Ian half caught Neil as he fell. Before anyone could react further, Steph stood up, ran across the room and was out the door. Annie dithered for a moment, then went after her, but by then it was too late. By the time she had reached the top of the stair-well, Steph's feet were slapping the steps two floors below.

Annie returned to the room, shaking. Neil was kneeling up now, touching his face gingerly. Ian wrung out a handkerchief he had been holding beneath the cold water tap and handed it to Neil.

'Cheers,' he said thickly, and pressed the handkerchief to his jaw, wincing at the pain.

'Are you all right?' Annie asked pointlessly.

Neil squinted up at her. 'I've had worse.' He rotated his jaw slowly as though to ensure it was still fully attached to the skull. 'Christ,' he said ruefully, 'she doesn't half pack a punch.'

Annie stepped up beside Ian, who put an arm round her without thinking. 'What now?' she asked in a small voice.

Ian glanced at her and sighed. He had an expression of dismay on his face. 'Search me,' he said lamely.

23

The sound of water hitting the tiled floor of the shower-stall was like tropical rain. Sometimes, during his morning shower, Howard liked to sit down at the periphery of the steaming jets and imagine that he was in a forest, his back against a tree, sheltering from a storm. Looking out at the rain, whilst remaining warm and snug inside, was for Howard the epitome of contentment. As a child he'd loved snuggling up in bed whilst listening to the rain battering against his windows. And the fiercer the wind and rain had become, the more deliciously secure he'd felt.

He was sitting now, cross-legged like a drenched Buddha, his eyes half-closed, his mind drifting lazily. Over the last few years, because he had felt a need to keep an almost constant surveillance over his mother, Howard had perfected the art of allowing himself to float to the brink of unconsciousness and then holding himself there. In a way, perhaps because he retained enough mental autonomy to channel his thoughts into whichever direction he wished, this precipice-walking was even more relaxing than sleep. Only when he was sure his mother was truly settled for the night and would not stir till morning would he give himself over to the erratic clutches of his dreaming mind.

He groaned, rotating his head on his shoulders, enjoying the sensation of his muscles relaxing, which felt as though he were sinking into himself. Running had been hard this week; the track was heavy from overnight rain, churned into a mud bath in some places thanks to the extra volume of pounding feet, eager students back from their summer holidays. Howard loved this part of the morning: the running and the shower afterwards. It was the only part of the day when he felt he could fully relax, the only time when he was truly his own person.

His eyes blinked open at the sound of an opening door. He sighed, fully expecting the clamour of students to disturb his reverie. But it did not. Instead he heard a single set of footsteps, muffled by the rush of the shower. The footsteps stopped outside his cubicle. A shadow loomed on the other side of the plastic curtain, like Norman Bates in *Psycho*.

'Howard?' a voice said. 'Howard, are you in there?'

He struggled upright, bare feet sliding a little on the tiled floor. 'Er ... yes,' he said. 'Er ... who is it? What do you want?'

'It's me, Howard, Paul Carmichael. Could you come out a minute, please?'

'Er ... hold on,' said Howard. He felt furious at Carmichael for disturbing his shower, for approaching him in such a vulnerable situation. Couldn't the man wait until they were in the staffroom? His anger simmered inside him, but as always failed to erupt. He had read somewhere that it was wise to bring out one's grievances, that bottling them up could be harmful, could make one ill, could even cause that awful disease whose name he tried never even to think about, let alone utter, for fear it would act as some sort of mystical trigger for its inception. But try as he might, Howard could not *make* himself angry. Not properly anyway. Not to the extent that he sometimes wanted to be.

'Howard?' the voice said again.

'I'm coming,' he muttered. 'Just a minute.'

He twisted the plastic dial until the water dwindled and died, then reached up and plucked down the towel he always draped over the curtain rail. He wound the towel carefully round his middle, securing it so it wouldn't come loose, and only then did he pull back the shower curtain. However, despite the towel, he was embarassed. He stepped forward carefully in the hope that it would prevent his stomach from wobbling, his 'breasts' from bobbing up and down. But Carmichael seemed not the slightest bit interested in his semi-nakedness. His expression was such that Howard felt prompted to ask, 'What's the matter? What's happened?'

'It's your mother, Howard,' said Carmichael evenly. 'She's had an accident.'

Howard felt his stomach lurch as though a great part of him had been ripped away. 'An accident?' he repeated. 'What ... what ... what sort of accident?'

'She's in hospital,' Carmichael said. 'Intensive care. I think she fell downstairs.'

Howard shook his head. 'But she can't have. She's not allowed upstairs. She can't have fallen down them.'

Carmichael placed a hand on Howard's bare shoulder. Even now, in his distress and confusion, Howard flinched and thought: I must feel like clammy jelly to him.

'Get dressed and I'll see you outside in five minutes,' Carmichael said. 'I'll drive you down there.'

Howard stared at him, clutching his towel like a giant baby trying to keep hold of a loose nappy. There was something obstructing his throat, a pounding in his ears.

'Five minutes, all right, Howard?' Carmichael repeated, then he turned and walked away.

Howard watched the door close behind him. 'She's not allowed upstairs,' he murmured to the empty room.

The only response was the delicate dripping of water, forming small but spreading pools around his chubby moon-white feet.

24

Forty-five hours before, in a dark dusty store-room, Jayne Trent's life had profoundly and irrevocably changed. With his violation, the man called Stitch had snapped her shackles, had given her the liberty she'd thought she would never attain, had filled her with the blinding light of revelation. 'Behold, I bring you sight,' he had whispered, his terrible face − his *true* face − writhing into a smile. He had touched her − there, where it was most intimate. And he had said, 'Now ... go home and look at yourself. Open the eyes I have given you. And be your own judge.'

The room was dark, close with shadow. Jayne, naked, was hunched in an armchair, staring at the opposite wall. The drawn curtains billowed a little as a breeze wafted through the open window. Like cool fingers the breeze lightly touched her skin, making her nipples stiffen, causing gooseflesh which drew an involuntary moan from her parted lips. Her hand, lying lightly on her thigh, began to stir, and her own fingers slipped between her legs, began to tenderly explore her vagina. But although Jayne moaned again, her eyes never moved. They remained fixed, rivetted on the opposite wall, where she was looking not at the Laura Ashley wallpaper but at a mind-screen that flickered behind her vision, a screen on which the sensory essence of her life was being replayed like a waking dream.

She blinked, groaned again, as her screen-life began to fragment, to draw to a close. As if on cue the telephone rang, its strident bell puncturing the silence like knife-thrusts. Jayne's fingers ceased their dabbling. She trailed her hand back across her thigh, leaving four slick-wet lines which merged into one. It was not the first time the telephone had rung in the past two days, but it was the first time she had heard it. She pushed herself upright, enjoying the movement of air on her naked skin. For the first time in years − in her life, perhaps − she felt unencumbered, felt freed by the miracle of divine sight, by the new perspective that her saviour, Stitch, had given her.

'Hello?' she said into the receiver.

'Miss Trent, is that you?' The voice, which Jayne recognised as belonging to the University's Chancellor, Douglas Parks, seemed surprised.

'It is,' Jayne confirmed.

'Miss Trent, where have you been? I've been trying to contact you for the past two days.'

'I've been here,' Jayne said. 'I've been ... thinking things over.'

'Thinking things over? What's that supposed to mean? Don't you realise you're supposed to be teaching? You've already missed six lectures.'

'So?' said Jayne simply.

Parks spluttered, thrown by her insurrection. 'So ... so ... get yourself down here now and resume your duties. But come and see me first. I think you owe me an explanation.'

Jayne sighed. 'No,' she said.

'I beg your pardon?' exclaimed Parks.

'I said no.'

'I know what you said. What did you mean by it?'

'I meant no, I won't resume my duties, I won't give you an explanation. I don't want to.'

There was silence on the other end of the line. Jayne giggled as she thought of Parks − the Walrus, his staff called him − sitting in his office, receiver to his ear, mouth hanging open in disbelief. After a moment there came a series of incoherent sounds, and then, finally, a stammered reply. 'Look ... Miss ... Miss Trent, I don't know what the problem is, but if there's something wrong perhaps we can ... we can discuss it. There *is* something wrong, isn't there?'

'No,' said Jayne.

'No?'

'No. In fact, Mr Parks, if you want to know the truth, everything is absolutely fucking marvellous.'

'Wha ... *What* did you say?' cried Parks, aghast.

'I said ...' And there Jayne stopped. For suddenly she realised what she *had* said. Never before had she used that particular word — indeed, the mere thought of it, and its associations, had previously sickened her. But now she felt a hot rush of release, a giddy sense of freedom.

'Cunt,' she said.

'*What*?'

She laughed. The word was delicious. A shudder of sheer joy, sheer abandonment, rippled through her.

'I said cunt, Mr Parks. Have you never heard the phrase before? It means clit, pussy, fanny. How'd you like to lick mine?'

Parks sounded faint. 'Miss Trent, are you drunk?'

'You could come over and you could lick my cunt and I could suck your cock. We could have such fun, Mr Parks. What do you say?'

The line went dead.

Jayne dropped the receiver and brought her hands to her face as an almost feverish wave of giggling swept through her. 'Cunt,' she whispered again, relishing the flavour of the word, revelling in her new vocabulary. She replaced the receiver, her body heaving with laughter. She knew she was losing control, that something primal was taking over, but her euphoria was such that she didn't care. Stitch's divine sight had shown her the truth, had made her face what she'd always known but had never admitted. She knew now that her life had been one of woeful inadequacy, self-imposed repression, that she herself had been a sanctimonious sham, a frigid failure whose Puritan ideals had been used not as a rule-book for life, but as a means of holding life at arm's length, of turning her back on responsibility. In short, she had been afraid of life, terrified by it. But now Stitch had changed all that. Now she was afraid no longer. She wanted to *live*. She wanted to wallow in life's excesses, immerse herself in its opportunities.

'Fuck,' she murmured and laughed.

153

She sank on to the hall carpet, legs splayed. Her fingers found her vagina again and began to explore. She eased her labia apart, caressed her clitoris lightly with one finger. She moaned, rotating her hips. To think that such pleasure had been available to her all these years, tucked away inside herself, and she had ignored it. She giggled through the waves of sensation that were sweeping her away. And as the climax crashed through her, she thought: Never again. Never again would she deny herself indulgence. Never again would she jump when the world shouted 'Boo.'

25

'Okay,' said Westey, 'what is it you all wanta talk to me about?'

Ian glanced round to see that Annie and Neil were both looking at him. It was obvious that they considered him their spokesman, presumably because approaching Westey had been his idea. He sighed and leaned forward, elbows on knees, like an old-timer about to relate some strange tale in a wayside inn. 'It's about a friend of ours,' he began, and then, haltingly, supported by contributions from both Annie and Neil, he told Westey the story of Dan Latcher and The Crack, of Steph's drastic change in character, of their confrontation earlier that morning.

Westey listened attentively, occasionally muttering, 'Jeez,' or 'Shit,' or raising a hand to ask a question. He smoked roll-up after roll-up; the window, opened wide in deference to Ian's asthma, plucked the smoke into ribbons like an inept vacuum cleaner sucking up dust. First Neil, and then Annie, stood up and walked through to Westey's tiny kitchen to refill coffee cups from the burbling percolator. Jimi Hendrix played quietly in the background, a muted though nevertheless frantic subsultus of tortured guitar strings.

When Ian was done, Westey crushed the butt of his latest roll-up into the overburdened ashtray and walked to the window. 'That sure is *some* story,' he said with feeling.

'It's true,' Annie replied a little indignantly. 'We didn't make it up.'

Westey turned, surprise on his face. 'Hey, don't get me wrong. I believe you, there's no reason you should lie to me. I just mean ... all this going on and me not knowing about it. It's like the fucking Moonies have come to town.'

'We were wondering if you could help us?' said Ian.

Westey shrugged. 'Sure, if I can. What is it you want?'

'Information on Dan Latcher for a start. You know, what's he like? Who does he hang around with? Where does he live? Also we were wondering if you could get us access to room G8? And if we decide to approach the Union President or the Chancellor with this, would you back us up?'

Westey considered a moment, then nodded. 'Yeah, all that sounds reasonable enough. Count me in.' He crossed to the stereo, replaced Jimi Hendrix with Ry Cooder, then turned with a chuckle. 'You know, I can't wait to see the look on old Walrus's face when you tell him his beloved pass-rate is under threat from some religious psycho who's turning his students into born-again zombies.'

Annie looked puzzled. 'Walrus?' she enquired.

'Parky the Chancellor,' explained Westey, still grinning.

'This isn't funny, you know,' Neil cut in, his voice so cold it froze the smile on Westey's face. 'There's a friend of ours involved in this. She might even be in danger.'

Westey glanced at Neil, then raised a hand, looking suitably repentant. 'Yeah, sorry, man, I didn't mean anything by what I said. It's in my nature to be flippant, that's all. It's how I deal with stuff.'

An awkward silence fell between the four of them. Westey sat down and began to pull at his beard, looking serious, thoughtful. Ian couldn't help feeling that there was some hidden sub-text to Westey's words; the warden's last sentence seemed to contain an undercurrent of meaning that he couldn't quite fathom. If he and Westey had been alone, and if he had known the hall warden a little better, he might have asked him what was wrong. Instead he said, 'Do you know this Dan Latcher guy at all, Duncan?'

Westey looked up, seeming to stir from some personal reverie. 'Not too well,' he admitted. 'He's a psychology post-grad, I know that much. Fancies himself a bit – you know, trendy suit, Vidal Sassoon haircut. I've only spoken to him a coupla times. Always found him a decent enough guy despite the pose.'

'Did you never think he was ... creepy?' enquired Annie.

'Creepy?'

155

'You know – strange? Weird? Shows too many teeth when he smiles? Stares at you like he's trying to strip your skin away?'

Westey seemed about to respond with some quip, then he looked at Neil's frowning face and reconsidered.

'No,' he said, shaking his head. 'Ida described him as your typical student. A bit cocky, a bit rebellious, a bit unsure of himself, concerned with looking cool, getting his end away and getting rat-arsed with his mates. All in all, a well-balanced middle-class individual, if such a thing is possible. Probably destined for some cushy little desk-job in Daddy's company somewhere.'

'Well, he's changed,' said Annie. 'There's something definitely ... not right about him now, something dangerous.'

'Can you tell us anything else about him, Duncan?' asked Ian.

'Yeah, like where he lives,' said Neil. His tone suggested all this pussy-footing around was frustrating him. He wanted to get to the meat – and quickly.

But Westey's information was not wholly illuminating. 'I can only tell you the area he lives in – Royston, which is where ninety per cent of Maybury's student population currently reside.'

'You've no idea of the street name?' probed Ian.

Duncan looked apologetic. 'Sorry, guys. But I do know the name of one of his house-mates – Nev Walton. He's a semi-mate of mine. He and I have scored dope together a coupla times.'

'Where can we find him?' asked Ian.

'Same place you'll find Latcher, I guess.'

'Very helpful,' said Neil heavily. 'Can't you tell us what course he does? What he looks like? Or better still, couldn't you find him for us and get his address?'

Ian glared at Neil, who was treating Westey as if *he* were the enemy. He could appreciate Neil's concern over Steph, but there was no need for him to take his frustrations out on others. However Neil failed to notice, or affected not to notice, his anger. In turn, Westey appeared to overlook Neil's sarcasm.

'I guess I could,' the warden said, scratching his beard, 'if I see him around, that is. Our paths tend not to cross too often. If you wanta track him down yourself, it's probably best to check out the History Department. Nev's a post-grad there so someone should know where to find him. As for what he looks like, well he's into Iron Maiden, Def Leppard, Motorhead, all that scene, and he dresses accordingly.'

Ian nodded and glanced at his watch. 'I don't suppose there's any chance of getting a look at room G8 before lunch, is there?' he asked hopefully.

156

'Sure,' said Westey, 'if I can get hold of Dave, the caretaker.' He stood up and walked behind the settee. Annie watched, puzzled, as he bent and picked up a crumpled shirt, wondering why he should choose this moment to start tidying up. All was revealed a moment later when he straightened with a red telephone in his hands and began to punch in a number. 'What do you guys hope to find in there?' he asked as the receiver burred in his ear.

Ian shrugged. 'We don't really know. A clue, maybe, to what this is all about.'

'This gets more like Sherlock Holmes every minute,' said Westey. 'Ah, Dave, hello. It's Duncan here ...'

Moments later the arrangements had been made. Westey would pick up the keys from Dave and go along to room G8 to collect some "research materials" he had left in there. At first Dave had suggested he come along too, but Westey had soft-soaped him into admitting he was far too busy to accompany him on such a fruitless errand. Within ten minutes of Westey replacing the receiver, the four of them were standing outside G7, Westey fitting the key into the lock. Ian smiled reassuringly at Annie, who was bravely trying to hide her nervousness. Neil was moving from foot to foot like a boxer eager for the bell.

Westey pushed open the door and stepped inside. Neil was a split-second behind him, then came Ian and finally Annie. The sickness that Latcher had induced in Annie a couple of days before had gradually faded to a dull nausea in her belly, a slight ache in her limbs, the odd bout of dizziness. Now, though, as she stepped into the silent, unremarkable classroom, a fresh wave hit her like a relapse. She halted, breathed deeply, closed her eyes and gritted her teeth. I will not be the weak link, she promised herself. This is just nerves, that's all. It's not real. The other possibility, that Latcher's perverse influence could linger in a room like radiation, was too disturbing to contemplate.

'Annie?' Ian said softly. She opened her eyes to see his concerned face. 'Are you okay?'

Beyond Ian, Westey was unlocking the door marked G8, Neil hovering impatiently by his shoulder.

'Yes,' she said, forcing a smile. 'Just ... memories, that's all.'

Ian nodded his understanding. He held out his hand and she took it without hesitation. They moved to the opening door of G8 together, the blind leading the blind into God knew what. Suddenly, remembering the crushed rose and the involuntary expulsion of her stomach contents two nights before, Annie glanced to her right.

157

Both flower and puke had been assiduously removed. Not a trace, nor even the hint of an odour, remained of either.

Ahead of her she heard Neil utter a wordless exclamation. As she turned he faced her and said, 'Are you sure this is the right room?'

Annie looked at him blankly. 'What do you mean?'

Neil stepped aside to let her see. Annie gasped at the sight of the tiny cluttered storeroom that lay beyond G8's wide open door. She stepped inside, stretching out her arms to ensure that the shelves to either side of her were not one of Latcher's illusions. The place was narrow enough to touch the wall at either side, many of the boxes stacked on the shelves furred with an accumulation of dust.

'I don't understand,' she said, swinging back to face them. 'Two nights ago this was a room, a small theatre. There were red drapes, candles, a stage at that end.' She pointed to the dingy back wall which lay not twelve feet away.

Neil looked around, as though in the vain hope of uncovering some secret hinge. 'Well, there's not even room to swing a cat in here now,' he muttered glumly.

26

When Catriona's parents' divorce proceedings had reached their final, most vindictive, stage late last term, Dan had been there to lend support and comfort. He had provided the emotional scaffolding without which she felt she would have crumbled to pieces. He had been whatever the circumstances and her fluctuating moods had desired: her protector, her agony uncle, the butt of her fury, and ultimately her lover. In her self-pity Catriona had taken, taken, taken from him with barely a word of gratitude. But now their positions were reversed, now Dan was the one in need of help; now, at long last, she had the opportunity to repay just a little of the massive debt that she owed him. But thus far she had failed him miserably, had procrastinated to the point of stagnation. Which was why, as she lifted aside the broken gate and approached the red-painted door of number 42 Cramer Road, her face was set in a new resolve.

Only that morning, whilst sitting through an interminable Economics lecture, Catriona had decided that the time had finally come for her to act. She would be patient with Dan, she would be calm, she would be sympathetic, but she would also be persistent. She would *make* Dan talk to her, argue with him until she was blue in the face if needs be; would coax and cajole the truth out of him even if it took all night. And if, after all that, she had still failed to reach him, she would revert with reluctance to her contingency plan. She would phone the police, his parents, the Samaritans, whoever she felt was best equipped to deal with the situation. She was determined to ignore Dan's problems no longer. From now on, whenever he needed somebody, she would be there for him.

She turned the key in the lock and pushed open the front door. The hall was silent, and seemed grimy with shadow after the stark whiteness of the autumn sky. Despite her intentions, Catriona could not help feeling nervous. There had been some strange rumours circulating about Dan in the past couple of days, rumours which she hadn't quite managed to dismiss as ludicrous. He had not been to a lecture yet this term, but that was not what concerned her. There was talk that he had fallen in with Satanists, Moonies, drug-gangs, Hare Krishna. Some of the wilder rumours suggested that he was indulging in blood sacrifices, drug-crazed orgies, was slowly but surely recruiting an army of quasi-religious zealots from among the University population. Catriona had managed to take most of the gossip with a pinch of salt and yet she couldn't help feeling that there was a grain of truth in there somewhere. In Spider she had seen for herself the type of person Dan was associating with nowadays. And in Dan himself she had seen a marked change; he was certainly not the same person she had known and all but fallen in love with last term.

And then of course there was the incident with Nev a couple of days ago. Try as she might to submerge what had happened in rationale, the image of those mangled metal studs kept bobbing to the surface of Catriona's mind like a childhood trauma. How in God's name had Dan had the strength to do that? Drugs, she kept telling herself obstinately, it was the drugs he was taking, that's all. Despite his bluster, Nev had kept well out of Dan's way since Tuesday. His wrist was now badly swollen and decorated with an impressive array of bruises. The wristband he had thrown away, as if by discarding the evidence of that morning he could pretend the incident had never occurred. Catriona had tried speaking to Nev

159

about it, but on each occasion he had hastily claimed he was 'too busy to talk right now,' and had left the room before she could contradict him.

She now stood in the hallway, looking at Dan's door, her breath coming too fast and too loud for her liking. Quietly she removed her shoulder bag, peeled off her jacket, feeling like a wildlife observer trying not to disturb a pack of dangerous animals. The house seemed almost preternaturally silent, as though something was about to break, but it was probably her senses heightened by trepidation which gave that impression. She moved towards Dan's door, raised a hand to knock. She lowered the hand again when she realised that the door was standing ever-so-slightly ajar.

'Dan?' she said. The word came out as a whispered breath which surely only she had heard. She placed the fingertips of one hand almost timidly on the door and pushed.

It swung open silently. She hesitated a moment, then stepped inside. The closed curtains gave the room a pre-dawn bleariness. She screwed up her face at the stink of stale, unwashed flesh, the more pungent and no less unpleasant reek of glue.

It took a few moments for her to make out the humped shape on the bed. When she did she gasped in shock, felt her stomach flip over, her legs turn to spaghetti. Spider was crouched astride Dan's prone body, his hair a smear of white in the gloom. The two of them were kissing like lovers, their mouths clamped together, their limbs locked as though their bodies had fused into an amorphous mass of flesh.

Catriona felt her skin crawl, though her revulsion was not due entirely to the scenario per se. There was something else, something about the entire situation, that was decidedly off-key. It took her numbed mind a few moments to work out what that was. And then she realised that though Spider and Dan were kissing there was no passion there. Indeed their bodies were hardly moving at all. Dan seemed stiff and motionless as a mannequin, Spider shuddering and twitching like a dog in sleep. Despite the evidence of her own eyes, Catriona felt sure that this encounter was not a sexual one. Spider didn't look as though he were kissing Dan, he looked more as if he were ... were feeding from him.

As the notion crept into her mind, Catriona gasped once more. Though Spider seemed unaware of her presence, she very clearly saw Dan's closed eyelids flicker open, his eyes swivel towards her. At first they contained nothing more than a bleary insensibility, then they widened in recognition. And suddenly they were animate with pain and fear and shame; they seemed to

160

scream silently at her: *Get out, get out, for Christ's sake, get out!*

Catriona did so. She stumbled from the room, fortunately retaining the presence of mind not to slam the door behind her. Moving as swiftly and silently as she could, she ran through to the lounge, from there to the kitchen, and from there out the back door. A cat sitting on a dustbin bolted when it saw her; weeds, growing between cracks in the flagstones that paved the back yard, nodded sagely in the wind. Catriona staggered to the back gate, threw it open, and began to run down the cobbled alley that ran behind Cramer Road and its neighbour, Cramer Place. She had no idea where she was going, she just wanted to get away. The fresh air stung her sinuses, caught in her throat like dry ice. Not until the wind began to freeze the tears on her cheeks did she realise she was crying.

27

'You're going to be all right, Mum. Trust me. You're going to be fine.'

Howard had been murmuring such senseless platitudes to his mother's inert form since they'd wheeled her into the intensive care ward ten minutes before.

He stared at the hand which he was holding gently in his own as though only now seeing it for the first time. It was pathetic and withered, brown-yellow with age. It looked as if it had been cobbled together from tree roots and dull, cracked leather, as if it was a makeshift thing, like the hand of a scarecrow, constructed with the aim of approximating humanity, nothing more. The stillness of it brought a lump to Howard's throat, tears to his eyes. He let the tears brim up and tumble down his cheeks.

'Fine,' he whispered. 'Fine, Mum.'

But at this moment his mother did not look as though she would be fine. Indeed, she looked anything but.

She resembled, in truth, a badly-dressed mummy. Both her legs and her right arm were in plaster (broken right femur, cracked left tibia, shattered left ankle, broken elbow), her head was swathed in bandages (fractured skull), and there was a large gauzy pad taped over one eye (left eyeball dislodged from its socket, resulting in serious corneal damage). Added to this was the extensive bruising which covered her body, one cracked rib and various lacerations. And the doctor had the gall to suggest she was "lucky" she had broken neither her neck, her back nor her pelvis.

It had been a long wait for Howard. He had arrived at the hospital to see Mrs Atkins slumped in a chair in the waiting room like a bundle of rags. Up to that point he had felt numb, as though operating on automatic pilot, but at the sight of the old woman he felt an intense anger engulf him, like a red-hot wire that started deep in his belly and threaded right up into his brain. He had walked over to Mrs Atkins, feeling with each step the fury build tremblingly inside him. When he was only a few yards away she had looked up. Her eyes were raw with crying.

'Howard – ' she began, but before she could say anything more his words came streaming out.

'You stupid old woman, what do you think you were playing at, letting my mother go upstairs? Didn't you realise something like this would happen? Haven't you got a brain in your head?'

Howard had never spoken with such open venom to anyone before. There were times when he had wanted to, but had never quite dared make the jump from thought to sound. Mrs Atkins stared at him, astonished, then abruptly broke down in tears. Howard felt a savage glee which he wasn't ashamed of at all. He wanted to see the old cow suffer for her stupidity.

'Well?' he demanded. 'How *do* you explain yourself?' He hadn't realised he was shouting until a nurse appeared by his side to placate him, and then he looked round to see everyone staring at him with wary but interested eyes. Howard demanded to see his mother, but the nurse told him he would have to wait; she would call him when the time came. He bought a cup of coffee from the machine and sat down on the next but one seat to Mrs Atkins, trembling all the while. He felt like shaking the old woman, shouting at her, but the nurse's intervention had somehow patched up the banks of the dam again and he couldn't reproduce the venom that had prompted his earlier outburst. He stared straight ahead, sipping his coffee without really tasting it; all it left in his mouth was a sense of heat that was faintly metallic. On the opposite wall, above a seated man's bald head, was a painting of two children running through a buttercup field. Howard stared at the painting until it became meaningless to him, until its colours seemed to scatter, to become

162

dispersed by his thoughts and eventually submerged by them. Mrs Atkins made occasional sobbing, conciliatory noises, but Howard ignored her and eventually she fell into silence. People came and went. The bald man's rustling newspaper boasted the headline: MP IN THREE-IN-A-BED SEX ROMP.

'Mr Duffy?' The voice came to him through a mush of background noise which seemed to underpin his orbiting thoughts.

He glanced up to see the placating nurse standing over him. 'Huh?'

'Mr Duffy, you'll be able to see your mother in a moment. She's been taken from emergency treatment to an intensive care ward. If you'd just like to follow me?'

Howard nodded and stood up; suddenly he felt nervous as a child at the dentist's. He glanced to his right. 'Where's Mrs Atkins?' he asked.

'Her son arrived and took her home a little while ago. All this was getting a bit too much for her.'

'Good,' said Howard.

The nurse gave him a strange look but said nothing.

Howard's vigil by his mother's bedside passed in dream-like portions, interspersed with the occasional cup of tea or coffee, or visits from nurses to monitor his mother's condition. She remained stable throughout that day, which to Howard meant little except that she was neither improving nor deteriorating, merely hovering in limbo. At nine that evening a nurse with frizzy ginger hair and the face of a street urchin came and crouched beside him. Howard had been staring at his mother's waxen features, willing them without success to flicker into consciousness.

He looked at the nurse. 'Hello,' he said dully.

'Hello,' she responded with a brightness that Howard found irritating. She made a token gesture of looking at the watch above her breast. Howard knew why she had come and what she was about to say.

'I'd like to stay with my mother. I don't want to leave her. She needs me here,' he said quickly before the nurse could speak.

The nurse looked momentarily annoyed that he had pre-empted her, then she adopted a look of professional condescension.

'She doesn't need you, Mr Duffy. She doesn't even know you're here, and it's unlikely she'll regain consciousness before the morning. I think it would be better all round if you went home and got some sleep. We don't want you getting ill as well, do we? It'll be better for your mother if you're bright and cheerful when she wakes up rather than dead on your feet. Honestly, Mr

163

Duffy, she's in the best possible hands. We'll ring you if there's any change.'

Howard simply looked at her. He didn't want to leave his mother, but he was too weary and uptight to argue, and also the nurse's words did make sense. He sighed, removed his spectacles, and massaged his face with his left hand.

'All right,' he said at last, 'but I'll be back first thing in the morning. Around eight o'clock, if not before.'

'Fine, Mr Duffy. Perhaps by then your mother will be awake, in which case the two of you could have breakfast together.'

Howard made no comment. He heaved himself up from the chair and, feeling drained and exhausted, followed the signs to the lobby. He phoned for a taxi and then went out on to the main steps of the hospital to wait for it. The night was cold, but Howard hardly felt it; he was much too engrossed in his own thoughts. Tonight, for the first time ever, he would be returning to an empty house, and that knowledge made him feel lonelier and more frightened than he had ever felt in his life.

28

Love was the answer, the One True Path. Love was light and perfection, baptism, creation, submission, emergence and sight. God is Love. Dan is Love. Tear out the blindness. Disconnect all thoughts.

In the past two days Steph had discovered the Truth. Doors had been opened within her, were still opening; doors in the maze created by the spirits, doors which led to the heart of her being, to Truth, to Epiphany. Dan would show her the way to herself, for Dan was Love, Dan was the key. Dan had thrown open the doors which the spirits had erected to hide themselves behind. He had shown her the extent of them, the influence they exerted.

And they were disgusting. They were Filth and Evil and Corruption. Their hooks were sunk deep into the soft flesh of the world. They had kidnapped creation, had buried the Truth in a mire of grossness and triviality. They had reduced Love to the heated mutterings of a squirting moment, a declaration to be used calculatingly – for spite, for profit, for personal gain. Dan had told her of the Mission, had warned her of the battles and conflicts ahead. The spirits must be eradicated, wiped from creation; there must be (he had said) a new Genesis. Dan would save whomsoever he could, but when the Reckoning came those souls too black would have to be cast into the cleansing fire. It was sad but inevitable. For the most part choices had been made. And now there remained only the Final Judgement.

These thoughts buoyed Steph. She felt high on conviction, her soul bonded with Love. Two days ago, she realised now, her mind had been a dark cell littered with traps. So cleverly constructed had the cell been that she hadn't even realised she was a prisoner. But now ... now she had been released like a bird into a vast blue sky with an endless horizon. Dan had unlocked her shackles, had flung her into the Light.

Freedom, she thought, her mind soaring. Giddily she back-tracked, recalling the beautiful process of her iiberation, the way her Saviour had come to her, shining with his Glory. He was a fisher of men, and each fish his net of Love ensnared was a soul saved. Unknown to her, she had been dark with the spirits then, though the instant he had touched her she had felt them sloughing off, losing their grip, though still their influence had been such that she did not fully comprehend the sensation. It had manifested itself as nothing more than a sense of well-being, a notion that in Dan Latcher lay the answer to a question for which she had been searching all her life. Together she and Annie had entered The Crack, and it was there where Dan's words had struck home, where his actions, his magic, had acted as a strange key, unlocking door after door within her, showing her the maze she must negotiate, guiding her through a confusion of false turnings and dead-ends. The scales coating her eyes had been ripped away. It had been an experience both pleasurable and painful, a necessary, and indeed delicious, rape. She had emerged from the baptism cleansed, full of a new Truth, a new purpose, full of Love.

But there had been a sadness there too. Actually being able to *see* for the first time was a curse as well as a blessing.

The spirits in Annie had been too strong. They had rejected Dan's word, and in so doing had gained a new strength, extending their threads of influence, binding her soul so tightly that there was no longer any prospect of escape. Annie, therefore, before the war had even truly started, was already a casualty, already one of the

165

Fallen. She was in thrall to the spirits. Everything she said and did was dependant upon their corrupt motivations, was intended to undermine Dan's burgeoning strength, to create weak links in an ever-lengthening chain of ascendancy. Once that morning already, Annie's spirits had tried to ensnare her, had allied with the spirits which controlled Neil and Ian and had tried to re-possess her flesh. She had felt them striving to ease shut some of the doors which Dan had thrown wide, attempting to block off the beckoning light of her Epiphany. But Steph had drawn on Dan's strength and Love. She had fought them, and she had *won*. And her victory had brought its own reward, for now, she knew, there was no going back. She had completed her rites of passage, had earned her place at the side of her Messiah.

But the spirits. The sight of them, too, was a curse to be endured. Steph was horrified by their seething proliferation, by the pervasiveness of their influence. Singly they defied the eye, but the overall impression was of a black bristling mass of multi-eyed, many-legged life. They were crustaceous, insectoid, octopoid, serpentine. They had shells and antennae and tentacles and claws. They were, Steph realised, all that she found repulsive. They were her own personal vision, her own living nightmares.

But they were *there*, that was the undeniable fact. Beneath the veil, the blind-sight of humanity, they were pulling the strings, forcing mankind to ride a subtle but undeniable down-slope. They offered up baubles and called it progress; they entranced the eye with glitz and called it civilisation. No one escaped their attentions. Indeed, Steph had seen people literally black with them, their bodies, their faces, their eyes, smothered with scuttling darkness. So abundant were they that when she walked she could not help but tread on them, crunching them underfoot. The sensation repulsed her; it was like walking on a carpet of scorpions and beetles and soft-bodied sea-creatures.

But at least, thanks to Dan's Love, they could no longer touch her. The radiance of her coming Epiphany was such that the spirits were repelled by it. She had seen them trying to alight on her skin, wings buzzing, and then wheeling away as though stung. She had seen Dan cutting a swathe through their bristling path, their bodies shrivelling in his aura, bursting into tiny puffs of cold white flame like debris which has drifted too close to the sun.

This, to Steph, was undeniable proof of Dan's divinity, if indeed she needed any. She felt honoured to be chosen by him, breathless in his presence, but she felt too that she had been born for this, that this was her purpose, her Destiny. To accept this Love, to find this

166

Truth, to be here now at this moment ... it all seemed so *right*. In the past two days, Steph's world had come together, a million separate points, separate aspects, converging into a single focus of which Dan Latcher was the living embodiment.

He was before her now, arms outstretched, teeth and eyes flashing, the combination of his words and his quick fingers unlocking more doors, and more, and yet more. She gasped, moaned, clapped and cheered as he probed her most intimate places, as he pushed her up and up and up, building one peak upon another, laying one blinding brightness atop the next. Sometimes she felt she would split with his attentions, felt his Glory would scatter her flesh, tear her limb from limb. Many times already she had felt she'd reached Epiphany, only for the glare to subside to reveal further doors, further passage-ways, further journeys.

She screamed her ecstacy. He was gorging her now, cramming her full; she felt her skin stretching like an over-inflated balloon. *Epiphany*, she thought, *this time for sure it's Epiphany* ...

But it was not. 'Enough for now,' she heard him say, and he lowered his hands.

She groaned as she dwindled, as her body, her soul, accommodated the result of these latest explorations. Looking around she gained an impression of light, of steam rising from sweating flesh, carrying away further impurities. She laid the tips of her fingers gently on her breastbone as though she could physically feel the new doors opened within her tonight. These meetings, these assemblies, were all essence to her, all sensation. Dan's message was ingested spiritually, instinctively; it was stored somewhere deep inside as race-memory was stored in the DNA of every human being.

She felt Love radiating from each and every one of the disciples around her. She stretched out a hand and it was taken and squeezed. The Crack now numbered thirty-six, plus Dan. Its growth was inevitable, unstoppable. This room, this secret chamber, was the only place she knew that was not crawling with spirits. And soon this place would be the world and the world this place. It was simply a matter of time.

29

'Enough for now,' said Dan, and grinned his predator's grin. Below him the congregation writhed, moaned, gratified by what he was pumping into them, absorbing it, replenished.

He spread his arms wide as though offering himself for crucifixion. The gesture said: *I have nothing to hide. There is nothing up my sleeves. I embrace you all.*

The curtains swished closed. Dan stood there for a moment, radiating, then his arms drooped a little; he swayed unsteadily on his feet. His lips closed over his vast grin. His fingers curled inward like hermit crabs retreating into their shells. His blazing eyes dulled, grew muddy and blank.

A figure slouched forward from the shadows at the side of the stage. Scrawny, ill-looking, white hair sticking up in gluey strands, Spider caught Dan as he started to topple sideways. Puncture-marks stood out, livid, in the crook of the glue-sniffer's elbow. He looked wasted, his skin a ghastly white, his eyes sunk in purple hollows. Yet despite his consumptive appearance he caught Dan as easily as if he were a balsa-wood scarecrow. He dragged him off-stage, paying no heed to the plaintive whisper issuing from Dan's barely-moving lips.

'Please ... please ... please ... please ...'

30

He had to knock twice and speak her name before Annie opened the door to him.

'Hello, Ian,' she said, tight-lipped.

'Hello,' he replied to her back as she turned away, and followed her into the room.

It seemed she had worked out her frustrations with a bout of tidying up. Steph's discarded clothes had been picked up, folded, and stacked on a chair; books, notes and tapes had been neatly arranged into piles. Annie had stuck up some posters on the few sections of wall that Steph had not claimed – one for Heathcote Williams' *Sacred Elephant*, another for Greenpeace, and one which depicted a mournful dog in a cage beneath which was the caption: "Every six seconds an animal dies in a British laboratory".

Annie sat down on the bed and looked at him expectantly.

Ian lowered himself into the armchair, clasped his hands together, smiled a sheepish smile, and muttered, 'Sorry.'

Annie nodded, though asked tersely, 'Is that all you came to say?'

'Well ... yeah ... and to talk things over, you know.' He stood up. 'Do you mind if I make some coffee?'

Annie shook her head, and Ian gratefully began to busy himself, his mind mulling over the most tactful way to re-open the subject. He filled the kettle at the sink, staring at his undulating reflection in the untarnished metal. Holding the brand new kettle in his hand gave him a pang of sorrow. An image came to him of Steph – the old Steph – excitedly buying this and other items for her university adventure. He swallowed the lump that was rising in his throat and tried to shift his mind on to a more determined track. Steph was under the spell of this Latcher guy, but the battle wasn't over yet, not by a long way. Ian suspected, however, that what was happening was getting too much for them to handle by themselves. Pretty soon they were going to have to hand the initiative over to someone more qualified, though just for the moment he felt oddly reluctant to do that. Admitting that Steph's behaviour was considerably more than infatuation, that the problem was too big for them, was rather a frightening prospect. He plugged the kettle in and switched it on. 'Have you seen Steph since this morning?' he asked.

There was a slight pause. 'No ... and I'm not sure I really want to either.' When Ian looked at Annie, raising his eyebrows, she muttered defiantly, 'All this is getting to me, Ian. It's ... it's really getting me down.'

Ian nodded his understanding. 'Yeah, it's not the most ideal way to start university life, is it?'

Little else was said until they were sat sipping their coffee. Then Ian mumbled, 'I really am sorry about what I said earlier, you know.'

Annie sighed. Smiled. The first real smile since Ian had arrived.

'I'm sorry too,' she said. 'I shouldn't have been so touchy. I just couldn't bear the thought of not being believed. I felt as though Neil and Duncan were thinking, "Silly woman", and then you started going on at me too and I couldn't take it any more. I just wanted some support, Ian, that's all. If you all think I'm making this up, I'll just ... I don't know what I'll do.'

Ian grasped his mug tighter as though the gesture could somehow project his earnesty to Annie. 'No one thinks you're making it up,' he said. 'We all thought you were mistaken, that's all, that you somehow got the wrong room. I mean, you're sure it wasn't F8 or G9, something like that? You said yourself you were reeling after that Crack meeting, you didn't know what was going on. Maybe you just −'

'No!' Annie said, shaking her head emphatically. 'No, it was G8, I'm sure of it; I've got it branded on my mind. G7 leading to G8. We went through a classroom − the same one as today − and into another room twice as big, with red drapes on the walls, candles, chairs, a big stage at one end.' She put a hand to her forehead. 'I can see it now, Ian. The door we went through. Definitely G8. Definitely.'

'But G8 was just a storeroom,' replied Ian, trying to keep his voice free from frustration. 'You saw for yourself. There was no way it could have accommodated all those things you were on about.'

'Don't you think I know that? Latcher must have done something to the room, hidden it somehow. It's another of his illusions.'

'But how −'

'I don't know!' exclaimed Annie before Ian could finish the question. 'But he did something, I'm sure of it. He's got ... he's got ... some sort of power.'

'But *what* power?' Ian said, aware that his voice was rising. 'What power can make an entire room disappear?'

'I don't know,' Annie repeated stubbornly, 'but he's got something, I know it. He could be the bloody Devil for all we know.'

It was a throwaway statement, but Ian asked, 'You mean you

think he's got some sort of *supernatural* power? Like something out of a James Herbert novel?'

Annie looked at him, scowling as though at some indelicate remark. 'Don't make fun of me, Ian.'

'I wasn't, honestly.'

'All I know is, two days ago that room was there and this morning it wasn't. I don't know how or why Latcher did it. All I know is that he did.'

There was a short silence, an impasse, during which Annie glared stubbornly, sticking to her story, and the thoughts seemed to grind like immovable rocks in Ian's head. Then all at once Ian's face cleared. He clicked his fingers. 'Of course! How could we be so stupid?'

'What?' asked Annie.

Ian looked at her. 'It's obvious what he did, isn't it? He swapped the signs around on some of the doors!'

He expected Annie to leap at this, to compliment him on his powers of deduction, but she merely frowned.

'I don't know,' she said doubtfully. 'From what I remember, that other room, G7, was the same, and in the same part of the corridor.'

Ian waved a hand as though tossing aside her argument. 'Yes, but maybe it was next door. All the classrooms along there would probably be the same layout, they'd even have similar views.'

It was obvious that Annie still wasn't happy, but she couldn't help admitting that Ian *might* be right.

'Of course I am,' he said confidently. 'It's the only solution, isn't it?'

Annie shrugged. 'I suppose. But which is the real G8, do you think?'

Ian considered. 'It must be the original one, the big one. Store-rooms aren't usually numbered like classrooms, are they?'

Again Annie's shoulders jerked in a shrug. 'No, I suppose not.'

Ian gave her a quizzical smile. 'You still seem very reluctant to accept this as a solution. Why is that? It makes perfect sense to me.'

Annie blushed a little as if she'd been found out. 'Oh, I don't know,' she said. 'It just ... I suppose it just doesn't *feel* right.'

Ian was silent for a moment, struggling with his exasperation. When he spoke he heard the condescension in his tone but could do nothing to stifle it.

'That's not much of an answer, is it?' he said. 'I mean, be

reasonable, Annie. It's logic we have to apply to this situation, not instinct.'

'Oh, and since when did you become Mister bloody Spock?' Annie responded, bridling.

Ian drew a deep breath. He had come here tonight with the intention of talking this matter through with Annie calmly and rationally. They had parted on bad terms earlier that day and he had resolved to make amends, listen to her side of things. But how could he take her seriously when she refused to accept what were obvious solutions to previously bizarre mysteries out of simple stubborness? Unable to stop the anger from flaring inside him, he snapped, 'That's a stupid thing to say. Just because I'm using a bit of common sense instead of getting all hysterical. I suppose you'd prefer to think that Dan Latcher was some sort of alien who can fire laser beams out of his eyes? Maybe he can shrink himself. Maybe he's got a spaceship hidden in a U-bend somewhere. Maybe he's hiding in the Nescafe jar, listening to us at this very moment.'

Immediately his outburst was over, Ian felt ashamed of it. He sat and glowered at the sink to avoid looking at Annie, and felt the air curdle between them. Just when he'd decided to swallow his pride and apologise, suggest they start again, he half-glimpsed something huge and white launching itself towards him. An animal! was the thought that flashed through his mind, and he half ducked, half turned as the pillow that Annie had thrown thumped against the side of his head and creased to enclose his face like a giant's gloved hand.

His attempt to avoid the projectile, and its unexpected impact with the side of his head, sent him toppling out of the chair. He flailed, but his hand encountered only empty air; the substance of the chair seemed to slide away from his kicking legs. He exhaled as the floor jarred the air from his body, felt pain jump briefly into his elbow and wrist and then out again before it could leave a mark. At last he oriented himself and groggily sat up. The first thing he saw was Annie collapsed across the bottom bunk, her body heaving with uncontrollable giggles.

It was the second time he'd seen her like this, and on each occasion it had been the same: some innocuously amusing event prompting a rush of hilarity that was really a purging of tension. He'd felt angry when he sat up, but now he too began to laugh. He threw the pillow back at her. She caught it neatly and replaced it on the bed. Still grinning he extended his hand towards her. 'Pax?' he suggested.

She nodded and reached for his hand. At the last moment Ian withdrew it and gave her a playful snubbing gesture, his thumb touching the tip of his nose, his fingers waggling. She stuck her tongue out at him. Ian reciprocated.

'You're incorrigible,' she told him.

'True,' he agreed.

He sat back in the armchair, stretching his legs out, crossing his ankles. 'Now where were we before you resorted to violence?'

'You were being a pain in the arse,' Annie reminded him.

'I'll ignore that. Cheap shots don't become you.' He grinned boyishly, winningly (he hoped). 'I'm sorry for what I said about the alien. That was a cheap shot too.'

'Yes,' Annie said, snooty as a school ma'am, 'it was.' She stretched out on the bottom bunk, elbow propped on the pillow, head resting on her hand. 'So what's our next move?' she asked.

'Another cup of coffee?' suggested Ian, but saw from her expression that she was back to wanting serious answers. He crossed his arms, shrugged. 'I suppose we have to find Latcher, confront him. Neil's been hanging around the History Department all afternoon, asking questions, but he's had no luck so far.'

'Is there no other way of finding out the address?' Annie asked. 'Surely the Uni would have a record of it somewhere?'

'Apparently not. We asked at Reception and at the Union Office, but students who live out aren't required to let the Uni know *where* they live. If anyone at Uni wants to get in touch with them, tutors or whoever, they just leave a note in the pigeon-holes.'

Annie tutted and shook her head. 'So what now? Just keep asking around?'

'I suppose so,' said Ian. 'In the meantime we could ask Duncan to get the keys again and look at *all* the rooms in G corridor.'

Annie pulled a face. 'Yeah, I suppose. It seems a bit pointless to me.' She was silent for a moment, obviously mulling something over. At last Ian said, 'What are you thinking?'

Annie picked at a tiny hole in the blanket she was lying on. In an almost apologetic voice she said, 'I think it's time we told someone else about this, Ian. Not just Duncan – someone in authority.'

Ian sighed. 'Yeah, I suppose you're right. I was hoping we could sort this out ourselves. I guess I didn't want to admit how weird and serious the situation was getting. The only problem is, who do we tell? Steph's parents? The Chancellor?'

'How about trying Mr Carmichael first? He's nice, he'll listen.'

Ian considered, then said, 'Yeah, okay. We'll talk to him in the morning after the lecture, though God knows how we'll explain the disappearing room and all that. He'll think we're a couple of nutters.'

'No, he won't,' said Annie. 'We'll make him believe us.'

Ian looked unconvinced but said nothing. He made more coffee and they sat around, chatting until well past midnight. Both of them were secretly hoping for, and yet dreading, the arrival of Steph. However by the time Ian kissed Annie on the cheek at ten past two and reluctantly murmured his goodnights, there was still no sign of her.

31

When the telephone began to ring, Howard snapped awake at once and was surprised to find he'd been sleeping at all. The anxiety in his mind must have expanded like a sheet and closed over his consciousness.

His fingers felt clumsy as they picked up the receiver. He put it to his ear and then found he had to swallow to release his gummy voice. 'Hello,' he said, his limbs and back aching as he eased them from the shape of the armchair in which he'd been sitting. The light in the room was soft, but still it hurt his eyes.

A voice said, 'Is that Mr Howard Duffy?'

The formality of the tone made Howard's heart and head throb like a distant drum.

'Yes,' he said, suddenly wishing it wasn't, 'it is.'

'Hello, Mr Duffy, this is Sister Cort from the Maybury District Infirmary. It's about your mother. I'm afraid she's taken a turn for the worse.'

The distant drum suddenly seemed much closer. Howard only just heard himself ask, 'A turn for the worse? What ... what does that mean?'

'She's deteriorating, Mr Duffy,' the nurse said calmly. 'We're trying to stabilise her, but I think it might be best if you came down.'

Unthinkingly Howard nodded into the receiver. 'Yes ... yes, I will. I'll be there in ten minutes.'

'There'll be someone to meet you when you arrive, Mr Duffy,'

Sister Cort said. 'Please drive carefully, or better still take a taxi.'

'Yes,' said Howard, 'thank you. I . . . goodbye.'

He put the phone down before she could respond. Immediately the ting of disconnection faded, to be replaced by a silence so profound it seemed sealed in plastic. For a few moments Howard simply sat, staring at nothing. He felt an urge to remain completely motionless, as though that could somehow halt his mother's deterioration. So brief had the phone call been and so abruptly had it plucked him from sleep, that it seemed almost unreal, like an extension of his forgotten dream. 'Mum,' he whispered, and all at once he was up out of the chair, rooting in his pockets for the keys to his VW Beetle as he blundered towards the front door.

There was no one on the roads, which was fortunate, for Howard unwittingly drove through two red lights. He felt almost surprised when he pulled up in front of the hospital – he could recall little of his journey here. He got out of the car and locked the door. Paradoxically his nervousness had given him a steady hand, an almost heightened sense of perception. Everything seemed very clear to him, very sharp. He trotted up the hospital steps and in through the glass doors to find the sister who had phoned him – Sister Cort – waiting with a strained smile.

'How is she?' Howard asked as she touched his arm briefly and motioned that he follow her.

'Not good, I'm afraid. Her pulse is irregular and her breathing is very shallow. At first her system was fighting hard against the jolt it had been given, but now I'm afraid she's tiring, as a result of which the initial shock is starting to exert a stronger grip. We're doing all we can to keep circulation moving, to keep vital organs supplied with blood, but there's only so much we *can* do. A large part depends on how strong she is, how badly she wants to keep going. At the moment she's fading, but I have seen patients in her situation rally their forces, give a final push and reverse the trend. I'd say at this stage, be prepared for the worst, but don't give up hope.'

'She . . . she's a strong-willed woman,' Howard said as though that proved everything would be all right.

Sister Cort gave him a faint smile. 'Well, that's half the battle won then, isn't it?' she replied, and led him into the intensive care ward.

It was like entering a chapel or a library. Howard felt instinctively he should be quiet, as though the sound of a raised voice would prove too much for many a fluttering heart. His mother's bed had been ominously enclosed on all sides by floor-length green curtains.

The nurse sitting beside the bed, monitoring his mother's condition, looked up with large brown eyes as Howard entered, reminding him of a doleful rabbit. His mother's frail bandaged body was hooked to a cardiac monitor. Howard wished he didn't have to witness just how erratic his mother's pulse was; it showed up as a jagged outcrop of constantly etching light on the dull screen.

'This is Mr Duffy,' Sister Cort told the nurse, 'the patient's son.'

The nurse smiled with a timidity that Howard found less than encouraging. 'Hello,' she said. 'I'm Alison.' She glanced at Sister Cort. 'Um ... Nurse Stevens.'

Howard nodded at her, finding this whole procedure grotesque. His mother's life was draining away, and here they were observing social niceties like guests at a cocktail party. Nurse Stevens was sitting on the far side of his mother's bed beside the ECG machine. The chair on this side, he presumed, was for him. He sat on it.

'Right,' Sister Cort said, 'I'll leave you to it, then.' She sounded, thought Howard, like a housewife who has led a plumber to a faulty cistern. This image was reinforced a moment later when she asked, 'Can I get you anything? A cup of tea or coffee?'

If the situation had been less grave, and if Howard had had a sense of humour, he might have smiled. Instead he looked up at her almost sulkily. 'Er ... no,' he murmured. 'No, thank you.'

Sister Cort nodded brusquely and left. As the curtains fell back into place behind her, Nurse Stevens – Alison – released a deeply held sigh.

'She's a real dragon,' she confided, once again flashing her timid smile.

Howard simply looked at her. Only when she blinked away, obviously unsettled, did he realise he'd been staring.

'Sorry,' she muttered. 'How I feel about Sister Cort is probably the last thing you want to hear just now.'

Howard felt his cheeks beginning to burn, despite telling himself there was no reason for them to do so. 'Er ... no,' he mumbled. 'Er ... not at all. That is ... it's all right ... I ... er ... I don't mind.'

He glared at his hands as he felt the old sense of inadequacy creeping up on him. He had always found social interaction a stressful process. The only person in whose company he felt un-selfconscious was his mother. Even at work he never initiated conversations with his colleagues; indeed, he felt himself shrinking away whenever anyone approached him. He had always loathed and envied people who could keep up a constant stream of chatter, who had an inexhaustible supply of smalltalk. Howard was not an unintelligent man, but verbal articulation intimidated him to the point of muteness, or at best a kind of bumbling idiocy. The only time speaking didn't bother him was in front of a lecture group, where he could plan beforehand exactly what he was going to say.

The cardiac monitor which had been emitting a fairly constant bleeping sound since Howard had been here, suddenly paused, chirruped twice in quick succession, then paused again before returning to its previous shaky rhythm. Jerked from his thoughts, Howard looked up, alarmed. Nurse Stevens' uniform rustled as though made of paper as she made a quick but thorough examination of his mother's inert body and her various artificial appendages. At last she sank back onto her chair and gave Howard a smile that aspired to reassurance, but fell, in his eyes, woefully short.

'Just a hiccup,' she said. 'Nothing to worry about.'

Maintaining eye-contact was something else Howard found discomforting, but this time it was Nurse Stevens who looked away. Howard's gaze shifted to his mother's waxen face, which was partially enclosed by an oxygen mask of transparent plastic. Clods of black shadow seemed to be weighing down his mother's cheeks, causing them to sink, stretching the flesh tight over the bone. He hesitated a moment, then took her scarecrow-hand. He had been afraid that simply touching her would upset the fragile equilibrium of her body, cause her to topple over the edge into darkness like a tightrope-walker distracted by a thrown brick. He held his breath for a few seconds but the mountain-range that was her pulse remained constant.

'Is ... is it all right if I ... talk to her?' he asked softly.

Nurse Stevens looked both touched and surprised by the question. 'Of course,' she said. 'It might do her good, give her something to cling to.'

Howard didn't like the implication that his mother's life was in his hands, that his voice was the rope which might or might not be lowered in time to prevent her vanishing into the quicksand. Nevertheless he shifted his chair a little closer to the bed as though about to share secrets with the still form − which in a way he was. He would have preferred to have been alone with his mother. He felt inhibited by the nurse's presence.

'Mum,' he murmured as quietly as he could, hoping the bleeping monitor would keep his words from reaching Nurse Stevens' ear. 'Mum, it's me, Howard.'

Not surprisingly there was no response.

Howard glanced up, saw Nurse Stevens watching him intently a

177

moment before she looked away, and furiously thought: *Mind your own business!* However he said nothing, merely leaned closer to his mother's ear, close enough to catch the slightly chemical odour of her bandages.

'Mum,' he whispered again, 'it's me, Howard. You're going to be all right, Mum. You've had an accident and you're in hospital, but you're fine now. There's nothing to worry about.'

He paused, not sure how to continue. His mother barely seemed to be breathing. At last, reducing his whisper even further, he said, 'Don't leave me, Mum. Not yet. Not like this. I'm not ready, Mum. Please fight, for my sake. I need you, Mum. I need ..."

His throat and eyes filled up. He bowed his head, terrified of Nurse Stevens seeing his naked emotion. Nevertheless she knew something was wrong. He heard her ask, 'Mr Duffy, are you okay?'

Leave me alone, you ... you bloody cow! he raged silently. He raised a hand, battling furiously to control the tears which had come all at once, catching him by surprise.

'Are you sure you're all right?' she asked. 'Would you like some water?'

He wiped his eyes with his sleeve, took a deep breath and looked up at her. He shook his head and managed to croak, 'No.'

Time passed and nothing changed. Howard clung to his mother's hand, murmured occasional words of encouragement to her, but beyond that the deep silence was broken only by the bleep of the cardiac monitor. Every so often Nurse Stevens checked his mother's condition – pulse, blood pressure, a gentle examination of the pupil beneath the unbandaged eyelid. Once Howard glanced at his watch and was surprised to realise it was the first time he had done so since the phone-call from Sister Cort. Because of this he had no way of knowing when that call had come or how long he had been here; he knew only that it was now 4:45 a.m. He stared into his mother's masked and bandaged face until its shape became meaningless to him, a blur of light and dark that seemed somehow to incorporate itself into the structure of his mind, prompting a stir of memories from years long past.

At five years old, or six, or seven, some boys had pushed him off a swing in the park, pushed him so hard that his body had slammed into the gravelly tarmaced ground face first. They'd run off, frightened, when he'd begun to yell. They weren't bad boys; afterwards, he remembered, one of them had approached him in the schoolyard and had silently and shame-facedly handed him a bubblegum as an apology.

178

Someone had taken Howard home — he couldn't remember who, but thought it was a woman — and delivered him to a shocked Mrs Duffy. The gravel had flayed Howard's forehead, nose and chin as effectively as a cheese grater. Howard vividly remembered seeing himself in the bathroom mirror, standing there in a white vest sprinkled with blood, his blue eyes large and frightened, but also a little excited, behind his spectacles. He'd never seen so much blood before; it looked as though someone had slapped him up the middle of the face with a brush dipped in red paint. At the age of five or six the possibility of future scarring was not an issue that Howard entertained. After the initial shock and pain were over, he felt almost proud to be hurt so badly, fascinated by the vividness and proliferation of his blood. He remembered his mother gently using a warm flannel to wipe the blood away, remembered a basin of steaming water that gradually turned pink, then red, darkening each time the flannel was wrung out in it. The worst bit was when his mother used tweezers to extract the bits of gravel from his face, but really even that was okay. His mother was kind and gentle. She counted each bit of gravel as she plucked it free as though it were a game. And afterwards she disinfected his wounds, holding him tight until the stinging went away, and then gently smoothed big pink plasters over his nose and chin.

Howard remembered the evening that followed as if it were yesterday. It was November; the air was cold, full of the mulchy smell of autumn and a lingering smoky sweetness that were the ghosts of bonfires. His father was out somewhere, so he sat with his mother in the lounge, eating crumpets dripping with hot butter and strawberry jam, sipping cocoa that had to be left to cool a little so that it wouldn't hurt his swelling lip.

He and his mother chatted quietly for what seemed hours — about school, about family, about the approaching excitement of Christmas. In the background classical music lulled from the wireless; it would be another five years before his father proudly brought home the family's first television set. His mother read him a story that night — the one about Brer Rabbit in the briar-patch — and afterwards he drew her a picture of Brer Rabbit and Brer Fox, concentrating hard to keep his colouring-in within the black lines of his illustration.

Despite the soreness in his face — the stiffening and bruising of his chin and nose, the swelling of his lip — Howard remembered that evening as one of sheer contentment. Time spent with his mother when she wasn't busy was always good, but that particular night was the best of all; it seemed that all the positive elements

179

in his world had come together to form an idyll that would never again be achieved. Of course, Howard was not fully aware of this at the time. It was only with hindsight that he was able to arrive at this conclusion. But thinking back, it was not difficult to recapture his impression of her at that time – as someone who was slim and beautiful, warm and loving. Instinctively his hand tightened on hers, an action which brought him rudely back to the present. He looked at her as she was now – scrawny and withered, life slipping from her grasp – and again tears sprang unbidden to his eyes, tickled his face as they traced a path down his plump cheeks.

Once she had been so strong, so steadfast. It seemed inconceivable that time could reduce such a woman to this. Howard remembered her at his father's funeral. He had been the one who had blubbered like a baby whilst she had endured the day with a straight back, a quiet dignity. It was she who had gone to the coroner's office, the bank, the undertaker's, she who had contacted the solicitor and arranged his father's affairs. Howard had been twenty-two at the time and even then had had to rely on his mother's strength to see him through. His relationship with his father had only ever been strained at best, yet the sudden savage intrusion of death, its hideous significance, its utter finality, had rendered him an incapable wreck.

And now here he was again, staring into the black hole that was Death's ever-hungry mouth, only this time there was real love involved, real fear, and it was an ordeal that he had to endure alone.

'Don't die, Mum,' he murmured before he realised he was doing so. 'Please don't die. I don't think I could live without you. I don't know what I'd do if I was on my own.'

He sensed Nurse Stevens looking at him and glanced up. She was smiling a smile that he immediately hated. It was sickly with compassion and false reassurance. It purported to identify with his anguish, and was all the more despicable because of its failure to do so.

'How ... how is she now?' he managed to ask, swallowing the fury that clawed at his throat and chest and stomach in its desire to erupt.

'She seems to have stabilised again,' Nurse Stevens said brightly. 'Perhaps you've done her some good, Mr Duffy. Maybe deep down she knows you're here.'

Howard nodded. It was a comforting thought, though one he found hard to accept. His mother had shown not even the barest acknowledgement of his presence – not the flicker of an eyelid nor the twitch of a finger. It was only that bloody machine that convinced him she was alive at all.

The curtains bulged and parted. Howard turned to see a young man with curly blond hair who was dressed in a white smock that made him think of an orderly in a lunatic asylum.

The man smiled as if he had wonderful news to impart. 'Relief time, Ali,' he said. 'It's six o'clock. How's Mrs D?'

Mrs D? Howard was outraged at the young man's lack of respect. He sat and fumed while Nurse Stevens stood and stretched.

'She's steady at the moment,' he heard her say. 'This is Mr Duffy, Mrs Duffy's son.'

'Hi,' the young man said, extending a hand, 'I'm Rod.' Unwillingly Howard offered his own sweaty, plump hand, which was squeezed and shaken, then allowed to drop like a piece of discarded fruit.

Rod settled himself into the chair vacated by Nurse Stevens. 'Ooh, nice and warm,' he said, squirming. 'You must be hot stuff, Ali.'

The young man's banter caused Howard's throat to tighten, his temples to pound. *If he doesn't shut up in a minute, I'll ... I'll ...*

'Would you care for some breakfast, Mr Duffy?'

'What?' said Howard stupidly. He looked up to see Sister Cort standing to his right, having entered behind Rod.

The sister's arrival precipitated Nurse Stevens' departure. She raised her eyebrows at Rod and slipped nervously past her superior.

'Breakfast,' Sister Cort repeated. 'We have a small canteen area on the first floor which serves English breakfasts between six and eight a.m.'

'Erm ... no ... I ...'

'Come, come, Mr Duffy. You look as though you need a break, and your mother's not going anywhere. You'll feel much better once you've got some nourishment inside you.'

Sister Cort's brisk and aggressive manner caused Howard's hackles to rise once more. He tried to formulate some disparaging put-down, but acerbic repartee had never been his forte. For long moments his thoughts wrestled, but with each second that ticked by the pressure of the sister's unwavering gaze squeezed out any hope of inspiration. Realising that the silence was becoming awkward, and that Rod's brow was starting to crease in a puzzled frown, Howard finally blurted, 'Well ... well ... well, yes! Maybe I ... perhaps ... um ... just a cup of coffee.'

His body seemed weighed down with his failure as he pushed back the chair and stood up. His face felt as though it were glowing like a ripe tomato; sweat had pasted the backs of his trousers to his ample buttocks. He wanted to take his mother's hand, to assure her that he would be back soon, but the eyes of both Rod and Sister Cort were on him. He dithered for a moment longer, then plunged for the gap in the curtains.

Though a hospital, out of necessity, was a round-the-clock concern, it seemed to Howard as he stepped into the corridor that at six a.m. the day's work was only just beginning. Patients were being roused, nurses were changing shift, and the first glimmerings of dawn were visible through the toilet window, which was Howard's first port of call after vacating the oppressive dimness of his mother's ward.

He locked himself into a cubicle even though the toilet was empty, and released a stream of urine that he'd been holding in his bladder for too long. After zipping himself up he washed his hands, then removed his spectacles and doused his face with cold water. The mirror confirmed his suspicion that he looked dreadful. His hair was untidy, his clothes rumpled, his eyes watery blobs in dark sockets. The shadow of his stubble was like a smear of grime. He raked podgy fingers through his hair, but it made no difference.

He put a hand on his stomach as it growled. Perhaps Sister Cort was right, maybe a little breakfast *would* do him good. After one last despairing glance at the mirror, he left the toilet and set off in search of the canteen.

He found it easily enough, and ordered coffee and a bacon sandwich. The bacon was fatty and undercooked, which was the opposite of how Howard liked it, and the coffee had oily globules shimmering on its surface. Nevertheless Howard found that his anxiety had imbued him with a surprisingly hearty appetite, and he devoured the sandwich in four bites. He was sipping his coffee and wondering whether to join the queue for another when the blond-haired nurse, Rod, entered the canteen and began looking around.

The plastic cup crackled in Howard's hand as he involuntarily tightened his grip. There was no flippancy in Rod's manner now. He looked grim, his movements urgent. He spotted Howard and seemed to gather himself before striding across. Something was certainly wrong: Howard saw it in Rod's closed face, in his brisk, almost robotic movements. His mouth felt suddenly dry; it tasted bitter, unpleasantly meaty. Rod's eyes seemed to meet his for the briefest fraction of a second before sliding away.

'Could ... er ... could you come with me, Mr Duffy, please?'
The initial hesitation was followed by a hurried tumble of words.

'Why?' asked Howard almost aggressively. 'What's happened?'

The young man looked uncomfortable. 'Sister Cort sent me to fetch you, Mr Duffy. She wants to see you immediately.'

'It's Mum, isn't it? Something's wrong with Mum?'

'Sister Cort will explain everything, Mr Duffy. If you'll just come with me.'

Howard got up so suddenly that the chair screeched and almost toppled. People turned to look, some with expressions of mild irritation, some curious, some merely blank-faced, like babies responding to a clap. In the corner a group let out a sudden burst of laughter and Howard was reminded of the time he'd farted into the silence of an exam room whilst sitting his 'O' levels. He'd tried so hard to release the fart slowly and quietly, but it had emerged like a staccato ripple of machine-gun fire. A wave of laughter had swept the previously still room. Around two hundred pairs of eyes had turned to look at him. Howard had never felt so embarrassed in his life. He had sunk his head into his arms and stayed there long after the silence had returned.

He followed Rod from the canteen, along a corridor, down a flight of stairs, along another corridor. Rod's haste and Howard's dry mouth prevented him asking questions. The bacon sandwich sat in Howard's stomach like a ball of acid. Howard's heart was a pounding fist inside his rib-cage. His mind seemed to float above his head.

They entered the intensive care ward and slipped through the curtains surrounding his mother's bed. Howard's first sight was of two men putting some equipment on a trolley; his second was of Sister Cort talking quietly to a doctor who looked like David Frost. The two of them turned to him with expressions of professional sympathy. There was an almost tangible sense of resignation about them. Howard realised with a shock that the steady bleep that represented his mother's pulse had ceased.

Howard's gaze found the bed – and relief swept over him. His mother was still there, still the same: grey and unmoving, but no different from when he'd left her fifteen, twenty minutes ago. Except that ... she was no longer wearing the oxygen mask. And the drip in her arm had been removed. He became aware that Sister Cort was addressing him and attuned his mind to focus on her words.

' ... very sudden, she didn't feel a thing, I can promise you that. She simply gave up, I'm afraid. The accident was all too much for her. You can stay with her for a while if you like, Mr Duffy. I promise you won't be disturbed. Perhaps it'd be best if you sat down. Would you like me to get you a coffee?'

For a few moments Howard simply stared at her as his mind assimilated the information being given it. Realisation came slowly, horribly. He saw the doctor glance at his watch, Rod hovering by the gap in the curtains. He turned and looked at his mother, a motionless bandaged husk. No, what they were trying to tell him was impossible, too enormous to contemplate, however critical his mother's condition had been. She can't have just ... gone. Not just like that. It was all so pointless, so anti-climactic, so ... so final.

'No,' he said, shaking his head, and felt an urge to smile at this blackest of jokes. 'No, it's not true. It can't be. It's all wrong.'

Doctor and Sister exchanged a glance. In her syrupy voice Sister Cort said, 'I'm sorry, Mr Duffy, but it wasn't entirely unexpected, you must have known that. It was a very bad accident and she was an old frail woman. Her end was very peaceful. Just a kind of switching off, of letting things go.'

Howard felt as though the back of his throat was crammed with rubber, as though the substance was draining from his legs. He groped blindly for the chair and sat down. His head flooded, filling his eyes and nasal passages, reducing his surroundings to a swimming blur of colour.

Sister Cort was talking again, but Howard didn't want to hear. He pressed his hands over his ears, lowered his head so that his tears dripped on to the floor. 'No,' he whispered, 'no. You cheated me. You cheated.'

And suddenly no one else mattered; he didn't care what they thought.

He began to beat his thighs with his clenched fists and to wail like a baby.

32

Jayne awoke with a smile on her lips and her fingers dabbling at her eager cunt. The dream had been a relentless outpouring of previously pent-up repression. Inside her head she had been a ruler of flesh, had bathed in sweat and semen. She had shirked nothing, had coupled and tripled and quadrupled and more, had sampled whatever new morsel was there for the tasting.

And now she was awake, her legs wide, the bedclothes beneath her rumpled and damp with her contortions. The daylight streaming through the uncurtained window caressed her skin, shimmered like gold on its surface, trapped and intensified by the soft down of tiny blonde hairs on her thighs. She raised her hand. Her fingers were slick and wet. She licked them, relishing the salty taste of herself, the hot touch of sex on her tongue. She shivered as a breeze raised goosebumps on her arms and legs. Outside birds sang an anthem to her liberty.

Footsteps on the stairs. Jayne turned her head slowly in the direction of the door. She was not afraid. Her sexuality was a tiger unleashed; its wild rage would protect her if needs be. She was untouchable except where she wished to be touched. She was mistress of all things physical. She felt this more profoundly than she had ever felt anything in her life before. She could not be hurt. It was an impossibility.

The door opened.

Jayne's lips curled into a smile. Unconsciously her pelvis rose like a primal greeting.

'My darling,' she murmured. 'My saviour.'

'Hello, Jayne,' said Stitch. 'Sleep well?'

She gave a throaty chuckle, cupped a breast with one hand, opened her legs a little wider. 'Mmmm,' she replied, a sound that was half affirmation, half evocation of the excesses in which her dreams had allowed her to revel.

'That's good,' said Stitch. He gazed on her splayed nakedness with interest, though also with a sense of detachment, like a surgeon assessing the healing progress of a previous patient's scars. 'It's time for the next stage if you're ready,' he said. He sat on the bed and almost idly inserted a podgy finger into her vagina.

Jayne moaned, her head rolling back on her shoulders. 'Yes,' she gasped, 'yes, yes,' though whether she was replying to Stitch's query

185

or encouraging his probings was difficult to tell. Her hair tumbled about her face and down her back. Her exposed throat was very white, the skin stretched like thin rubber over the tendons. Her hips rose, thighs trembling, heels digging into the bed. Stitch pushed in his finger as far as it would go, smiling as she screamed her ecstacy.

Though Jayne was shuddering and panting towards orgasm, Stitch showed no sign of shedding his dispassion. He gave the air of a man servicing a machine, cajoling it gently to a peak of performance. Jayne's fingers clawed at the sheets beneath her. Stitch smiled in satisfaction, fleshy lips peeling back from his pointed teeth. At the optimum moment he inclined his head towards Jayne's exposed body and began to lick her breasts. Her nipples stiffened immediately, straining to meet his tongue.

She gasped, a hand curling around his bald head, pulling him firmly towards her. Buried in flesh, Stitch clamped his mouth over her nipple and began to suck. Jayne was writhing, but Stitch's body was motionless, twisted awkwardly towards her, feet still on the floor. He showed no desire to divest himself of his shabby suit, nor even to release his penis. He allowed her shiny, swollen nipple to bob from his mouth, moved his head lower as he licked lightly at the curve of her rib-cage, then lower still as his tongue left a trail of gleaming spittle across her stomach. His finger made a squelching plop as he extracted it from her vagina. He pushed Jayne's legs up until they were at right angles to her torso, then lowered his face to her hungry cunt.

She cried out as his tongue began to lap at her, then probed deeper, straining for the places where his finger had been. Her body writhed against him. His face was like a rock between her legs, the nub of his nose nudging her clitoris, sending shivers of sensation, like tiny delicious starbursts, into her womb and beyond. 'More,' Jayne groaned as though he were showing an inclination to stop, 'more ... yes, more.' She pushed herself hard against him, her flesh slurping, excited by the abandon of the moment, by the thought of how wet, how slippery it must be for him, how he had no choice but to drink her, breathe her, live her sex, at least for this moment in time.

But she was wrong. Stitch *did* have a choice. There was a purpose to his abrupt seduction; his tongue was performing neither for his gratification nor hers. Jayne was lost in the crash of orgasm, her head thrown back, eyes closed, hands clutching his head, and so she didn't see what happened next, which was exactly what Stitch intended.

186

What happened next was Stitch's real purpose for being here and for indulging Jayne in this way. Unseen by her, his mouth began to open wider, and yet wider, around his still-flickering tongue. It opened as wide as a man's mouth *could* open ... and then more ... and a little more. Stitch's eyes and nose seemed to concertina above his mouth like a rubber mask, to become nothing but folds and ridges of flesh. And still his tongue worked within her. And still her body shuddered with orgasm, her head thrown back, moans and gasps escaping from her slack lips. She was oblivious to the curl of movement in the cavern of Stitch's mouth, to the glimpse of something white, segmented, which uncoiled at the back of his throat and oozed along his tongue towards her desperately straining vagina.

The thing used Stitch's tongue as a platform, a red carpet, to emerge into the light. It was a small snake, milk-white and gleaming, with black unblinking eyes and a tiny flickering tongue. It opened its mouth briefly, as though yawning, to reveal curved needle-sharp fangs set in bloodless gums. Grotesquely a voice emerged from its scaly lips — Stitch's voice. 'I offer you temptation, Jayne. Tell me — will you take it?'

Jayne was lost in her own thunderous pleasure. Whatever Stitch was offering she would accept.

'Yes,' she whispered, 'yes.'

Stitch and serpent smiled together in chilling unison.

Jayne gasped as the snake flashed forward in a blur of white movement and entered her vagina. The tip of its tail flickered for a moment within the folds of pink flesh. Then it slipped all the way inside and was gone.

187

33

When Annie awoke on Friday morning, the sun was shining as if to refute the fact that autumn was just around the corner, and the birds were squalling like small, shrill children. It was the kind of day when one ought to be bouncing out of bed, throwing the curtains wide, breathing in a few good lungfuls of sweet country air, and declaring to the blue sky just how damn *good* it was to be alive. But although Annie felt physically fine − almost back to normal, in fact, since Dan Latcher's poisonous influence had laid her low on Tuesday night − mentally she felt as though pinballs were popping and springing and jumping in her head. She felt an urge to turn over and go right back to sleep. But instead she stared up at the bottom of Steph's unslept-in bunk and reflected on her first week of University life.

Well, hardly a week. She had arrived on Monday and today was Friday, so it was really only ... could that be true? Had she really only been here for *four days*? Considering all that had happened it seemed an impossibility. It was as though the days had stretched to contain an inordinate number of hours and events. In a strange way it reminded her of something her crazy brother, Ed, and his friends had once done in a pub car park, which was to cram seventeen people into a Mini Clubman. She had been the one who had rung Directory Enquiries and, giggling under the influence of six port and lemons, had asked for the telephone number of the Guinness Book of Records. After a few minutes of inane conversation, during which the groans issuing from the tiny car had begun to sound not unlike those which might drift from a torture chamber, the woman on the switchboard had muttered something about wasting her time and had abruptly rung off.

At the memory of Ed, Annie smiled. She wondered what he was doing now: sleeping off a hangover, most likely. Ed was twenty-two, four years older than her, by far the most outgoing of the three children her mother and father had produced. With his blue eyes and mop of straw-blond hair he was a real heart-breaker. He was currently at the intermediate stage of signing off the dole and going full-time as a self-employed landscape gardener with a friend of his, Asif, a tall slim Indian with a sweep of jet black hair and a beautiful, almost aristocratic face. Asif wore expensive suits and silver cufflinks, but − also like her brother − he was wild despite his surface glamour. Whenever Annie had been out with Ed and his friends, their antics had inspired feelings in her which wavered somewhere between fear and exhilaration.

According to her father, Ed had inherited his hellraising tendencies from their mum, who, in her youth (or 'bobby-sox days', as Dad always called them), had been something of a wildcat herself. Mum always blushed and denied this, though secretly Annie thought she was rather proud to carry the image, however erstwhile, of smart'n sassy teenage rebel.

As for herself and her other brother, Matthew (who was twenty years old and studying law at Loughborough University), they had largely inherited their father's characteristics. He was a shy man, friendly but reserved, who liked comfort and security in his life, familiar things around him. In his own quiet, steady way her father ran the household. He had a wry humour and was prone to the occasional bout of silliness, but this side of him emerged only rarely, and always strictly within a select company which included his family and his very few but very good friends. Never had Annie known him, for example, perform his Deputy Dawg impression in the company of strangers or even mere acquaintances. As a result some people found him a little cold, a little distant, as was also the case with Matthew. However if she had had to make the choice, Annie would have said that she was closer to Matthew and her father than she was to Mum and Ed.

In some ways, she supposed, Ian was like her father. True, he was more open than Dad was, but he was also sensitive and caring and perceptive. Looking back Annie realised that almost from the start her instinct had been to trust him, even to confide in him. She was amazed at the depth of their friendship considering the short time they had spent together. They had met, become friends, had even had their first row, and now, unless she was reading the signs all wrong, they were teetering on the brink of romance. And all in the space of four days! It seemed incredible, and yet intense situations, she supposed, prompted intense reactions. The crisis they had had to deal with almost immediately had left little opportunity to pussyfoot around with social conventions. The one consolation of this business with Steph and Dan Latcher — though it was scant consolation indeed — was that her mind had been too busy coping with the turmoil it had been thrown into to worry about homesickness.

She got out of bed, wondering what this new day would bring. She was nervous about seeing Mr Carmichael after the lecture, however amenable he might be. She washed and dressed and brushed her hair until it crackled. She didn't really feel hungry, but she made herself go to the dining hall and eat two slices of toast with butter and marmalade. She looked around for Ian or Neil, or even Steph, but she saw no one that she knew. When a scrawny, bespectacled student in a grubby shirt sat opposite her and started devouring a plate of sausage, egg, black pudding, baked beans, tomatoes and fried bread, she left.

She had arranged to meet Ian in the coffee bar at eight forty-five (their lecture was at nine), but she was there by eight-thirty. At this hour the place was virtually empty, though the addicts, as always, were playing on the video machines. On a platform attached to a bracket, set so high up the wall that it made your neck ache to watch it, a television was on. Annie listened to the morning news for a moment, but the sight of tar-coated birds and seals being washed ashore on the southern coast sickened her and she had to turn away.

She would write to someone about that, she decided, as she joined the short queue for coffee. Nothing made her angrier than the way man was casually destroying his planet simply through ignorance and greed. She was a member of Greenpeace and the World Wildlife Fund and in her spare time she worked for Conservation Volunteers. She had campaigned against pollution, vivisection, the fur trade and the destruction of the rain forests, had wept for the plight of whales and elephants and gorillas.

She retreated to a corner of the room and watched the comings and goings in the coffee bar. On the TV, Jeffrey Archer was now talking about his latest book and smilingly avoiding questions about his sex life. A girl entered the coffee bar with a mane of blonde ringlets and dungarees striped in bright primary colours. Annie stared at her. What was it about the girl? And then suddenly it clicked.

At the Crack meeting, which Annie had attended, this girl had been sitting near the back.

Heart beating rapidly, Annie watched the girl as she bought tea and a pancake from the snack bar. The girl seemed to share a joke with the formidable Mrs Blake: Annie quite clearly heard her silvery laughter. Then she bought a newspaper from the rack on the other side of the room, found a spare table and sat down.

Annie watched her as a transfixed bird might watch the stealthy prowling of a nearby cat. Apart from Steph, this girl was the only other person Annie had seen who had been at the meeting on Tuesday night. Why was the girl here now? To spy on her? Did Latcher know that she and Ian and Neil were conspiring against him? The girl seemed oblivious to her presence but was that just an act? If Annie stood up and walked out of the room, would the girl fold her newspaper and stroll nonchalantly after her?

Annie tried to stop her hand from trembling as she sipped her coffee. She couldn't. She put the coffee cup down and clenched her fist. Ought she to challenge the girl? It was said, after all, that attack was the most effective form of defence. But even as the thought formed, Annie shied away from it. Perhaps when Ian was here, but not alone.

She watched as the girl slowly ate her pancake with a plastic fork and read her newspaper. If she was a spy, she was an incredibly cool one. And now that the initial shock of seeing her had worn off, two other thoughts occurred to Annie ... occurred to her and puzzled her. The first was, why, if Latcher had wanted her discreetly watched, had he sent *this* girl, who with her clownish dungarees and blonde hair could not have been more conspicuous? Did he want Annie to *know* she was being watched? Was it a tactic employed to scare her, to let her know that their every move was known to the group, and thus to warn her against taking any action?

The second thought was that the girl simply did not *act* as if she were being controlled. Certainly she was not like Steph, who resembled a puppet whose strings were being pulled from afar. When Steph had not been moving there had been an eerie stillness to her, a stillness so complete that Annie had the uncomfortable impression she was neither blinking nor even breathing. Steph's eyes had been alive, but in an impenetrable, strangely refracted way. It was as though she were staring at a horizon that lay hundreds, perhaps thousands of miles in the distance. And as she stared she was listening to some inner voice, a voice whose message was immeasurably vital, but which was so faint and fragile that the slightest movement might shatter it.

But this girl ... she was totally different. Annie had heard her laughter, and it had been natural laughter, not forced or calculated. And her movements ... she was swinging her foot as she ate, shifting in her chair, scratching, flicking hair out of her eyes — was engaged, in fact, in the minutiae of bodily motion which so distinguished her from the living automaton that Steph had become.

But was this evidence enough of her humanity? Perhaps different Crack members simply reacted to Dan in different ways? Or perhaps this girl had been conditioned to act naturally? Annie found it a little unreal to be thinking in these terms, but they were nevertheless questions which had to be considered.

191

A more frightening notion occurred to her. What if this girl was the norm? What if the majority of Crack members were indistinguishable from their previous personae? Though they had not discussed it fully, Annie knew that hers and Ian's interpretation of events hinged upon further evidence coming to light — from tutors admitting that, yes, now you come to mention it, John or Jane had been strangely distant and inattentive of late; from students who had been troubled by their room-mate's behaviour, but had thought it simply a phase or a private problem, none of their business.

But *if* this girl was the norm, *if* Steph was the exception, then their story might prove very hard to corroborate. Dan, and indeed the other Crack members, would pooh-pooh their accusations, dismissing them as over-reaction or perhaps sour grapes because Annie did not feel she had fitted in. Annie had no doubt that, without sufficient evidence, Latcher would find it very easy to silver-tongue any prospective jury into believing his accusers were cranks or trouble-makers. She felt a wave of despair and anger and frustration sweep over her. She wished Ian would hurry up. Together they could confront the girl, hear what she had to say.

As if guessing her intentions, the girl glanced at her watch, folded her newspaper, put it in her bag and stood up. It was two minutes after twenty to nine and Annie turned to look at the coffee bar entrance, willing Ian to enter, but of course he did not. Her stomach began to churn, and unwittingly she let out a groan of exasperation, as the girl slung her bag over her shoulder, skirted round the obstacle course of tightly-packed tables and chairs, and dropped her greasy paper plate and plastic fork into a nearby metal waste basket.

Annie squirmed in her seat as the girl strolled casually towards one of the three doors that led out from the coffee bar. Then, acting before she even fully realised she was doing so, Annie jumped up and hurried after her.

'Hey!' she called as the girl stretched out a hand to the swing-doors. 'Hey, wait a minute!'

The girl turned, a startled expression on her face.

Didn't expect this, did you? Annie thought with terrified glee. Didn't think I'd have the courage to come running after you? And you know what — neither did I.

She stopped two yards from the girl, who was now clutching her shoulder bag protectively against her bosom as if she expected to have it snatched. The girl's face flickered into a nervous smile. 'What's the matter?' she asked.

Now that she had come this far, Annie wasn't sure what to do next. It would have been opportune if Ian had stepped through the door behind the girl at that very moment, but of course such acts of providence were the exclusive trademark of crime shows and soap operas. It never happened in real life.

'Look,' the girl said when Annie didn't respond immediately, 'what is this? I've got to –'

'Can we talk a minute?' Annie asked.

Those words were the first that came to mind, and struck Annie as ludicrously inappropriate given the situation. The girl stared at her for a few seconds longer, her eyes searching Annie's face.

'What about?' she responded finally.

'You know,' Annie almost said, but inhibition prevented her. Steph – the old Steph – would have come right out with it, as would Ed and Mum, but Annie had never been happy with direct confrontation. She was covert, cautious, even secretive by nature. She gestured vaguely at a cluster of empty chairs. 'Could we just sit down first?' she said.

The girl's gaze jumped briefly to the chairs, then back to Annie. It's a good act, Annie thought. She's really behaving as if she doesn't know what this is all about. And she looks genuinely worried, which suggests that she did not expect to be challenged. This thought, that Dan had underestimated her, that behind his ghoulish grin he was fallible after all, gave Annie a surge of confidence.

'Let's sit down,' she said a little more firmly. 'We've got something to discuss.'

The girl's eyes widened. 'I don't know what you're talking about. I don't even know who you are,' she blustered.

'Are you sure?' said Annie. 'I think you do know me. I certainly know you.'

The girl continued to stare at her. As well as consternation, there was now a deep-seated bewilderment in her eyes. Then all at once they cleared. This is it, thought Annie, she knows there's no use pretending any more.

'You're not Helen are you?' the girl said. 'Steve's girlfriend?'

Annie was taken aback. 'What?'

'There's nothing between us, you know,' the girl began. Then, noting Annie's obvious surprise: 'You're not Helen, are you? So who are you?'

Annie raised a hand briefly to her head as if to get a grip on her thoughts. 'Look,' she said, 'can we sit down?'

'Why?' the girl said again.

'Because ... because ... oh, for God's sake, it's about Tuesday night! You know it is. You know what I'm talking about.'

'Tuesday night? What do you – ?' and then an expression of horrified realisation came over the girl's face. She reared back, pushing herself into the corner between door and wall as if she had just been informed that Annie had some lethal and highly contagious disease.

'You're one of *them*, aren't you?' she said. It was such a dumb line that, had it cropped up in a low budget (or even high budget) alien invasion movie, it would have raised a howl of laughter from the audience.

Annie, however, merely looked at the girl, feeling nothing but exasperated surprise. She had time to reflect that this was all wrong, it wasn't going the way it was supposed to at all. She stammered, 'What ... what do you mean? One of what?'

'You know,' the girl said, stealing Annie's unused line. She looked as though she would be crawling up the wall backwards now if she was able.

Annie thought: Maybe she didn't know I'd be here. Maybe the Crack members are actually *scared* of me and Ian and Neil because of the way we interrogated Steph yesterday. Then she looked at the girl again and suddenly it clicked what she really *did* mean.

'You think ... you think *I'm* one of The Crack, don't you?' she said.

The girl drew in a deep breath like someone about to swim a length underwater. She actually flinched when Annie used the group's name.

'Well, you are, aren't you?' she said. Fear was making her aggressive. 'What is it you want?'

Thoughts whipped through Annie's mind like a rain of arrows. It struck her that to the casual observer she must look like the school bully, demanding money from a pupil she had pinned against the wall. Simultaneously she was wondering: How do I interpret this behaviour? Is she genuine? Or is this simply an act to throw me off-guard?

'I want ...' she floundered, then decided to plunge in. 'I want to know if you were spying on me?'

The girl uttered a shrill laugh which wasn't really a laugh at all. 'Spying on you? Why would I do that?'

She was opening doors to rooms that Annie didn't yet want to enter. But she felt she had no choice. She wished Ian were here. She stammered, 'W-well, because ... because *you're* a member of The Crack, aren't you? I saw you there on Tuesday night. Don't tell me Dan Latcher didn't put you up to this.'

She felt both frightened and emboldened by her accusation. But

194

she felt confused too, had the unpleasant sensation that she was wallowing out of her depth. She was beginning to wish that she'd let the girl simply walk away, after all. *Was* the girl pretending or had she, like Annie, been genuinely unmoved by Latcher's performance? Annie cast her mind back to the meeting. Certainly at the time she felt that she alone was mentally unaffected. But perhaps the acute discomfort of her physical condition had blinded her. Certainly her main objective had been to get out of that place as quickly as possible. It was therefore feasible, she supposed, that this girl had reacted as Annie herself had, had concealed her revulsion beneath a veneer of smiling complicity as Annie had tried to do.

In which case − Annie felt her heart leap a little − didn't that mean there were grounds for hope here? That she was not unique, that Dan Latcher could be resisted? She tried to stem her surge of excitement as she focused on what the girl was now saying.

'Look, whoever you are, Dan Latcher didn't put me up to anything. I haven't seen him since Tuesday night and I don't intend to. There's something about him ... he's more than a creep, he's dangerous. And if you've come to try and persuade me to go back there, to give it another try, then I'm afraid you're wasting your time.'

This, more than anything that had gone before, suggested to Annie that the girl was telling the truth. Even if she had been conditioned to deny any link with The Crack if challenged, Annie did not think that conditioning would have extended to the besmirching of Latcher himself. Of course she may have been wrong, but Annie felt instinctively that she was not. Latcher had shown such enormous conceit. He had not only encouraged adoration, he had expected it. Annie had sensed an outrageous ego in him, an ego that was undoubtedly the source of his influence and attraction, but which could yet prove to be his Achilles Heel.

'Please,' she said to the girl, 'let's sit down. I'm not a member of The Crack, honest. I hate Latcher too. But there's a friend of mine − Steph. She's fallen for Latcher in a big way. There's a group of us trying to get her back.'

She was aware of what she was giving away here, but it was a calculated risk, one she felt prepared to take. The girl was looking at her thoughtfully. At length she said, 'I didn't see you there on Tuesday night.'

'You might have seen my friend, Steph, though,' Annie replied, 'the one I was telling you about. I came with her. We sat at the front. Steph's bigger than me − red hair, loud voice.'

'Oh,' the girl said as if she'd been told something surprising. 'Yes. I think I do remember her.'

Annie gave a wry smile. 'Most people do,' she said.

She sensed the girl relaxing a little now, as though, like herself, she was wanting, and even beginning, to trust the other. The girl glanced at the chairs Annie had indicated.

'Okay,' she said, 'I'll talk to you for a few minutes. But I've got a lecture at nine.'

'Yes,' said Annie, 'me too.'

They sat down. When they were settled, Annie said, 'Okay. So what's your version of Tuesday night?'

The girl gave her a knowing look. 'Ah, no. You first.'

'But if you're a Crack member you'll just agree with me. You'll say that's how it was for you too. How will I know you'll be telling the truth?'

'How will I?' the girl countered. 'This knife cuts both ways, you know.'

They were silent for a moment, then the girl said, 'Look, I've got some paper in my bag. We can write down what happened and then swap accounts. How does that sound?'

Annie shrugged. 'Fine.'

The girl took an A4 pad from her bag, ripped out two sheets and gave them to Annie who thanked her and rooted in her own bag for a pen.

'What's your name?' the girl asked.

Annie looked up. Her expression seemed innocent enough. And surely there was no danger in disclosing such innocuous information. Via Steph, Latcher must already know all that he needed to about her.

'Annie,' she replied. 'What's yours?'

'Heather,' said the girl.

This established, they bowed their heads and began to write.

Five minutes later, Annie had written two sides. She felt it unpleasant stuff to regurgitate but it was nevertheless good to expel it. Heather finished just before her and sat waiting patiently, her pad on her knees. Annie's hand sped over the page, her thoughts translated into a scrawl of blue biro.

At last she put her pen down and flexed her aching hand. 'Finished,' she said.

'Me too,' replied Heather.

Annie glanced at the clock. It was eight minutes to nine. Heather stretched out both hands, one of which contained the pad, one of which was palm up like a beggar's plea.

196

Annie, too, stretched out both hands. They exchanged documents simultaneously, like spies. They began to read, though Annie was so eager that she had read the first eight lines before realising she had taken nothing in. She forced herself to go back to the beginning and start again slowly. Neither of them noticed the coffee bar emptying as people began to drift away to lectures.

Annie read almost a carbon copy of her own experience, though without the follow-up. Heather, having attended the meeting alone, had merely put the episode behind her, had tried to forget about it. Like Annie and Steph she had met Latcher at the ECA Fair, had been eighty per cent entranced by him, twenty per cent repulsed. Certainly she had been intrigued enough to ignore her better judgement and attend the Crack meeting that evening. There she had experienced, as Annie had, a sense of trepidation that had burgeoned into nightmarish fear. She had found Latcher's rantings to be meaningless, absurd, though nevertheless frightening in their idiot intensity. She had been astounded by the rapturous response from the audience, had thought at first they were mocking him, but had quickly realised that their devotion was genuine. Around half-way through the meeting she had begun to develop stomach cramps, bolts of pain in the head, had felt nauseous, dizzy, as if poisoned. She had barely made it from the meeting, had slipped away whilst Latcher was occupied with his entourage of admirers. Back in her room she had vomited into the sink, had taken two paracetomols and had gone straight to bed. All that night and the following day she had felt utterly dreadful. Her room-mate, Sandra, had looked after her, had wanted to call the doctor, but Heather, for some reason she couldn't articulate, had forbidden her to do so. She had told Sandra it was just a bug, and a particularly bad period, that she would be okay within a couple of days. Secretly she had fretted, wondering what had been done to her, wondering if she would recover. By Wednesday evening she had been relieved to find that she felt a little better, by Thursday better still, and now she was almost back to normal.

Annie looked up to see Heather still reading. One detail in the girl's account had leaped out at her as though written in lights. In a voice that sounded strangely suppressed, as though not daring to admit she might have found some kind of answer, Annie said, 'When you went to the meeting, you'd got your period.'

Heather looked up, surprised. 'What?' she said.

'It says here you blamed the way you felt on a bug and a bad period.'

'So?'

197

'So I had my period too,' said Annie. 'You don't think maybe . . . that somehow . . . I don't know how, but somehow . . . that protected us, do you?'

Heather looked blankly at her.

Annie realised how ridiculous this must sound, but the idea had grabbed her, had shaken her, as if it had a will of its own. She persevered, 'What I mean is, Latcher's influence somehow couldn't keep hold of us because of our periods. It was just a physical thing to us. It made us ill, but that was because our bodies rejected it, got rid of it in the quickest way it could. Don't you see what I mean? Somehow we had some sort of built-in immunity system. As Latcher's . . . poison entered us, it bled right back out again. It never got the chance to reach our minds.'

She felt triumphant, breathless. She looked at Heather who had paled slightly, whose lips were pursed in thought.

'But . . . but that's silly. It doesn't make sense.'

'None of this makes sense,' said Annie. 'But there was something in the air at that meeting. Some . . . some *bacteria* . . . I don't know. There was something more to Latcher than just what he did, what he said. There was some sort of otherness to him, some evil magic, something he projected out from himself like a drug.'

She paused. What she was saying was crazy, but what was crazier still was her own certainty that she had come very close to the truth. Nowadays menstruation was seen purely as a physical process, as a function allied to procreation, but in ages past, when humankind had only nature to sustain it, a woman's monthly cycle was widely believed to have mystical properties, was believed to be linked to the moon and the earth and the elements. Hadn't Annie heard it said that a woman's menstrual blood was the stuff of her magic, was at the core of her largely untapped power? Was it, then, too outrageous to assume that faced with the threat from Latcher, with his evil magic as she'd named it, her own defence mechanism, the substance of her white magic, would be stimulated into counteracting the threat against her body?

Her soul?

She shuddered as these thoughts, arcane and alien, flitted through her head. It was like seeing ghosts inside herself, was like having long-buried memories come suddenly to the fore. If there was a grain of truth in these thoughts, what did that make Latcher? A black magician? Certainly it seemed he was infinitely more dangerous than they'd suspected. But then again, was she simply allowing her imagination to run away with her? She exhaled, blinked, as

198

though the pressure of these theories was expanding in her skull, blocking her ears.

Heather was clutching Annie's account of the Crack meeting and shaking her head slowly. 'This is all too much,' she said. 'I need time to think about this.'

'Take time,' said Annie. She scribbled her name and room number on Heather's pad. 'If you want to help us, get back to me. It'd be good to see you again. We need all the support we can get.'

Heather took the pad with a forced smile of thanks. Annie glanced at the clock on the wall — and suddenly noticed that apart from the two of them the coffee bar was empty.

'Hell,' she said. 'It's almost nine. I wonder where Ian's got to.'

The instant the words left her lips, in he came, sleepy and tousled, breath wheezing, inhaler clutched in his hand like a grenade he was about to throw.

'Sorry I'm late,' he gasped as he hurried across. 'It's bloody typical — the first time I forget to set the alarm and my body-clock finally decides it's on holiday.' He noticed Heather and gave her a cursory nod. 'Hello.'

'This is Heather,' explained Annie, swinging her bag on to her shoulder. 'She was at the Crack meeting on Tuesday night.'

She saw Ian's eyes widen, his mouth open to ask a question. The clock on the coffee bar wall was now inching past nine.

'I'll explain later,' she said. 'Come on, we're late.'

She took Ian's hand and they hurried away. Heather, looking troubled and bemused, simply sat there.

34

When Neville entered the house, he was humming the new Motley
Crue single and so didn't immediately hear the sound of weeping. It
was only when he was halfway along the hallway, and had paused
in preparation for the guitar break, that he heard it.

It was a small sound, little more than a snivelling judder of
breath, but it was so forlorn that he couldn't possibly ignore it.
He bypassed Dan's closed door with a scowl and tapped lightly
on the lounge door, also closed, from behind which the sound was
coming.

'Hey,' he said, 'who's in there? It's me, Nev. Are you okay?'

Normally he would have barged straight in. The lounge was
common ground, after all; if you wanted privacy you went up to
your bedroom and bolted the door. But so much weird shit had
been happening in this house the last few days that Nev felt an
instinctive trepidation. He glanced at the bandage on his right wrist
and hand which was now a dirty greyish-brown colour. Beneath the
bandage his wrist was a swollen rainbow of flesh. He was having
to rely on Tom Broadbent's carbon-copied notes in lectures because
he couldn't yet write, and judging by the stiffness and pain that his
wrist was giving him, he thought that that situation would endure
for a little while longer at least.

The weeping continued. Nev said, 'Cat, is that you? Can I come
in?'

The timbre of the weeping changed a little; it sounded as though
the sufferer was trying to pull him or herself together. A bleary
cracked voice spoke a word which Nev took to be, 'Yeah.' Aware
that his throat was dry and his heart was pumping harder than it
ought to, he opened the lounge door and stepped inside.

He was almost relieved to see Catriona curled up at the end of
the settee, wiping at her red tear-stained face with the backs of
her hands. The question 'What had you expected to see?' occurred
to him, but he pointedly ignored it. His relief was followed by a
confusion of emotions – disquiet, sympathy, resignation, annoyance. The incident with Dan on Tuesday morning had shaken him
badly – more than that, had really frightened him – and since
then he had felt disinclined to discuss the matter. He had kept
out of the house as much as possible, had thrown himself into
his work with more gusto than at any other time in his academic

life, and had, thus far at least, successfully deflected every approach from Catriona on the topic. This had not prevented questions from rearing their ugly heads in his own mind, however, but each time one had broken the surface he had ruthlessly stamped it back down again.

Now, though, through her misery, it seemed Catriona had ensnared him. Nev had never been able to ignore the sound of another human being in distress, a response which stemmed from the experience he had had with his sister, Carol, who had come running to him every time her bastard of a husband had beaten her up. You're just a soft cunt, Nev told himself bitterly. He knew in truth this was a strength, not a weakness, but right now he wished he could drum up a little indifference. Whatever was happening with Dan, it was something worse than drugs or a breakdown – something far worse – and Nev wanted to keep as much distance between it and himself as he possibly could.

'Hey, Cat,' he said, walking across and sitting down beside her, 'what's wrong?' He already knew the answer to that one, but he felt loath to claim responsibility for resurrecting a subject which, in his own mind, had become taboo. Besides, there was a slight chance, *very* slight, that he might be let off the hook. Hell, perhaps her pet dog had died or something. Maybe some wanker had pushed her down outside the supermarket and run off with her handbag.

But no. The reply was inevitable. In a voice squeaky with upset, Catriona said, 'It's Dan. I don't know what to do. Nobody seems to want to help him.'

Nev shrugged, feeling uncomfortable and ashamed. 'Maybe he doesn't want our help.' he said.

Catriona swung round on him. Her blotchy face was furious. 'He might not want it, but he *needs* it,' she stormed.

Nev felt uncomfortable. He held up his bandaged arm as though waving a white flag.

'We tried to help him the other day and look what happened. He threw it right back in our faces.'

'He wasn't himself,' said Catriona.

'You can say that again! For my money, I'd say he was doing a very passable impression of the Incredible Hulk.'

Catriona shook her head, swiped away the last of her tears. 'He's ill, don't you see that? There's something wrong with him.'

'He seemed strong enough to me, a real three Shredded Wheat man, in fact. He can't exactly be sickening for something, can he, crushing my wrist the way he did?'

Nev heard Catriona's breath whistle out through gritted teeth and got the impression she was physically restraining herself. Her verbal punches, however, were hard and hurtful. 'Don't be an utter prat, Nev. Dan is ill. When I came back on Monday he sounded really sick, then on Tuesday he comes bounding out of his room as if he'd just o.d.'d on vitamin pills. But even then there was something wrong with him; even an arsehole like you could see that. His eyes, his manner, everything about him was warped, off-key, aslant. Maybe it was just drugs, I don't know. But there's something else as well, something I've not told anyone about ...' In a voice thick with distaste, she described the scene she had stumbled on yesterday, the grotesque and passionless clinch between Dan and his new friend, Spider.

'Well, that explains it then, doesn't it?' Nev said. 'Dan's become a gay acid-house freak.' His humour was desperate and a little brutal. The image of Dan lying motionless beneath Spider's twitching etiolated body was almost too nauseating to contemplate.

Catriona's glare looked as though it could melt steel. 'How can you joke?' she exclaimed shrilly. 'How can you live with yourself, not doing anything at all? Some fucking friend you are. I bet if you saw your mother being cut to pieces in the street you'd turn the other way.'

That hurt. It was an almighty kick to Nev's pride, to his loyalty, to his sense of worth. It brought the anger bubbling up even as the rational part of him said: She doesn't mean it. She's upset. She's just hitting out blindly.

'Well, you haven't exactly gone out of your way to help him either, have you?' he said viciously. 'I mean, considering all the shit he took from you last term, I'd've thought he deserved at least a little concern.'

That was unfair and Nev knew it, but then so was Catriona's previous comment. They were both blaming each other for their personal burdens of guilt, shame, wretchedness. There were no real excuses for their inertia, so they were each hiding behind a shield of furious accusations. Nev felt no sense of triumph to see his words hit home. Indeed, he felt like the biggest heel on Earth as Catriona's face crumbled once more into tears.

'Shit,' he murmured. 'Aw, I'm sorry, Cat, really I am. I shouldn't have said that. My gob's quicker than my brain, that's my trouble. Here.' He produced a scrunched-up Kleenex, unused but covered with bits of fluff, and offered it to Catriona. She instinctively reached for it, then, seeing what it actually was, blurted, 'I'm not using *that*!'

The petulance in her voice and the indignation on her face, which was red and wet and screwed up like a baby's, suddenly caused him to bark with laughter.

'I don't blame you,' he said. 'I don't think even I'd blow my nose on that.' He flung the offending object into the wastebin.

This time, fortunately, his humour proved positive. Catriona picked up on it and gave a tearful laugh. It was like seeing the sun glimmer briefly through a dark bank of storm clouds.

'That's better,' Nev said. 'Hey, I really am sorry about this, Cat. We shouldn't get at each other over this, you know.'

'No, I know,' Catriona agreed. She reached into the pocket of her purple corduroy slacks and produced a white uncrumpled Kleenex. 'Now, this is what I call a tissue,' she said before proceeding to blow her nose.

'Very impressive,' Nev said, 'but rather too minimalist for me. I thought the screwed-up, bedraggled look of my own tissue, coupled with the liberal sprinkling of un-nameable gunge, was a more vital and convincing statement on the nature of today's society.'

'Arsehole,' responded Catriona, giggling. She tossed her now used Kleenex towards the wastebin, but it missed and hit the gas fire. She sighed, raking a hand through her hair, pushing her fringe out of her eyes. 'I only got upset because what you said was the truth,' she admitted bleakly.

'Aw, c'mon, Cat, I didn't mean what I said. I know you care about Dan. You wouldn't be crying otherwise.'

'I care about him, yeah, but how much? If I *really* cared, I'd have done something about this by now. I wouldn't have just let it drift.'

Nev shrugged. 'I dunno. There's not a lot we *can* do.'

'We can try talking to him. We've hardly done that. I mean, we said on Tuesday that if we couldn't get through to him we'd tell someone – his parents or whoever. But have any of us bothered? No, we've all left it to each other. We've just passed the buck around and around while meanwhile Dan's just been getting into deeper and deeper trouble.'

Nev had hung his head a little so that his hair covered most of his face. He looked like a little boy who had been called before the headmaster.

Now he looked up and said, 'We don't know for certain that he's actually in any trouble.'

Catriona nodded. 'He's in trouble, all right. Deep shit, I'd guess. You've heard the rumours going around? That he's started some sort of weird religious society?'

'I heard something,' Nev admitted. 'Whispers, that's all.' He glanced at her, his face locked in a grimace as though these disclosures were causing him pain. 'I have to admit, it doesn't sound much like our Dan.'

Catriona gave a harsh laugh. 'That's an understatement. You know what Dan's like – a trendy, atheist, arrogant, lovable Scouser; he's not the Hare Krishna type at all.'

'Yeah, but ...' Nev's voice trailed off.

'But what?'

Nev shrugged. He looked ill at ease. 'But he's always been ... well ... a bit sensitive, hasn't he? Vulnerable, like? I mean, put it this way: Dan's a more likely candidate to fall for this sort of stuff than I am.'

Catriona frowned, but said nothing. That Dan had been dragged into something against his will and wanted out was a notion she could readily accept. But the very idea that he might be a willing protagonist in all of this ... that was a concept she categorically refused to entertain.

She cast her mind back to yesterday, to the repulsive scene she had stumbled upon in Dan's bedroom. She remembered Dan's eyes: full of suffering and horror and shame. No, there was no way Nev was right; Dan was a prisoner, a victim, not an assenter. In a dull voice she said, 'Yesterday I was going to talk to him. I'd resolved to make him listen to me. I still *want* to talk to him, Nev. Before I bring anyone else in on this, I want the chance to ... to just *talk* to him.'

Her eyes blurred again. She looked at Nev and saw only a wavering image – brown hair, blue eyes, pink face. Her tears prevented her from seeing Nev's expression. She asked him, 'Am I being selfish, wanting that?'

Nev shifted slightly beside her. She blinked away the tears as best she could and saw surprise on his face.

'Selfish?' he repeated. 'No, I don't think so. Why do you think you're being selfish?'

'Because ... well ... because *I* want to try and talk to him before anyone else does. Because I'd like to think that the person he'd respond to would be me. The thought of someone else ... *rescuing* him, bringing him out of this ... makes me jealous.'

Then yes, Nev thought, you *are* being selfish. But he didn't say so. He draped an arm around Catriona's shoulders, gave her a reassuring squeeze.

'No, you just want what's best for him,' he said, 'like we all do.' He kissed the side of her head. Her hair smelt of lemon. 'Have you tried talking to him today? Is he in his room now?'

Catriona shrugged. 'I don't know. I banged on the door when I came in, but there was no reply.'

'Is the door locked?'

'I couldn't open it.'

'Then he must be in. These doors only lock from the inside.' He stood up. 'Come on.'

'What are you going to do?' Catriona asked, standing up too.

'It's time for action,' Nev said. 'No more sitting around, no more shirking responsibilities.' In true heavy-metal fashion he raised his bandaged right arm and clenched the fist like a club. Then he rather spoiled the effect by screwing up his face and muttering, 'Ow, that hurt.'

'Prat,' said Catriona, smiling. They trooped out into the hallway. Nev knocked purposefully on Dan's door with his left hand.

'Dan?' he said. 'Are you in there? It's me, Nev, with Cat. We want to talk to you.'

Their only reply was a stubborn silence. Nev glanced at Cat and raised his eyebrows. He saw his nervousness, which he was trying hard to conceal, reflected in her face. He knocked again.

'Dan, will you open this door? We're not going away this time.'

If Dan was behind the door, he remained unimpressed by the threat. Nev sighed deeply, clenched his jaw muscles. He banged harder and longer, ceasing only when he thought his knuckles might be starting to bruise.

'Dan,' he shouted, his voice echoing, 'open this fucking door, will you!'

'We just want to talk to you, Dan,' Catriona said more gently. 'We know you're in trouble and we want to help. I saw you yesterday with Spider, remember?'

They paused, waiting for the padding footsteps, the click of the bolt. It didn't come. Nev punched the door in frustration, making a tiny dent in the white-painted wood.

'You'll knacker that hand too if you're not careful,' Catriona said disapprovingly. She rapped daintily. '*Please*, Dan, open up. If you don't speak to us we'll have to call your parents. But we want to avoid that if we can. We want to try and sort this out between us.'

'I'm sick of this,' Nev said when this latest appeal broached no response. 'I'm gonna kick the door in.'

'You can't do that,' exclaimed Catriona, 'what about the land-lord?'

'Fuck the landlord. This is more important. No excuses this time, remember?'

205

Catriona hesitated for just a second, then nodded stiffly. 'Okay, but just let me tell Dan what we're going to do. If he realises we mean business, he might come out.'

'Be my guest,' said Nev, stepping back, waving a hand at the door. Catriona rested her forehead against the wood and told Dan of their intentions. There was no reply. Nev stepped forward again.

'Okay, Dan, ready or not, here we come.' He lifted up his right leg, then pistoned it out, hitting the door just to the left of the handle with the sole of his Doc Marten boot.

The slam of his kick resounded from the walls like the aftershock of an explosion. Underlying this was a more subtle sound, the crunch of wood giving way. However, despite this, the door appeared to remain obstinately sturdy. Nev shook his foot, as though checking to ensure there was nothing loose in there, then muttered, 'Stand back, I'll try again.'

His second kick was altogether more successful. There was a splintering noise and the door bowed inwards, like a man struck in the midriff trying desperately to remain upright. The door's glossy white veneer split to reveal jagged flesh-coloured shards, like a snarling mouth of serrated wooden teeth.

'Once more,' grunted Nev, and kicked the door again, hard, before it could recover.

This time the lock shattered. A whole chunk of wood, containing both bolt and handle, gave way and clanked to the floor. The door itself seemed to groan and sag further inwards, shedding slivers of wood and paint. Nev put his shoulder to it and wrestled it gratingly open.

'Fuck, what a stink!' he cried, recoiling, after taking no more than two steps.

Catriona, standing in the doorway, felt she was going to be sick. The pungent wave which boiled over and around her was like the body-heat of some vast malodorous animal. She stepped unwillingly into the cauldron, the hand clasped over her moth and nose offering scant protection. The source of the reek, it seemed, was manifold: there were animal smells of piss and shit and sweat and vomit, odours of fruit, meat, fish and eggs gone rotten. Of milk turned sour. Of cheese so rank it had liquefied.

She saw Nev ploughing into the stink and the gloom, waving his hands before him like a man fending off demons. He reached the drawn curtains on the other side of the room and hurled them open. The next moment air which smelt almost dizzyingly fresh was swirling in through the windows he was throwing wide, making

206

inroads in the cloying farrago, slowly dispersing it.

She looked round the room as her senses stabilised. The place was a mess, but an empty mess. Despite the bolted door, Dan was not here.

'What the fuck's he been doing?' Nev said, staggering back into the centre of the room. 'This place smells like a zoo. Was it as bad as this yesterday?'

'I ... no, I'm sure it wasn't. But the door was already ajar. I only stood in the doorway. I remember it smelt of ... B.O. And glue. But it was nothing compared to this.'

Nev wafted a hand in front of his face. 'He must have held the annual zombie convention in here last night then.' He looked distastefully around at the rumpled bed, the clothes strewn over the floor, the paper that was scattered in and around the waste-paper basket. 'Fucking hell, Danny-boy,' he murmured, 'what have you got yourself in to?'

He strolled over, picked up one of the discarded sheets of paper and began to read its type-written message. Catriona said, 'If the door was bolted and the windows were all locked from the inside, how did Dan get out?'

Nev looked up from the sheet he was reading and regarded her with a steadiness he didn't feel. 'Don't ask awkward questions,' he advised. He handed her the sheet. 'Look at this,' he said. 'It's really weird.'

Catriona took the sheet from him and glanced at it. One word was typed over and over again, covering the sheet from top to bottom, from side to side:

EMPTY   EMPTY   EMPTY   EMPTY   EMPTY

She shuddered. The single word, mindlessly reproduced, was like a chant. 'What does it mean?' she asked.

'Pass,' said Nev. 'Here's another.'

This sheet held the single word, endlessly repeated:

ABYSS   ABYSS   ABYSS   ABYSS   ABYSS

'This is weird,' said Catriona.

'With a capital W,' agreed Nev. He began to range about the room, like Sherlock Holmes searching for clues. His eyes alighted on the wardrobe and a strange look came over his face.

'Cat,' he said. The sudden urgency in his voice made her look at him sharply. 'You don't suppose ...' Nev left the rest of his sentence unfinished. Instead he pointed very deliberately at the wardrobe and raised his eyebrows.

Catriona knew immediately what he meant. Unless there was

a secret passage somewhere that they didn't know about, it was impossible for Dan to have vacated the room. Which meant that he was hiding somewhere.

She shivered and hugged herself, feeling suddenly cold.

'Are you going to open it?' she whispered.

'You bet,' said Nev, though he looked rather more reluctant than he sounded. Both of them edged towards the wardrobe, Catriona with her arms still tightly folded as if to say: This is your idea. It has nothing to do with me. Whatever happens, it's your responsibility.

Nev reached out and took hold of the handle on the wardrobe door. He turned to Catriona and grinned, though she could see that the corners of his lips were quivering slightly. 'Time for Dan to come out of the closet,' he said. '*Voilà*!' He plucked the door open.

A smell hit them, not as overtly disgusting as the cheese-thick stench which had assailed them upon entering the room, but nevertheless in its own way just as unpleasant. It was a dry, musky, hot smell, like the dusty remains of old stale spices. Catriona threw up her hands and screamed shrilly, though it was not the smell itself which prompted the scream, but its source.

Piled high in the wardrobe, so high that they cascaded out in a plump white wave, were the headless blood-spattered bodies of countless doves. They spilled around Catriona's and Nev's ankles, bumped against their shins, left smears of red on their clothes. Feathers hovered and spun as though striving mindlessly for autonomous life. Instinctively Catriona stepped back and dove-corpses burst and slid beneath her heels, making her scream all the more.

'Fucking cunt, fucking sick cunt,' Nev was saying, horror and repugnance bunching his features. He tried to close the wardrobe door again, but could not. The doves blocked it in a roiling, tumbling wave, puffing out their musky death in fetid wafts. Abandoning his efforts with the door, Nev turned and hopped-skipped-jumped out of the dove-heap like a man leaping across hot coals.

'Come on,' he said to Catriona, who was releasing a strange moaning sound into clenched fists that were pressed to her mouth. Her eyes danced with hysteria; she was rigid yet trembling, buried in dead doves almost up to her knees. A feather settled in her hair like a delicate snowflake. She didn't notice. 'Come on,' he repeated. He leaned across the dove-heap and took her arm.

She tensed, and just for a moment Nev thought she was about to throw a screaming fit. Then she relaxed, though her trembling intensified. Shaking her head slowly from side to side she blubbered, 'I can't, I can't, I can't.'

208

'You can,' Nev said gently. 'Take my hands, then leap across. You won't land on any of them, I promise.'

Catriona hesitated a moment longer, then did as he asked. She took his hands, bent her knees, closed her eyes, and pistoned herself forward. Nev used the strength in his arms to boost her momentum. Pain flared in his bruised wrist, bringing tears to his eyes, but he gritted his teeth against it. Catriona barely cleared the pile; in fact, the heel of her left foot came down on the tip of one snowy outstretched wing. She collided with Nev, who stumbled backwards, off-balance. His head hit the wall, causing a further starburst of pain and a muzzy fall of black sparks across his vision which took almost a minute to clear.

'Fuck,' he muttered, head and wrist throbbing in unison. 'Fuck, fuck, fuck.'

Catriona was staring down at the headless doves, her face as white as their feathers. 'Why did he do it?' she whispered. 'Why did he kill all those beautiful things?'

Even now a witty response occurred to Nev (maybe they were first prize in an Ozzy Osbourne competition), but he refrained from voicing it. The why he could guess: maybe Dan's new friends went in for devil-worship, blood sacrifice, stuff like that. The question that perplexed him, however, was how? There must be two or three hundred birds here. Simply acquiring them must have been a feat in itself, but the thought of decapitating each and every one was mind-bogglingly awful.

Nev tried to picture the scene: Dan and Spider, sitting in this room, surrounded by cages and floating feathers and the sound of cooing. He imagined them concentratedly lifting cage after cage on to their laps, twisting the heads off the birds inside and tossing the two lifeless portions into handy receptacles – the bodies into the open wardrobe, the heads perhaps into a black plastic bin liner. He wondered whether they had worn aprons, like butchers, to protect themselves from the blood, whether the birds had sensed their fate and had raised their voices in a tumult of panic. The image was dreadful but somehow unconvincing. It was hardly the stuff of Dennis Wheatley; sounded more like the chicken factory job that he had been forced to take two summers ago to pay off his overdraft, the one that had turned him into a vegetarian for six months.

'Come on,' he said without answering Catriona's question, 'let's get out of here.' Gently he took her hand and led her from the room, pulling the vandalised door closed behind them.

Out in the hallway he went immediately to the telephone, picked

209

up the receiver, and began running his finger down the list of useful numbers they had tacked to the wall until he came to: Dan – home.

'What are you doing?' asked Catriona.

'Ringing Dan's parents. This shit has gone far enough.'

He placed his finger in the first number of the Liverpool code and put the receiver to his ear. Then, so loudly that it made Catriona jump, he shouted, 'Fucking hell!' and slammed the receiver back down again.

'What's the matter?' asked Catriona.

'Fucking thing's dead. I'll have to use the one at the end of the road. Do you want to wait here? I won't be long.'

'No,' said Catriona. 'I'll come with you.' She cast a glance at Dan's closed door. 'I don't want to be left in here with those ... those things.'

Nev's disgust at what he had seen had changed to a fury that he found frustratingly directionless. His anger was not aimed purely at Dan, but was rather inspired by the entire situation and his inability to comprehend it. For this reason he felt like snapping at Catriona, 'For fuck's sake, Cat, they're only a bunch of dead birds', but with a gargantuan effort of will he managed to bite back his vitriol. Instead he muttered, 'Come on then, let's go,' and strode down the hallway to the front door, rubbing at the bump that was beginning to swell like a mushroom on the back of his head.

Catriona trailed a few steps behind, feeling weak and sick and cold as though on the verge of 'flu. Above the door was a simple floral design in stained glass which bled trails of coloured light, blue and red and orange, across the ceiling. Catriona was looking at this, perhaps hoping that the colours would soothe her, when Nev opened the door. The shadow of a figure fell across them. She lowered her gaze. Standing on the doorstep, smiling, was a plump middle-aged man with green eyes and a perfectly bald head.

Catriona's first thought was that he was a salesman, but then she noticed he had nothing to sell. A preacher then? But no, where was his Scripture? And surely no religious man would come dressed in threadbare suit, scuffed boots, shabby stained overcoat? She sighed, realising his clothes were the clue. He was obviously a down-and-out, come to Royston because it was a soft touch, full of students who were suckers for a sob story or who merely paid up because his presence intimidated them. Well, thought Catriona, today he had chosen the wrong house. Nev was not in a charitable mood.

'Who are you?' he demanded, recent events making him sound aggressive.

210

''ere, mate, no need to get narky', was the kind of wheedling response that Catriona expected to hear. Instead the man's smile became wider, more voracious somehow. Catriona shuddered again. It was becoming a standard response.

'Stitch,' said the man, 'Peregrine Stitch. Pleased to make your acquaintance.' He proffered a chubby hand, which Nev ignored.

'Look, mate, we're in a bit of a hurry. Whatever it is you want, it'll have to wait.'

Nev tried to push past the man, but Stitch side-stepped, blocking his way, still smiling as though it were a game.

The surprise on Nev's face was quickly superseded by anger. 'Look, pal, I'm warning you. If you don't shift I'll throw you down these fucking steps.'

Stitch said nothing. He just smiled. Then, very deliberately, he crossed the threshold into the house. Catriona felt suddenly, horribly, afraid, and not merely at the prospect of an unpleasant confrontation. Stitch carried an aura with him, something dark and cold and intrinsically awful. She felt the sort of panic she would feel if a Great White Shark suddenly entered a pool in which she was bathing.

She wondered if Nev felt the same. If he did, he was courageous enough to stand his ground. Catriona could not see Nev's face, but she saw his body stiffen. The fingers of his bandaged right hand straightened as though he were a gunslinger about to draw. His left hand clenched into a fist so tight it was almost white from the blood being squeezed from it.

'Get out of this fucking house now.' Nev's words were measured, his voice dangerously low, oozing with menace.

Stitch smiled wide enough for Catriona to see that every one of his teeth were pointed, like a row of large white bullets set into his gums. 'I think not,' he said calmly.

'I think *so*,' replied Nev, and stepping forward he shot out his left arm, palm flat, to shove Stitch backwards. What happened next was so quick and so unexpected that Catriona couldn't immediately take it in. She stood, dumbstruck, as Nev started to scream. When she finally realised what was happening, she began screaming too.

In the split-second it had taken for Nev to raise his arm and propel it forward, the layers of clothing covering the centre of Stitch's chest had shrivelled away like cellophane exposed to heat. Nev's hand had passed through the ragged-edged hole and impacted with bare flesh. But not only had it impacted with it, it had been *consumed* by it. Catriona wasn't sure, but she thought she had seen a lipless mouth open, lined with jagged teeth, in the space between

Stitch's flabby man-breasts; a mouth which had allowed Nev's left hand to pass inside before biting it off at the wrist.

Nev was now holding up his foreshortened arm and staring at the stump in utter disbelief. His screams were shrill, sickeningly primal, as though raw pain was being ripped out of him. Blood fountained from the wrist and wrote its gory signature on walls and ceiling; bone pushed up through the meat like a splintered stick. Nev's body whipped this way and that; he spun and ducked and bounced from the walls, as though by so doing he could somehow shake off the dreadful truth of his mutilation.

Stitch simply watched and smiled, and even when a spurt of blood splashed across his left cheek he didn't flinch. Through a haze of shock, Catriona saw him turn and quietly close the front door. Doors now were closing inside her own head too, their black echoes dragging her into a waiting void of calm. She struggled against their closure but her system had taken too much; her strength was ebbing. Before she succumbed completely she heard the shock of silence as Nev's screams were abruptly curtailed.

35

The ringing of the telephone in the silent house was like the plaintive bleating of a lost lamb. If Howard heard it he didn't register the fact. He just sat and stared into space, still as an art class model.

Mother is dead. Mother is dead. I'll never speak to her ever again. Beneath the bland red-eyed mask of his face, the thoughts tumbled and swarmed, simple truths that were nevertheless ungraspable, too enormous to accept.

Yesterday morning she had sat and eaten porridge, her last bowl, little knowing she had only two hours of consciousness left. She had spent those last two hours arguing with the television, cackling over pointless gossip with Mrs Atkins, wracking her failing brain for answers to *Daily Mirror* Crossword clues.

It all seemed so pointless somehow, so trivial. Howard couldn't help feeling the two of them had been cheated, short-changed by some higher authority. He should have been prepared in some way, forewarned. His mother's death should have been momentous and sombre and dignified. But instead it was almost as if Fate or God or whatever had cut her off on a whim. She'd come through all these years unscathed, and then suddenly – *BANG*. The End. No right of appeal.

His eyes, not for the first time, filled with tears. They were tears of injustice, tears of anger, but they were also tears of panic at what was to come. Howard felt that not just his mother's life but his own had been rudely, uncaringly, terminated. There was nothing left for him now. His entire direction, his meaning, had been stolen from him. There was simply no point to what was left, no sense in carrying on. He might as well just sit here and rot. Nothing else mattered.

The world, he thought, is shit. God is shit. Life is shit. Normally Howard didn't use this word, barely even allowed it to cross his mind because Mother had said it was wrong. But Mother had been taken away, squashed out of existence like a fly on a window. Whoever, whatever, had done that obviously had no conscience at all – which therefore meant that the moral precedent, the Image, that Mother had urged Howard to follow for all these years simply did not exist.

The telephone stopped ringing. Silence more deafening than the sound of its bell, made Howard look up. Who was calling him?

213

It didn't matter. Everything was ended now, there was nothing to be said.

The ornaments, the pictures, the wallpaper, the carpet, the furniture, all were extensions of his mother's personality. But Howard felt no comfort in these things. They were horrendously empty, almost mocking because they reflected something that no longer existed. The thought that he could, if he wished, see his mother's flesh and yet never again communicate with it terrified him. Was she locked in there, unable to get out? Why couldn't Howard just shake her and wake her up? It seemed so easy and yet so impossible, both at the same time. The conundrum repeated itself over and over in his head, searching desperately for a solution to itself that could never be found.

Time. That was an illusion. The world had simply shifted onto a new reality, one in which his mother no longer had a part. Howard had sat in this chair for how long? It didn't matter because only the present existed. The passage of time was a human conceit invented for convenience sake, for a way of rationalising the constant change, the ever-advancing march of entropy and decay.

'You're best out of it, Mum,' Howard murmured. 'The whole thing's shit anyway.' He looked up at the ceiling and raised his voice. 'And I don't care if you *are* listening. You can do what you like. It doesn't matter.' He pushed himself suddenly out of the armchair. He felt heavy, breathless, as though his grief, the burden of his thoughts, was like a sack of rocks that he carried inside him. He strode to the mantelpiece and snatched an ornament from it, a china figurine of a rosy-cheeked girl in Victorian dress holding a parasol. 'This is what I think of you,' he shouted. He hurled the figurine across the room. It hit the edge of the old sideboard and shattered. Feeling suddenly weak and sick, Howard sank to his knees and began to cry. He buried his face in his hands, searching for darkness. 'No,' he moaned, 'no, no, no.'

When he had done, he stood up and went into the kitchen. There was no method to his movements. Everything was utterly pointless. He had no desire to eat or drink, hadn't even felt like going to the toilet for a long time. He felt neither tired nor alert. He simply *was*, floating like a mindless balloon.

He wished he *was* mindless. Wished he was utterly empty. He was full of emptiness, but it was the wrong sort. It was the painful sort, not the oblivion he craved for.

On the kitchen table were two bottles of milk. He couldn't remember bringing them in from the doorstep. One of those bottles was for his mother but she didn't exist any more. The blackness of

214

that, the awfulness of it, clutched Howard as though he was only just realising it for the first time. He pushed the milk bottles off the table and watched them smash to the floor, a white explosion.

'That's that,' he said, and walked across the broken glass to the back door. If he didn't clean up the milk soon it would stink, but so what? It didn't matter. Howard went outside, pulling the door closed behind him, but not bothering to lock it. He knew he should play by the rules, but he didn't want to, and so he wouldn't. He walked round the house to his car, got in, started it up and drove away. He didn't know where he was going and he didn't care. There was no destination, no choice, nothing. Wherever he was going there would be no sense in it.

36

Annie looked in the mirror. A cat twitched its nose back at her. She chuckled, delighted by the costume, and carefully drew an extra whisker on each cheek.

It was Friday night, the night of the Fancy Dress Freshers Ball. Annie had barely given the Ball a thought until this afternoon; indeed, since arriving at University, socialising had been very low on her list of priorities. It had seemed obscene, somehow, to go and enjoy herself whilst the situation with Steph prevailed. But tonight she felt justified. She was certain her meeting with Heather that morning had been a major step forward, even if, for the moment, she wasn't quite sure of its full implications. And their conversation with Carmichael after the lecture had proved heart-eningly fruitful. By mutual consent, she and Ian had understated the really weird bits, and had been met with a sober, concerned response. Carmichael had promised to investigate the matter, stir up a few people, starting with Dan Latcher's Head of Department and progressing, if needs be, to the Registrar, the Student Union, the Welfare Officer and University Chaplain, even the Chancellor. He had promised to get back to them on Monday morning, by which time large and influential wheels would hopefully be grinding into

215

motion. She and Ian had left Carmichael's office feeling buoyant, full of fire. They'd show Latcher he couldn't mess around with them. Thanks to their perseverance he was about to be leaped upon from a great height.

Annie put the finishing touches to her cat woman costume and wondered whether the black body-stocking was a little too *risqué*. Nah, it hugged the contours, but she wasn't actually showing any bare flesh except for her face and hands. She slipped into a pair of black pumps on to which she had carefully stuck claws cut out of white paper. Checking to ensure that her cardboard ears were standing upright, she turned to the door ... to find her room-mate walking silently towards her.

'Steph!' said Annie, shocked, and for the first time felt a pang of real fear at the sight of her. Had news of their instigations reached Latcher's ears? Had he sent Steph along to ... to what?

Don't be silly, Annie told herself. This is still Steph's room. She has a right to be here. There's nothing sinister in it.

On that score, at least, she appeared to be right. Without acknowledging Annie, Steph walked into the room, climbed up on to the top bunk, and lay on her back, crossing her hands over her chest like an effigy on a tomb.

'Steph?' Annie ventured, edging towards her. 'Steph, are you okay?'

There was silence for a few moments; it seemed that both girls were holding their breath. Then in a flat voice Steph replied, 'Fine.'

Annie hesitated. She could think of nothing else to say. Or rather, she *could*, but they were all questions to which she was certain Steph would give her no answers.

She had been shocked not merely by Steph's entrance, but by her physical state. Gone was the vivacious red head with the glowing skin and buzzing personality. In her place was a pale, haggard, lank-haired imposter with rumpled clothes and body odour. Annie was certain that Steph had neither eaten, slept, washed, nor changed her clothes for at least two days. She felt rage and disgust at Latcher for reducing her room-mate to such a level. The momentary pang of fear she had experienced on first seeing Steph dissipated, to be replaced by pity and a resolve to do right by her friend. Her immediate problem now, though, was how to keep Steph here. Now that she had returned, Annie didn't want to lose her again.

Ought she to stay in, not go to the Ball? But she couldn't remain here with Steph forever, could she? And what about Ian? She had arranged to meet him in the bar. Besides, what could she do if Steph did decide to leave? Restrain her physically? She balked at that prospect. If Neil had been unable to do it, then she very much doubted that she could. Maybe, then, she could persuade Steph to accompany her to the bar. Perhaps a night on the tiles amid friendly company would help to break Latcher's spell.

Annie was aware that she was clutching at straws, but she had to do something. She approached the bed, wrinkling her nose as she caught a whiff of unwashed flesh. She shook her head free of the thought that with her eyes closed and her hands crossed over her chest, Steph looked like a corpse. Speaking almost directly into her friend's ear, Annie said, 'Steph? Are you awake?'

Steph did not reply. Her body was perfectly still, her face composed. She looked like a machine which had switched itself off. It was good, thought Annie, that she was getting some sleep. But she could not fully convince herself, could not help feeling uneasy. No sleep should be as profound, as still, as this; Annie felt an urge to shake her friend awake, merely to assure herself that Steph was still capable of waking. Cautiously, as though being goaded to feel the skin of a venomous snake, she reached out and touched Steph's hand.

It was cool but not cold, as Annie had half expected. Nevertheless she wondered whether her friend ought to be examined by a doctor. She dithered for a moment, undecided. Then, slowly and carefully, watching Steph's face all the while, she began rooting through the pockets of the clothes that her room-mate was wearing.

She found what she was looking for in the right-hand pocket of Steph's grubby blue culottes: a set of keys attached to a Garfield key-ring. Snatching up her own keys she vacated the room, pulling the door closed behind her. As she locked Steph in, her hands trembled uncontrollably. Ridiculous though it was, she couldn't help thinking that Steph would wake up, realise what she was doing, and come after her like an avenging ogre.

The door locked, she hurried down the stairs, out of the hall and across to the main building. The chilly night and her nervousness made her shiver. Already she was regretting wearing this costume; she had to keep glancing down to convince herself she wasn't naked. She blushed at the admiring glances she received from a group which consisted of a caveman, a Cavalier, the Incredible Hulk and Ronald Reagan, who were standing just inside the main building, sharing a four-pack of Kestrel lager. Her nipples seemed to rear up, unbidden, as though intent on embarrassing her. Their outlines were clearly visible through the thin black fabric of the body stocking.

She was grateful that the bar was seething; it made her feel less exposed. However she was convinced that the bodies which pressed against her own, the hands which brushed against her bottom and breasts, were not all accidental. She pushed through a crowd of Roman emporers, Mafia hit-men, zombies, assorted royalty, human cereal packets, superheroes and celebrities in the hope of finding Ian dressed as Dracula. But if he was here, she couldn't see him. And neither could she see Neil, though she had no idea what he was coming as, or even if he was coming at all. For all she knew, he might even be the Cyberman who was standing beside her. She found a relatively uncongested spot by the jukebox where she could see the bar entrance, and stood with her arms crossed over her breasts, the heat created by the crush of bodies causing the body stocking to glue itself ever more tightly to her contours.

After a little while, trapped in the noise and the heat and the crush, she began to feel almost soporific. She was pleased to see that Gayle Jacobs, who seemed to revel in her scurrilous nickname, Bike, was dressed in a mermaid costume which made her own seem positively priggish. Men were hanging round her, all but drooling. Annie found it funny and dismaying both at the same time. So intent was she on the mating rituals of her contemporaries that she almost leaped out of her body stocking when a large hand slipped roughly round her waist and squeezed her right buttock.

She turned to see a large sweaty muscle-man with a partly-shaven head grinning down at her. His face was smeared with boot polish; his eyes were glassy with drink and stupidity. He wore enormous black lace-up boots from which ballooned a pair of green army-issue camouflage trousers, and was bare-chested but for two criss-crossing ammunition belts which stretched from left shoulder to right hip and vice versa. He smelt like a cross between a men's locker room and a brewery. Annie took a sudden step forward in the hope of shaking him off, but was unsuccessful. His hand stayed where it was, clinging to her hip like a large crab.

'Do you mind?' said Annie curtly. She was boiling inside, but was reluctant to make a scene for fear of drawing attention to herself.

'I don't mind at all,' slurred the muscle-man, and belched. For the second time his hand slipped down to her buttock and squeezed.

Annie twisted to evade his attentions, shoved at the encircling arm, but it was sweat-slippery and immovable as rock. Trying to keep the anger in her voice, to hide her distress from this oaf, she said, 'Will you please stop doing that? I'm a person, you know, not a piece of meat.'

For some reason the muscle-man found this funny. He threw back his head and laughed. Beer sloshed in the bottle he held in his left hand.

'I don't know what you find so amusing,' Annie muttered.

To her horror the muscle-man hugged her closer. He inclined his head towards her in a conspiratorial manner.

'You, love,' he replied blearily. 'All this playin' hard-to-get bollocks. I know you want it really, I can tell, I'm not stupid. So c'mon, how about it, eh? We got a coupla hours before the band comes on. How about the pussy givin' me some pussy?' He grinned delightedly, struck by the piquancy of his own wit. 'That's a good 'un, eh? The pussy's pussy. Y'know, I've always wanted to skin a cat.'

He guffawed at this and plucked at Annie's body stocking. She twisted so quickly that it sprang from his pinched fingers like an elastic band, stinging her waist. Her voice was full of fury but still measured; she wasn't yet shouting.

'Just go away, you disgusting pig. I wouldn't choose you if you were the last man on Earth.'

Even this insult failed to penetrate the muscle-man's thick, polish-smeared skin. Grinning inanely, he placed his bottle carefully on the juke-box and swung his left arm around Annie, crushing her to him in a bear-hug. She gasped, overwhelmed by his heat and stink. The ammunition belts he wore pushed painfully into her breasts. She tried to raise her fists to protect them, but she could not move her arms.

'Get ... off ... me ...' she panted, struggling, trying to kick. She couldn't believe this was happening with so many people around, but ironically the crowd worked to the muscle-man's advantage; there was such a crush of bodies and such a cacophony of noise that it was evidently not apparent she was even in distress.

'C'mon, little pussy, just one kiss,' the muscle-man coaxed.

As he lowered his slobbering planet of a face towards her, Annie saw from the corner of her eye the Prince of Darkness enter the bar.

37

Like Annie, Ian felt that voicing their concerns to Carmichael was the wisest decision they had made. The English tutor's positive response had made him feel like celebrating, so much so that he had driven down to Maybury that afternoon and splashed out at the only costumier's he could find. He was standing now in the bar entrance, soaking up the admiring looks, playing his part to the full. He flared his nostrils, bared his fangs and licked them lasciviously, twitched his black silk-lined cape over his shoulder, and made for the bar.

He would have liked to have adopted a dignified, aristocratic stroll, with perhaps a hint of seductive menace, but the free-for-all at the bar prevented him. Instead he pushed and shoved with the rest of the throng, hoping his cape would not be ripped from his shoulders, his ruffled shirt not be crushed and crumpled like tissue paper. He wondered whether he ought to go the whole hog, drink Bloody Marys instead of pints, but whatever he drank he would have to remove his fangs, which would spoil the illusion. He felt a trickle of sweat squeezing out beneath the black, strange-smelling wig with the widow's peak, and blotted it with the tip of one white-gloved finger. He didn't want pink stripes caused by runnels of perspiration to ruin the effect of his deathly-white, red-lipped face. He smiled at a girl wearing a romper suit and shaking a rattle, and then froze. Over her shoulder he saw Annie grappling with Arnold Schwarzenegger.

It was immediately obvious to Ian that she was not enjoying the experience. The Schwarzenegger clone had her pressed back against the juke-box, enclosed in an intimidating crush of gleaming muscle, and was trying, it seemed, to suck her face off. Ian changed direction, much to the annoyance of a giant hedgehog with drooping spines, and made his way towards the tusslers.

'Hoy!' he shouted when he was close enough. A couple of people turned, but the decibel-level was so high in the room that his challenge was lost in the general bedlam.

Annie's eyes, however, flickered briefly, gratefully, towards him. Then they skimmed away as she twisted her head to avoid another slobbering assault.

'Hoy!' Ian yelled again, and this time the he-man's head turned slowly towards him. There was a look of mild irritation in his glazed eyes. It was obvious he considered Ian little more than a minor distraction – like an itch or a buzzing insect.

'What the fuck do you want?' he said, and immediately Ian realised this was Stu from the Welcoming Committee. Ian hadn't recognised him with all that black shit smeared over his face. He looked at Annie, and noticed there were smudges of the stuff on her face too.

'What do you think you're doing?' Ian said. He hoped the tremour he felt in his throat was not evident in his speech.

'What's it fucking look like?' Stu retorted. 'What's it to you anyway? Piss off.'

Ian stood his ground. He clenched his fists and his teeth, purposely stiffening his body. His chest began to tighten up. He coughed, cleared his throat in an effort to loosen it.

'Let her go,' he said. 'Can't you see she's not interested? Let her go now.'

Stu looked as if he couldn't believe what he was hearing. 'Fuck off,' he said scornfully. 'Me n' pussy-willow here are having a great time. Aren't we, puss?'

Ian saw that Annie was too close to tears to speak. She shook her head and renewed her ineffectual wriggles.

'You see?' said Stu. 'She's snuggling up to me like the little pussy she is.'

Stu looked as though he truly believed what he was saying. Rage swept through Ian, almost choking him, rising in his body like a scream of red, causing pinpricks to dance in his vision.

He lunged forward and grabbed Stu's wrist, wrenching it from Annie's waist. 'Let go of her you fucking ugly cunt!'

An expression of surprise, so stark it was almost comical, appeared momentarily on Stu's face. Then brutality crunched into it, a mindless, idiot fury. He dropped Annie as though she were a forgotten toy, and swung round on Ian, ammunition belts jangling. He didn't speak, he didn't trade insults. He merely swung his fist like a ponderous but lethal hammer and smashed it into the side of Ian's face.

Annie screamed as Ian fell to the floor. A ripple seemed to run all through the crowd, like an echo of the violence. Ian struggled feebly like a beached fish. Stu bent over him and began a relentless pummelling – left fist, right fist, left fist, right. Ian was knocked this way and that. He could do nothing. Blood appeared on his face and on his white shirt and on Stu's fists. Annie was so shocked and so sickened and so terrified that she could only stand and scream.

The violence, for those witnessing and for those involved, was strangely timeless; it seemed to last for both an age and an instant.

221

Suddenly from the crowd around the combatants, most of whom were struggling to get out of the way, erupted three figures – a harlequin, a lumberjack and Batman.

The lumberjack was Neil. He hit Stu on the head with his axe. The axe was made of plastic, though there was a second, during which Annie went cold, when she thought it was real. The blow made Stu flinch and look up. Before he could react, all three of Ian's rescuers smashed into him and sent him sprawling across a table, scattering bottles and glasses. Stu heaved and roared, but the weight of his assailants bore him down. No punches were thrown. Evidently Neil's aim was to restrain; even, if possible, to placate. Annie peeled herself from the juke-box, which had continued to play *Happy Hour* by The Housemartins throughout the fracas, and knelt beside Ian's stricken body.

'Ian,' she said, voice shrill with upset, 'Ian, are you all right?' Ian was panting, gasping for breath, one hand groping in the folds of his now bedraggled costume for his inhaler. His nose was gushing with blood, as was a cut above his right eye. His wig, not surprisingly, had come dislodged and was lying flattened on the floor like a squashed cat on a motorway.

'Take him out of here,' Neil shouted. It was obvious that Stu's rage would not abate until the object of his aggression had been removed.

A couple of people came forward from the crowd to help Ian sit, and then stand up. He seemed oblivious to his surroundings, though he nevertheless had enough of his wits about him to place the mouthpiece of his inhaler between his lips and press down hard, twice, on the vial of Ventolin. His arms were draped across the shoulders of the two students and he was all but carried from the bar, the crowd parting to admit him. Annie picked up the wig and followed. Outside the bar one of the students asked, 'Where to?'

'Er ... Merlin Hall,' said Annie. She led the way, feeling dazed. It was cold and quiet outside the bar. It was like stepping from a dream, being suddenly given back her senses. She had been sickened and shocked by Stu's attempted violation of her and by the ensuing brutality. She began to shudder from delayed reaction and found she could not stop. She swallowed tears as she led the Samaritans and their bloodied patient up to room 34.

By the time they reached her landing, Ian was walking unaided, albeit a little unsteadily, and bemoaning the state of his hired apparel. Annie paused outside the door, turning to the two bene-factors as she extracted her keys from the small purse attached to a black belt at her waist. Strangely she was reluctant for them to see Steph. She felt a desire to keep her hidden, like a guilty secret.

'Thanks a lot,' she said. 'I think I can mange on my own from here.'

'Okay,' said one, who was dressed as a vicar. The other, Robin Hood, merely nodded.

They trooped away down the corridor, the vicar wiping Ian's blood from his hands with a piece of tissue. Only when they had rounded the corner did Annie open the door. She ushered Ian in. He was now tilting his head back in an attempt to stem the blood-flow from his nose. All was quiet in the room. Annie glanced at the top bunk: it was empty. A cold breeze whispered in through the wide-open window.

'Oh, no!' she cried and ran to the window. She looked out fearfully, part of her wanting to close her eyes at what she might see. She couldn't believe that Steph had been desperate enough to make her escape this way. It was at least fifty feet to the ground, and the window frames were so narrow and well-spaced they would be virtually useless as foot and hand-holds.

But escape she must have, for the ground beneath the window was clear. Annie looked right, left and even above to ensure Steph was not balanced precariously on a neighbouring window-sill. She was not. She scowled, perplexed by the puzzle, when suddenly there was a loud bang from behind her, so unexpected that she almost leaped out of the window in shock. She dragged her upper torso back into the room and spun round to see the wardrobe door hanging open and a glimpse of Steph's back as she fled from the room.

'Steph!' Annie cried, and ran after her. Ian was sitting on the bottom bunk, reddening handkerchief held to his nose, too dazed by the sudden turn of events to react. He half-stood as Annie ran past, but his legs felt alarmingly unsteady and he sat down again. A couple of minutes later she returned, looking exasperated.

'Why didn't you stop her?' she said unfairly.

Ian answered her question with another. 'Was that Steph?'

'Yeah. She came back earlier. She looked awful. I locked her in the room and came to find you. Then you got beaten up. And now she's escaped . . .' Her voice cracked and she sat down on the bunk. A tear rolled down her face. 'What a night,' she half-sobbed.

'Yeah,' said Ian. 'It was supposed to be a sort of celebration, wasn't it?' He put an arm around Annie's shoulders and tried to smile: it made his face hurt. 'I suppose it'd be funny if it wasn't so bloody serious.'

223

Annie wiped her eyes, let out a long sigh, and stood up. 'Let's get that face of yours seen to,' she said.

'I think Stu's already done that,' replied Ian. 'Actually, when you think about it, Stu's a good name for him, isn't it? I mean, below the neck he's all meat, and above he's a vegetable. Get it? Stu: meat and vegetable?' Annie turned from the sink, which she was filling with warm water, and gave him a condescending look. 'I'll shut up, shall I?' Ian proposed.

'It might be a good idea,' she said. 'Now do you think you can walk over here or do I have to rip this sink off the wall and bring it to you?'

He sat on a chair as she gently bathed his face. Occasionally he winced and drew back, Annie hissing in sympathy each time he did so.

'How do you feel now?' she asked when she had cleaned him up.

'Sore,' said Ian. 'How do I look?'

'Just slightly uglier than usual.'

'Thank you so much.' Ian looked down at his shirt. 'It's really this I'm worried about. Look at the state of it.'

Annie pulled the plug from the sink, draining the basin of warm, soapy water. She began to refill it with cold clear water. 'Take it off and we'll soak it overnight. We'll wash everything else tomorrow. Maybe it'll be okay.'

'I lost my teeth,' said Ian. 'The fangs, I mean. I don't suppose you picked them up, did you?'

'No, only the wig. Sorry.'

'Ah, well, not to worry. They were only cheap plastic things anyway. They hurt my gums.'

'If it's any consolation,' said Annie, 'I thought your costume was very nice.'

'Thanks,' replied Ian. He gave a slow, careful grin. 'Yours is pretty stunning too.'

Annie blushed a little. 'Unfortunately that's what that moron thought. That's what caused all this trouble.' She watched as Ian struggled out of his costume, and took the blood-stained shirt from him. 'If they complain at the fancy-dress place, just say you wanted the costume to look more authentic.'

'Oh yeah,' said Ian, 'they'll love that.' He touched his nose and winced. 'Do you mind if I shut this window? It's bloody cold in here with no shirt on.'

While he did that, and looked through Annie's t-shirts for one large enough to fit him, she washed as much blood out of the shirt

224

as she could. She emptied half-a-dozen basinfuls of pink water, each less garish than the one before.

'You'll make someone a lovely housewife,' he observed, straight-faced.

Annie turned and flicked water at him. 'Watch it or I'll tap you on the nose.'

Ian grimaced at the thought. 'Why do you think Steph came back tonight if all she was going to do was run away again?'

Annie sighed. 'I don't know. Oh God, Ian, she looked awful. It was obvious she hadn't eaten or slept or washed since we last saw her.'

'Bastard,' he muttered and caught Annie's quizzical look. 'Latcher, I mean. The sooner Carmichael gets the authorities stirred up, the better. I hope that sod gets expelled for what he's done.'

'You do think they'll listen, don't you?' Annie asked anxiously.

'Course they will. They've got to, haven't they? They can't ignore something like this.'

They were silent for a moment. Annie looked thoughtful. At last she said, 'Maybe Steph came back tonight because she wanted help. Maybe her instincts brought her back here, but Latcher's influence was too strong for her. If that's the case, she might come back again, mightn't she?'

'She might,' agreed Ian, though in a neutral voice. He thought it just as likely that Steph had been sent by Latcher to see what, if anything, they were up to. He groaned, rotating his head on his shoulders. After a period of dormancy his wounds were beginning to throb. The skin around his nose and eye felt tight, a little puffy; his cheekbones were like blades pushing against the flesh from within. 'I think I'd like to try a new face,' he said. 'This one's getting too small for me.'

'Poor Ian,' said Annie, walking across and sitting on the bunk beside him. She took his hand. 'You should have come to the Ball as a white knight, not as a vampire.'

She leaned forward to kiss his cheek. Ian turned, and she found herself making contact with his mouth instead. She froze, though only momentarily, and then she responded to his almost chastely puckered lips. Ian slipped his arms around her as their kisses became more passionate. Soon they were fervent enough that it was making his face hurt, but he couldn't have cared less. However acute the pain became, he didn't want this moment ever to stop.

38

He watched the tail-lights of the cars ahead of him and listened to their collective voice. They moved in sly, secret patterns, converging, dilating, winking, contracting, a blood-code which only he understood. They spoke to him of his mission, filled his senses with it, gorged him, so that his concentration was utter, all else oblivion. Though his touch on the steering wheel was confident, his feet on the pedals sure, he saw nothing of the motorway or its traffic. His mission was all that mattered, and it was his mission which would protect him. The propriety of it swathed him like an enchanted cloak which rendered the wearer invulnerable.

On the passenger seat beside him, arrayed like ceremonial artefacts, were a carving-knife, a meat skewer and a machete. Their blades were polished to lethal perfection, alternately springing to flashing life as orange light slid over them, then sinking back into brooding shadow. These, too, filled him with his mission, singing their thin and vicious song, a song which he had heard once before in his childhood, and which he only now realised was a hymn to the ultimate glory. And tonight he would have that glory. Tonight it would be his. To someone out there he was the fast-approaching shadow.

He was Destiny.

He was Doom.

He was the Unmaker.

39

'*I'm* the leader!' Gary Glitter yelled, and the audience cheered and clapped in obeisance. He stomped to the middle of the stage, red-sequinned suit glittering like a ruby, and began to gyrate his hips as the music started, puffing out his exposed hairy chest like a cockerel.

In the audience an over-excited skeleton lifted his hands above his head to clap, inadvertently stepping back on someone's toe. Before he could turn and apologise, he had been hit hard in the small of the back and was sprawling forward, grabbing at the checked trousers of a Mad Hatter in a vain attempt to remain upright.

'Watch it, dickhead,' slurred a growling voice, and the skeleton turned to see a man-mountain rising drunkenly above him. The skeleton said nothing: he didn't trust himself not to voice his indignance. The man-mountain glared at him a moment longer, then turned and shambled away, ammunition belts jangling as they slapped against his bare torso.

Stu was in a foul mood. He just couldn't understand why the birds were avoiding him tonight. He thought they'd go mad over his body, thought they wouldn't be able to keep their eager little mitts off him. But, mysteriously, the opposite had been the case — he'd been given the brush-off time and time again.

Maybe, he thought, they felt intimidated by him. Maybe these snotty University birds were too fucking uptight to go for a real man. How he longed for the girls of Rochdale, his home town. In his experience they were honest, down to earth, just out for a good time. He thought of Shirley and Rita and Collette and Wendy; now *they* appreciated a bit of muscle. They didn't look down their noses at him as though he was something they'd just discovered on the bottom of their shoe. They got pissed with him, had a laugh, and, more often than not, one of them would end up sitting on his dick in the back of his car, or lying underneath him, legs wrapped round his back, at some party somewhere.

He allowed himself a brief, bitter smile. He wished he was in Snappers now. What he wouldn't give for a piece of that Collette tonight. He looked around him and felt like hitting someone. They were all such fucking wimps here.

He scanned the crowd for that pussycat bird he'd been chatting up earlier, but he couldn't see her anywhere. He'd been getting on all right with her. She'd been playing hard to get but that had been all show; in truth, Stu could tell she was *begging* for it. But then that fucking ponce had come along and started bleating. And then them other bastards had come from nowhere and pinned him down. Ha! Fucking cowards. They daren't take him by themselves, dare they? If he saw any of them around again tonight, they wouldn't live to see tomorrow.

People moved aside for him as he marched through. Stu liked that. 'Fat old bastard!' he turned and shouted, but Gary Glitter was in full flow now and couldn't possibly have heard him. Stu contented himself by flipping a two-fingered salute at the stage, then he leaned against a pillar and took a bottle of Pils from the side pocket of his voluminous army trousers. Pils was Stu's trademark: on his nineteenth birthday, four months earlier, he had drunk twenty-seven bottles of the stuff. The previous Uni record (it was said) had been twenty-five, which meant that Stu had now gone down in the annals of beer-guzzling history. He was proud of his record, even though he'd been as sick as a dog afterwards. He'd rather be remembered for something like that than for getting a fucking first-class Honours Degree.

He stood and watched the women in the audience for a while, occasionally tilting the bottle into his mouth in a way he'd seen Marlon Brando do once. The majority of birds were with boyfriends or in groups; the few that weren't were mainly dogs, misfits — he'd resort to one of them only if he became *really* desperate. He considered going to look for Freddy and Gav and the rest of the lads, but he had a feeling they'd already fucked off into town. Stu wished that he'd gone with them, but he'd been so certain that once he put his body on show the birds would have been flocking round him, tongues hanging out, desperate for it, that he'd decided to stay here.

'Hello there. Could I have a suck on your bottle?'

The voice, so close to his ear, and so unexpected, caused Stu to jerk back his shaven head, the momentum of which was abruptly and painfully halted by the pillar behind him. He tried to grin through his pain at the leather-clad goddess who had sidled up to him and was now pressing her breasts against his right elbow.

'Course you can, darling,' he said, regaining his composure with admirable speed. 'You can suck on my bottle any time.'

He handed over the bottle. She took a sip from it and handed it back. Then she closed both hands around his right bicep and squeezed.

'Ooh,' she gasped, 'you're so strong. You must lift an awful lot of weights and things.'

'Yeah,' said Stu. 'Every muscle in my body is in the peak of condition. *Every* muscle. Know what I mean?'

The goddess giggled. Her breasts, barely restrained behind a skimpy leather corselette, rubbed once more against Stu's arm, causing a spontaneous stiffening in his boxer shorts. In truth, he was a little bemused by this sudden turn of events. All evening he had been plugging away in vain at the female population, and then out of the blue up pops this vision from a wet dream and virtually throws herself at him! His erection rejoiced. Somebody up there likes me, after all, he thought. He took a subtle step back from the goddess, not because her proximity disturbed him (on the contrary!), but simply so that he could admire the full vision.

She was gorgeous. Absolutely fucking gorgeous. Slim with big tits, long legs, nice arse. She was dressed all in black — straight black wig, wraparound shades, corselette, mini-skirt, fishnet stockings, high-heeled boots and lacey fingerless gloves which reached almost to her elbows.

'Fancy a dance, darling?' he said, slipping an arm around her waist.

The goddess leaned into him, filling his nostrils with her perfume. Her lips, red as a clown's nose, she placed to his ear and murmured, 'I'd rather go somewhere quiet.'

Stu was rendered almost speechless. Almost. Not quite. 'C-come on then,' he managed to stammer. 'What the fuck are we waiting for? Let's go back to my place.'

He grabbed the goddess's lacey hand and all but dragged her away before she could change her mind. Blissfully ignorant of what was to come, he congratulated himself on his seductive powers.

40

Peter Daniel Simpson swayed out of The Fighting Cock at ll:25 p.m. with his friend John Salisbury.

'Fuck me,' Simpson said as the cold wind ambushed them.

'No thanks,' replied Salisbury, 'I'll wait till I get home. Betty's bettier ... bettie ... better looking than you are.'

The two of them snorted laughter at Salisbury's tangled phrases. 'You're pissed, you are.' Simpson accused. 'You're getting all your worms wrong.'

'Betting all my worms dong? Don't be chilly.'

'Chess you are. Fission to yer. All your turds are completely long.'

They dissolved into schoolboyish laughter. This was a long-standing private joke between them. Simpson fumbled with the zip of his jacket, trying to get the teeth to mesh. At last he managed it.

'Fancy a coffee? Our Elaine'll still be up. She can make it for us.'

Salisbury looked at his watch. 'No ta, Pete. Like I said, I wanna get back before Betty falls asleep.'

Simpson chuckled and gave his friend a playful punch, almost overbalancing in the process. 'You randy sod. I'll see you tomorrow then, eh?'

'Yeah. Tell you what, I'll pick you up about half-twelve and we'll go for a couple of pints before the match.'

'Great,' said Simpson. 'I'll give Les a ring as well, see what he's doing.'

'Yeah, all right. See you, mate.'

'Aye, see you, John. Have fun with Betty.' He grinned as Salisbury flipped him the V, then turned and trudged off in the opposite direction.

It was a clear night, though bloody cold. The stars looked hard as ice-chips. Simpson gazed up as he walked, trying to make out the constellations, but in his present state it was worse than hopeless. He wondered what it was like being an astronaut, gazing down on the world from above. His drunken musings were interrupted by his foot skidding on something slippery, almost up-ending him. He looked down at what he had stepped in, then grimaced disgustedly. Why the fuck did people spend good money on chop suey if all they were going to do with it was dump it on the pavement?

He used the kerb to scrape the mush from his shoe. What a shithole this place was. A man couldn't even look up at the skies and dream without planting his foot in something revolting. When he'd transferred as much as he could of the chop suey to the gutter, where it belonged, he continued on his way.

His house lay fifteen minutes' walk away through a grid of sooty back-to-backs, across an unlit patch of litter-strewn scrubland, beyond a line of fast-food shops where hunks of sweating meat revolved slowly on skewers. He ignored the skateboard gang acting tough outside the chinky, dipped his head into the collar of his jacket when they jeered at him, knowing that the slightest reaction would provoke them. When he had turned the corner he looked back to see if any of them were following. It didn't appear so. He sighed with relief and hurried on, alert for the slightest sounds of pursuit, his drunkenness causing the pavement to sway gently like the deck of a ship beneath him.

He strode beneath a railway viaduct, water slimy as phlegm trickling down its walls. He passed a schoolyard in which the burnt-out shell of a car sat like a greasy black toy, and a garden in which a discarded mannequin with painted features and a caved-in head slumped on the disembowelled, mildew-speckled remains of an armchair.

Beneath a stuttering lamp standard he stopped to light a cigarette. He had cupped his hand around the flame, and was bringing it to his mouth, when from the silence behind him came a sudden sharp sound, like metal dragging over stone. He turned, the match spinning from his fingers and sizzling out on the pavement. Gritty mustard light struggled feebly to dispel an army of hulking shadows.

'Who's there?' he wanted to ask, but thought it best to remain silent. Had the skateboard gang followed him after all, or was he simply allowing his beer-sodden imagination to run away with him? He had cause, he told himself, to be jumpy. After all, he'd been attacked on this route before. And not just once but three times! Twice for money, the third time for the sheer hell of it.

The irony was that, in his younger days, with his mates, Simpson himself had handed out his share of beatings. He therefore understood the pure animal satisfaction that could be gleaned from violence, the sense of self-worth, of power. To overwhelm a fellow human being, to dominate them physically, pound them to a pulp: ah, yes, there was a thrill in that the equal of sex.

231

But understanding such motives did not lessen his fear. On the contrary, it increased it, for Simpson knew that no amount of reasoning would save his skin. Absently he flicked away the unlit cigarette and began walking. He listened as he did so. He would know within a minute or less whether he ought to run.

But he heard nothing more – or at least, nothing that could be construed as threatening. An old man choking his life away above a tailor's shop; a bad musician grimly repeating chords on an out-of-tune guitar. Simpson lit a cigarette on the move, sucked the smoke deep into his lungs to calm himself. He felt shame and anger as well as fear. He was still relatively young, but sometimes the kids around here could make him feel like a toothless old lion. No longer king. Easy meat.

'Fuck 'em,' he muttered, kicking at a wall. His defiance filled him with bravado, but it was easy to feel brave when he could see his house at the other end of the street. He began to walk towards it, face set, swinging his fists. He *was* a man. He *was*. He'd soon show Elaine how much of a man he could be.

The privet hedge leaned towards him over the wall, bulky and black as a whale in the darkness. Elaine had been going on at him for ages to cut the fucking thing. He'd do it on Sunday if he wasn't too hung over from Saturday night.

He pushed open the gate and walked up the short path towards the front door. Something stirred in the privet. He spun round, eyes and mouth gaping.

'What the fuck's that?' he said, partly to himself. He was about to step towards the privet, but then thought better of it. His hand tightened around the key he was holding, the cold metal pressing into his palm like a sharp-edged tooth. The minuscule lawn and the shaggy hedge was a fusion of black. The hedge-top was so overgrown it acted as an umbrella, blocking the light.

Whatever was in the privet shook it again. Branches and leaves rubbed together, sussurating. If Simpson didn't know better, he might have thought that the privet was trying to tear its roots free from the earth and come shambling towards him. Keeping his eyes on the patch of darkness, he extended his hand towards the door, rattling the key around, and then into, the lock.

Before he could turn towards the door, a white face oozed, grinning, from the blackness. Simpson jumped into his own front door as though forgetting it wasn't open, the handle slamming into

232

the soft flesh beneath his ribs. He started choking, his head spinning with beer and shock.

'Hello, Simmsy. Want some fun?' said a voice.

Before he could reply a cleaver flashed, blue-white, from the darkness and opened a red wet yawn beneath his chin.

Part Three
Happy as Larry

'Peaceful, pale flesh on a bed
Real and beautiful — and
dead.'

Dennis Nilsen

Monochrome Man: Sad Sketches

41

Later, when Mally was alone and had locked himself in, he performed the sacrament.

He stood in the middle of the floor and slowly, almost ritualistically, stripped off the clothes he was wearing. As each garment was peeled away he held it to his face, breathing in the dizzying copper scent that was the soil of his Art, before letting it drop to the floor. When he was naked he bent and gathered up the bundle, then padded to the bathroom. He reached out and yanked down on the light-pull. The electric light was an intense glare, hiding nothing, reflecting from the white tiles in dazzling splashes, like small suns.

The light was good. Mally looked at his hand; it was sticky with a redness so livid it made him squint. He looked at the light-pull: that was red too. The hot copper-smelling pile in his arms seemed to be aflame with redness. It was a deep, deep Artist's redness, a redness so intense, so rich, that Mally knew there was blackness at its core even though he couldn't see it.

Mally dropped the clothes on the floor. His face and chest and groin were daubed with delicate patterns, smears and stripes and blotches which were the sacred symbols of his Art. He smiled. It was a good thing. He could feel its essence sinking into him, giving him power and insight – the power of the Hunter, the insight of the Artist.

'I am the Unmaker,' he said, and was so delighted with the words that he giggled like a child. By his actions, his Art, he was changing the world, transcending his status, soaring above the offal, the Pit, the darkness. He was challenging God, and winning. He giggled again, then reached down and plucked his shirt from the pile. Holding it in both hands he wiped it across the wall, leaving startling slithers of red – like violent shouts, like screams of colour – on the white walls. Ah, it was so good. So *good*. Each garment left a new scream, a statement of his Ascension. He painted his voice on the white world. And it was a new voice. A strong voice.

At last the Artist sat back, sweating but happy. The white walls

237

were covered with his symbols, with bold declarations of his power. This was good, but Mally was not so arrogant that he was apt to be reckless. Once the sacrament was over he would clean these walls, he would clean his car, he would clean the tools of his Art, he would clean the soil from his clothes and he would clean himself, and then he would step into the blackness that separated the day-world from the night-world. For the two could not meet. Not yet. Not while the threads of Destiny were being woven, not while the child of transcendance gestated in the womb. Soon he would transcend, and then he would be invincible. But, in the meantime, the watchword was 'Caution'.

He walked, naked and daubed, back to the bedroom. On the bedside table was a large glass storage jar which he had bought earlier that day for this most crucial part of the sacrament. On the bed were his tools, their blades gleaming, alive. Beside them was a small polythene bag, the organ inside like some form of sea-creature, a mollusc or a tiny squid, leaking red.

Mally smiled and picked up the bag. The organ slithered to the bottom on an oily slide of red. He unscrewed the jar, then opened the bag and upended it over the jar. Blood ran into the jar like a reluctant trickle of urine. The organ followed, plopping into the jar with an insignificant splat. Mally's fingertips were red. He licked them, smiling at the salt-copper taste, the thrill of sampling this most forbidden of fruit.

He discarded the polythene bag, placed the storage jar back on the bedside table, and lay down on the bed. As his weight sank into the mattress, his tools clinked together, a short metallic phrase of compliance, approval. One of them pressed up against his leg in a cold, sticky kiss. Mally sighed, then raised his head a little and looked down at his slab-pale body. He saw his penis, striving to raise itself. The scar-tissue etched across its surface gleamed silver-white, stretching from a puckered grimace to a tight shiny grin as his cock awakened. He encircled the organ with his hand and began to masturbate. It was an experience both of pleasure and of pain. His lips curled at the exquisite torture.

As always, orgasm was reached only after a long and arduous journey. And inevitably the destination was disappointing, a listless twitch prompting a sputter of milky slime. Mally lay for a while, recovering, his breath scraping in his throat like nails. His semen sat on his stomach, a quivering marble coin.

At length he reached out with his left arm, closing his hand around the storage jar. He drew it to him and unscrewed the lid, releasing a strange smell that was sickly and secret and somehow exhilarating.

238

Mally used the edge of the lid to scrape the semen from his belly. He allowed it to plop sluggishly into the jar, where it did not quite mingle with the blood, but created white whorls in its redness, like blind, bloodshot eyes. Now there was just one more stage to go before the sacrament was complete. He sat up and stretched forward, reaching for the machete that was still pressing against the side of his leg like an adoring pet. Unhesitantly he drew the keen blade across the underside of his arm between wrist and elbow, opening a deep red stripe which had barely healed over from the first time he had done this. The blood began quickly to flow, to drip on to his legs and the bedclothes. Mally held the jar beneath the stripe, watching as his blood joined with the elements already contained within, completing the sacrament. When he was satisfied he screwed the lid back on to the jar, then stripped off his pillow-case with his right hand and wound it tightly around his bleeding arm.

The next hour he spent cleaning up, dealing methodically with the evidence of his night's artistry. He swabbed the walls and floor of the bathroom, soaked his clothes and his bedsheets time and again before hanging them up to dry, scrubbed his car seats with buckets of soap and hot water.

Though he was thorough, pink stains lingered, but Mally was not too worried. He would be transcending soon, and as such his aim was not to eradicate evidence, but simply to destroy enough that it would slow down anyone who happened to come stumbling after him. He cleaned and bound his wound, then took a bath, divesting himself of his Hunter's soil, his war-paint. When he was dry and smelling sweet, he padded back to the bedroom, wearing a white bath-robe and leather slippers.

He perched on the edge of the bed and picked up the jar. Taking it in both hands he began to shake it as though mixing a cocktail. The organ slopped and slithered within a red froth of blood and semen. Mally placed the jar back on the bedside table and stared at it intently.

The contents were settling, curtains of oily red fluid oozing and merging as they sank down the inside walls of the jar. At first Mally thought the sacrament had not worked, but then he saw the subtle shapes beginning to form from the quintessences, saw the organ writhe, transform, like dough worked by unseen hands, in the vital soup. The blood began to separate into beads and strings and globules, stitching itself a life. The semen also, until the jar itself began to shake with its inner activity, a glass volcano in which sentient lava was both Creator and Creation, ready to erupt.

Mally stared, fascinated, dry-mouthed, burning with exaltation.

Somewhere, far far away, he heard again the Hymn of Pain, and he rejoiced in it, affirming his acceptance of it with an eager, though unconscious, nod of the head. The air in the room became close, cluttered with its own dusty heat. To Mally's eyes the room seemed to dim, all light drawn to the jar and to the struggling transmutation of its contents.

And then ... yes ... Mally saw definition. Saw the face within the jar, eyes milky blobs of semen, flesh running like the molten tallow of a red candle. And a moment later the one face became two, a tortuous division of flesh and blood, like the hacking apart of Siamese twins, or, worse, the excruciating scission of two personalities, one enmeshed within the other, each intrinsic to the other's needs.

Two faces. One pain. Mally saw the tiny mouths move, the blind eyes blink in hideous synchronisation.

Larry. The word, coaxed from tortured flesh, itched and scratched behind Mally's eyeballs. He winced and scrabbled at his forehead, but the voice was inside.

Larry, came the voice again.

'Stop it,' Mally blubbered. 'Stop it ... hurts ... I am the Unmaker.'

Immediately the itch subsided, the masks of false flesh within the jar registering dismay. Mally felt his dominance returning.

'Now,' he said. 'What is it that you want?'

The faces paused, blinked, and in that instant Mally recognised them. Once they had haunted him, used him, but now he had them trapped, sealed within a glass prison like helpless insects.

'I am the Unmaker,' he whispered. The itch behind his eyes formed words again, only this time their touch was whisper soft, reverential.

Hello, Larry. Want some fun? they asked as they had done so many years before.

And Mally smiled, for now he had the choice. 'Yes,' he whispered, holding the jar close to his face. 'Yes. I do.'

42

Ian awoke with the sleep-muddled certainty that spiders were about to crawl into his nostrils. It was the thought of them descending en masse, filling his lungs, that made him snap open his eyes, sit up and jerk back his head all in the same movement. Immediately a sizzling wire of pain zigzagged across his features – nose to cheek to eye. 'Ow! Shit. Ow,' Ian groaned, bringing up his hand and holding it gently to his face in lieu of a compress.

Beside him, on the bed, a figure stirred. It had been Annie's hair, not spiders, which he had been about to inhale. Remembering the previous night he smiled gingerly. He could still taste her lipstick on his tongue. They had fallen asleep on top of the bed, fully clothed. Neither had had the courage to suggest undressing and slipping beneath the sheets.

Ian's smile widened, his face seeming to creak with pain, at their chasteness. Annie would be disgusted if she knew, but Ian could not help feeling warily protective towards her. She was only eighteen, after all, and her first week here had been spent mostly in emotional turmoil. But that wasn't the sole reason: Ian himself had been single for nine months and it felt strange, though extremely nice, to be getting close to someone again. He didn't want to rush things, make any wrong or hasty moves. Whatever happened between them would happen in its own good time.

'God, you sound like a bloody saint,' he murmured. He swung his legs over the side of the bunk and stood up. Immediately he shivered; the mutual warmth they had shared seemed to remain with Annie like an invisible blanket. She made a contented sound and huddled closer to the wall, drawing up her arms as though dragging the blanket around her.

'Oh God,' Ian muttered as his battered face stared back at him from the mirror. His nose and cheekbone were swollen and bruised, his eye a bloodshot slit within a cushion of purple-black flesh. He turned on the tap and gently doused his face with cold water. It hurt. He dabbed at it carefully with a towel, looking glumly at the pink stains, faint but noticeable, on the ruffled shirt which Annie had draped over the radiator.

After a trip to the bathroom he made coffee, which he carried over to the bed. He sat down, careful not to bump his head on the top bunk, and leaned forward to kiss Annie's ear-lobe. She murmured wordlessly at the touch of his lips. 'Annie,' he said, 'I've made some coffee. Do you want some?' She groaned again and rolled over on to her back. Her arms came up as if sleep was a weight she had to push away.

Her eyes opened with an effort. She looked like a small child, and yet paradoxically this quality made Ian feel suddenly amorous. She stretched, arching her back. She still wore her costume from last night, though she had added an enormous lilac sweatshirt which reached to her thighs. Ian put the coffee on the floor and stretched out beside her, encircling her waist with his hand. God, this felt good. He smiled, making his face flare.

'You look like James Dean after the car crash,' she muttered blearily.

'I love you too,' he said, and leaned forward to kiss her.

They kissed gently, carefully. Ian was very aware of her softness, her femininity, the smell and taste and shape of her.

'Mmm,' Annie said after a few minutes, lying back, a contented smile on her face. She stretched again, then yawned. 'Did I hear you say something about coffee?'

Ian reached down and picked up the two mugs, one of which he handed to Annie. 'At your service, madam. What's it like having a slave?'

'Very nice,' said Annie and took a sip. 'Mmm, that's good. How do you feel?'

Ian wanted to say, 'Randy', but didn't; they weren't quite that intimate yet. Instead he asked, 'Emotionally or physically?'

'Both.'

'Physically — as if half my face has been set in concrete. Emotionally ...' he paused, looked at Annie and grinned his slow, swollen grin ' ... pretty good. How about you?'

Annie smiled coyly and traced the shape of an elephant on the mug she was holding. 'Very nice, thank you,' she said.

'Does this mean, then, that we're sort of, like ... *officially* going out?'

Annie feigned a look of surprise. 'I don't know. Does it? I can't recall being asked.'

Ian shook his head. 'You're merciless, you know that?'

Annie shrugged, eyes still all innocence.

With exaggerated courtliness Ian took her mugless hand in both of his. 'Miss Annie O'Donnell,' he said solemnly, 'I will be most delighted if you'll do me the honour of being my belle.'

'Your what?'

'My belle.'

242

'Oh, I see.' She took a sip from her mug.

'Well? Will you?'

'Will I what?'

'Go out with me, you clutz-brain?'

Annie pulled a dismissive face, as if she couldn't be bothered one way or the other. 'I'll think about it,' she said.

Ian rolled on to his back, pretending anguish. 'You're a hard woman, Miss O'Donnell. I risked my life for your honour last night, you know.'

'Oh, and now you expect something in return, is that it? Well, I'm sorry, Mr Raven, but I won't submit to emotional blackmail.'

She took another haughty swig from her mug, and then abruptly gave an impish grin. 'Ian?' she said.

'Hmm?'

'Yes.'

'Yes what?'

'Yes please.'

Ian looked at her, then they both laughed and kissed, which for him was a painful procedure. Annie got up, rooted through her drawers, dragging out clothes, regarding them, pulling a face and putting them back, until she was satisfied with her ensemble. She stuffed toiletries into a bag and retreated to the bathroom, reappearing ten minutes later, looking bright and refreshed in yellow Snoopy t-shirt, tight stone-washed jeans and white espadrilles. They went for some breakfast, where Ian's pummelled face received much attention, and where he was asked for the first time a question which was to crop up with maddening regularity over the next few days: 'What happened to you?'

Over breakfast they decided to take a trip into Maybury, see the town and return – with much apology and explanation – Ian's costume. He went back to his room to change, arranging to meet Annie in the coffee bar at ten. At five to he was trotting down the stairs to the ground floor when he almost literally bumped into Duncan Westey emerging topless from a shower room, damp towel slung over one shoulder.

'Hi, Duncan,' said Ian amiably. 'How are you?'

For a moment Westey stared at him as though he'd never seen him before. 'Er ... fine, Ian, thanks. Yeah ... okay. Er ... what happened to your face?'

Ian told him. He'd got the story down to a few concise sentences. Westey nodded, though he seemed preoccupied. When Ian had finished he said, 'Shit. Well ... s'long,' and turned to move away.

'Yeah,' said Ian. 'See you, Duncan.' He began to walk away too.

He'd taken no more than three steps when Westey called, 'Hey, Ian, hang on a sec.' Ian turned. 'I got something for you,' said the warden.

'What is it?' Ian asked, but Westey had turned his back and was shuffling towards his flat. From behind he looked like an old man: thin, straggly hair, stooped back, knobbly vertebrae and flesh as white as dough.

He entered his flat, leaving the door open behind him. Ian followed, wrinkling his nose. The place smelt of stale tobacco and alcohol fumes. The curtains were three-quarters closed, a single bar of insipid daylight straining across a floor which was a minefield of empty beer cans, heaped ashtrays, discarded magazines, grubby clothes, screwed-up sheets of paper, record sleeves and food wrappers. Westey disappeared into the part of the flat that contained his bedroom, kitchenette and tiny bathroom. Ian perched on the arm of the settee, first removing an ashtray quivering with butts.

Westey was gone for no more than a minute. When he reappeared he was wearing a Frank Zappa t-shirt which was already damp on the shoulders through contact with his partly dried hair. His face was very pale apart from the dark pouches under his eyes. He handed Ian a grubby piece of paper without a word.

'Must have been quite a party,' Ian said, looking around.

Westey followed his gaze and shrugged. 'I guess I haven't had much time for housework these past coupla days.' He nodded at the piece of paper which Ian was now looking at. 'That's Dan Latcher's address. I got it from a friend of Dan's, guy called Bongo.'

Ian looked at the address, then folded the sheet of paper and put it in his inside pocket, next to his inhaler. 'Aw, great. Thanks for this, Duncan. Annie and I went to see Paul Carmichael yesterday, and it looks as if things are really starting to move at last.'

He briefly told Westey of the latest developments, but had the impression the warden was only half-listening, that he was anxious to get on with something that Ian was holding up. 'You're still prepared to back us up if we need you, aren't you, Duncan?' Ian concluded by asking.

Westey looked evasive. 'Er ... I don't know, Ian. I'll have to see. I've got rather a lot on my mind at the moment.'

Ian was disappointed, despite the fact that Carmichael's involvement might have rendered Westey's vow of support redundant anyway. 'But you promised,' he blurted.

Westey shrugged. 'That was before.'

'Before what?'

'Before ... before what happened happened.'

'What's happened?' Ian asked. 'Maybe I can help.'

Abruptly Westey scowled. 'I don't think so.'

'Try me.'

There was a brief, ugly silence and then Westey's head snapped up. The vehemence on his face surprised Ian.

'Look,' the warden muttered, 'I don't have to explain myself to you or anyone. I never signed no fucking contract or anything, you know.'

Ian stepped back, holding up his hands. 'Hey, okay, I'm sorry. There's no need to fly off the handle.'

As quickly as it had come, Westey's anger faded. He looked down at the floor as though ashamed to meet Ian's eye and vaguely waved a hand.

'Aw, sorry, man, I shouldn't take it out on you. Like I say, I've got a lot on my plate. Overworked and underpaid, I guess.'

Ian smiled. 'That's okay.' There was a pause, then awkwardly he went on, 'If there's anything I can help you with, anything you want to talk about, you know all you have to do is ask.'

'Yeah, sure. Thanks, man. But ... like I say, it's somethin' I gotta work through myself.'

'Okay,' said Ian. He moved stiffly across the room, turned at the door and held up the piece of paper. 'Well, thanks for this anyway. See you, Duncan.'

'Yeah.'

In the car, during the short drive to Maybury, Ian and Annie discussed Westey's behaviour. Annie suggested that maybe the warden was scared to help them.

'Scared?' repeated Ian, surprised.

'Yes. It's possible, isn't it? Perhaps Latcher's got to him in some way, warned him off. He's a pretty scary guy, you know.'

Ian thought about this for a moment, then he said, 'No. I don't think that's it.'

Annie was facing the open window, screwing up her eyes against the wind which was whipping through her hair. She turned to Ian. 'Why not?'

Ian slowed the car, indicated, and glanced into his rear-view mirror. He turned right, passing a primary school bearing the date 1885, and a field in which two horses and a donkey grazed beneath a massively regal oak tree.

'Because I don't,' he replied.

'But you can't just say that. You've got to have a reason.'

Ian was silent for perhaps ten seconds. 'Well, he wouldn't have called me in to give me Latcher's address for one thing, would he?

And for another ... I just felt whatever was bothering him was more personal than that. It was something he was finding tough to cope with.'

Annie shrugged. 'Well, I'm not convinced. I still think it might be Latcher's influence.' She hung out of the window again, letting the wind redden her face.

Ian said, 'Your friend Heather never got back to us, did she?'

Annie pulled her head back in, wound the window up. 'No,' she said, 'not yet.'

'What was it the two of you talked about anyway? You said you'd tell me, that you'd found out something amazing, but then when I asked you later you said you wanted time to think about it a bit first.'

Annie looked embarrassed. 'I still think I need time to think. If I tell you now, you might laugh.'

Ian looked indignant. 'I won't.'

'You might. It sounds pretty crazy.'

'Go on, I promise I won't laugh.'

Annie didn't reply immediately. She stared blankly at the scenery, at the large country houses and modern farms they were passing, at the sky which was as blue and as bright as a summer leftover. At last she said, 'Okay, I'll tell you. But promise you won't go all patronising on me like you usually do.'

'What do you mean? I don't do that.'

'Yes you do. You know you do.'

Ian grinned, then said, 'Ow. Remind me not to do *that*.' A red Ferrari overtook him on a tight curve. 'Prat,' Ian muttered, then he continued, 'Okay, I promise. Cross my heart and hope all my hair falls out.'

Annie was silent a moment longer as though still unsure. Then she told him.

When she had finished it was Ian's turn to be silent. Annie glanced at him, but the swelling and bruising of his features made them difficult to read. 'Well?' she said at last. 'What do you think?'

Ian breathed out slowly. 'Very weird,' he said.

'Do you think I'm right?'

'I don't know. All this stuff about white magic and black magic, and about ... bleeding Latcher's influence out of you.' He frowned, then asked, 'Do *you* think you're right?'

Annie paused for just a second, then surprised herself by saying very definitely, 'Yes. Yes I do. I know it sounds totally cracked, but deep down, instinctively, I feel certain that I *am* right, or at least on the right lines.'

Ian just shrugged.

Annie probed, 'Come on, Ian, tell me what you really think. You think I'm a fruitcake, don't you?'

Ian raised a hand from the steering wheel, then slapped it down again, a gesture of exasperation. 'No,' he said resignedly. 'Not you specifically. It's this whole situation that's crazy. But the thing is, I find I don't actually disbelieve any of it. I should, but I don't. I feel as though, with all that's happened, I'm prepared to consider anything. And that's what makes it *really* scary.'

They were silent for a few moments, then Ian asked, 'This ... this magic. Do you reckon you could use it again?'

'What do you mean?'

'Well ... you said it felt like an instinctive, natural thing, something long-buried that the threat from Latcher had ... had woken up.'

'So?'

'So can you control it? Can you harness it and use it whenever you like?'

Annie paused. 'I don't think so,' she said at last. 'I don't know. I'd be scared to try.'

Little more was said on the subject as they entered Maybury proper and cruised around in search of a parking space. They found one in the carpark behind Maybury's only cinema, a quaint though elaborate pre-war structure which Ian knew from reading his *What's On In Maybury* leaflet had been owned and lovingly maintained by three generations of the Howitt family since 1932. Carrying his Dracula costume in the cardboard box in which he'd been given it, Ian led Annie through the town's wide and partly cobbled streets to the costumiers, a shabby, narrow building between a Pizzeria and a second-hand bookshop. As Ian professed his sins to the portly proprietor, Annie browsed amongst the brown-faced mannequins, looking at the costumes. A Roman centurion which had lost most of the left side of its face made her shudder. Only a few hunks of crumbling plaster adhered to the wire-mesh framework, including the painted portion of an eye.

Ian agreed to give the man an additional ten pounds to make up for the lost plastic fangs and damaged shirt. Though he felt the supplement a little steep, he really couldn't be bothered to argue. After they had returned the costume, Ian and Annie wandered around the town, exploring second-hand clothes, book and record shops, hunting for bargains in the open-air market.

Though picturesque, Maybury seemed a little self-conscious; too many of its establishments had edged across the border into the

247

Land of Twee. A glut of olde-worlde façades fronted shops which sold 'antiques', dried flowers, patterned linen, pine furniture, and which, more often than not, served tea and dainty cakes upstairs in mock-traditional ambience. Ian and Annie were relaxing in just such an emporium when Ian, idly exploring his pockets, pulled out the piece of paper which Westey had given him. He unfolded it and thoughtfully re-read the address.

'Annie?' he said.

'Hmm?'

'Why don't we pay Dan Latcher a visit?'

Annie's cup, which she had been lifting to her mouth, halted in mid air. She looked at Ian with wide, wary eyes. It was an expression not unlike the one he had been given by the staff here when he had entered their pretty tea-parlour resembling a street fighter.

'What ... now?'

'Yeah, why not? There's no time like the present.'

Annie lowered her cup slowly back to its saucer, contents unsipped. She appeared calm, though the brief musical chattering of china on china betrayed her trepidation.

'Wouldn't it be better to wait until Monday?' she said. 'Speak to Mr Carmichael first?'

'No,' said Ian, 'I don't think so. Look, we've got the address here. It seems wrong not to do something about it.'

Annie sighed deeply. Though her body was still, the expression on her face suggested she was squirming inside. She looked at the table, picked up the sugar spoon and allowed grains to trickle from it back into the bowl. Ian could see that her hand was trembling. At last she said, 'I don't know, Ian. I don't know if I could face it. I'm scared.'

She let go of the spoon. Ian reached out and closed his hand around hers before she could draw it back.

'There's nothing to be scared of,' he said. 'I'll be with you. And what can Latcher do? He's only human. He's no different from you and me.'

'Isn't he?' said Annie, unconvinced.

'Course not.'

She shook her head. 'I don't know about that. I think he *is* different. He's ... powerful.'

Ian clasped her hand tighter. 'No, he's not, Annie. He's a human being. There's nothing special about him.'

'There *is*,' Annie insisted. 'No, not special, but bad. He influences people. Uses them. He's like a magician or a hypnotist, but worse.'

Ian felt frustrated, but he was determined to be gentle. 'Look,

I know you've had a bad experience with him, but you have to admit that the circumstances were pretty exceptional. You went to his meeting unprepared. He disoriented you with tricks and games, threw your senses into confusion. He may even have used some sort of drug, some gas or something. But if we go and see him now, we'll catch him off-guard. It'll be daylight, we'll see him in normal surroundings, we'll have the upper hand. It might even help, Annie. You'll see what an old fraud he is. Maybe even Steph'll be there.'

Annie didn't respond, but Ian knew she was listening. He squeezed her hand tighter.

'You know we can't just sit back and do nothing,' he urged. 'We have to act on this for Steph's sake.'

Annie was still staring at the table, looking miserable. In a very small voice she said, 'I know, Ian, but you haven't met Latcher. You don't know what he's like.'

'That's why I want to go,' Ian said. 'To see what we're up against.'

They were silent for a few moments. Aware that he was being manipulative, and not much liking himself for it, Ian said, 'Anyway, what about this white magic of yours? It protected you the first time, didn't it?'

Annie looked sharply at him, unsure whether he was making fun of her. If he was he concealed it well; his face was deadly serious. She replied, 'Yes, but it made me really sick, Ian, and like I said, I don't know if I can control it. Maybe it only works when I've got my period. And besides, it'd be a one on one this time. We'd get Latcher's full ... force. His full attention.'

'But you can always make those sorts of excuses,' Ian said. 'We won't help Steph by avoiding things all the time.'

Annie pulled her hand away from his and sat back in her chair. She sighed again and half closed her eyes, anguished by the decision she knew she had to make. Doggedly she said, 'But we're not avoiding things, are we? We went to see Mr Carmichael yesterday.'

She knew before she said it that that was no sort of argument. Ian replied as she expected he would.

'We can't leave things up to other people, disclaim all responsibility. Carmichael won't be able to do anything until after the weekend, probably not till Tuesday at the earliest. We've got to go, Annie. You know we have.'

Fear made her irritable. She flapped at the conciliatory hand which Ian was stretching towards her, knocking it aside. 'All right, all right,' she muttered. 'I suppose as usual you won't shut up until you've got your own way. But don't blame me if ... if anything happens.'

'We'd better go now,' Ian said, standing up. 'It'll be dark if we leave it much longer.'

He paid the bill and they left, walked back to the car with barely a word passing between them. As Ian put the keys into the ignition, he turned to Annie and said, 'Look, if you're really scared, we can just pass the house, have a look at it.'

Annie shrugged. 'What would be the point of that?'

Ian didn't reply. He simply looked at her a few seconds longer, then started the car and edged out into the late-afternoon traffic.

Royston was on the University side of town, no more than five minutes' drive away. They had bypassed it on the journey into Maybury, Ian preferring to take the scenic route. Now they crawled through the maze of seemingly identical terraced streets, Ian calling out street names for which Annie searched scowlingly in the A-Z. When she had her bearings, she directed him, though unwillingly. 'Left here, then first right,' she murmured after some minutes of tentative cruising.

Ian followed her instructions, raising his eyebrows in doubtful satisfaction as they turned into Cramer Road. It was not dark but the sky had lost a little of its lustre, was becoming just the tiniest bit hazy in its prelude to twilight.

'Number forty-two,' Ian muttered. 'It should be on that side.' He gestured to the right.

Annie gazed out of the window, face blank with inevitability. 'There it is,' she said in a flat voice.

Ian parked across the street and the two of them stared at Latcher's house. It was unimpressive, anonymous even: broken gate, red door and white windowsills, garden overgrown, though not desperately so, roof in need of minor repairs.

'Looks quiet,' Ian said. The interior of the downstairs room was hidden from view by thick curtains, drawn tight. Through the upstairs window they could make out a lightshade which was a white paper sphere and part of a wall adorned with posters or hangings too dim to identify.

'Hmm,' said Annie, and added hopefully, 'Maybe no one's at home.'

Ian stroked her arm. 'You don't have to come with me, you know, if you don't want to. You can wait here. Raise the alarm if I don't come out.'

He smiled to show the comment was a joke, but Annie didn't smile back.

'No way,' she said. 'We'll go in together. I don't want you falling under his spell like Steph did.'

250

'No chance of that,' said Ian. 'I've got a will of iron.' They sat in silence for a few seconds longer, then Ian purposefully tapped Annie on the shoulder and opened his door. 'Come on then, let's go.'

Ian led the way across the road and through the broken gate to the front door. He gave Annie a reassuring smile, then rang the bell. They waited, Ian shifting from foot to foot, clasping and unclasping his hands before him as though unsure which was the best stance, Annie shivering though it was not cold. They heard feet thudding down stairs, approaching the door, saw the handle begin to turn. Both of them took an involuntary step back as the door was opened to reveal a figure they both recognised. The girl recoiled a little at the sight of Ian's mauled face, though of the three of them she was quickest to recover her composure, and said enquiringly, 'Hello?'

Ian stepped forward, waving a finger. 'It's ... it's Emma, isn't it? Emma Chettle?'

'Yes, but ...' The girl frowned at him, then her face cleared. 'My God, you're Ian, aren't you? And you're ... er ...'

'Annie.'

'Annie. Yes, of course. Well ... what brings you two here?'

'We ... er ... we came to see ... er ... someone else,' Ian mumbled. 'Is this Dan Latcher's house?'

'Dan?' Emma said guardedly. 'Yes it is, as a matter of fact. Are you two friends of his?'

Ian and Annie exchanged a look. It was obvious Ian was a little embarrassed by the situation. If they had not been standing on Dan Latcher's doorstep, Annie might have found the scene wickedly amusing.

'Er ... no, not exactly,' Ian said. 'But we need to talk to him. It's about ... er ... a mutual friend of ours – oh, of course, you know her. Steph.' Emma nodded. Ian continued, 'This address was given to us by ... er ... a friend of Dan's.'

'A friend? Who?'

'Oh, well, maybe not really a friend. More of an acquaintance. Duncan Westey. He's a hall warden at the Uni.'

'Oh, right,' said Emma. She seemed to relax a little. 'Well, Dan's not in just now. Perhaps you'd like to wait for him, though God knows where he's gone or how long he'll be.'

Ian glanced at Annie, who was obviously relieved that Latcher was not home. He said, 'Well, I dunno. Perhaps it'd be better if we came back at another time.'

Annie nodded in agreement. The two of them half turned away. Ian flinched in surprise as Emma clutched hold of his jacket sleeve.

'Please,' she said, 'don't go.' There was a hint of desperation in her voice.

The two of them turned back to look at her. She said, 'I've been dying to talk to someone. Please, won't you come in? Just for ten minutes?'

Ian looked at Annie. She seemed resigned, as if this was somehow inevitable. 'What is it you want to talk about?' he asked. 'Is it about Dan?'

'Partly, I suppose,' Emma replied. 'It's just ... everything's so weird. I don't know what's going on any more.' She pressed the back of her hand to her face as though in an attempt to stop herself breaking down, and took a backward step into the house.

'Please,' she repeated, 'come in. If you came to see Dan, then maybe you can tell me what it is you wanted. Maybe we can help each other.'

Ian hesitated for just a second, then followed her. Reluctantly Annie followed him, pulling the front door closed behind them.

Emma made coffee and they sat and talked for considerably longer than ten minutes. She told them about the way Dan had changed, about his new friend, Spider, who she herself had not seen, about the incident with Nev. Annie, in turn, told her about The Crack and how it had affected both Steph and herself. Emma muttered, 'Oh God,' at frequent intervals throughout Annie's account, smoked cigarette after cigarette, fingers trembling, drawing deeply on the smoke as if somehow its effects could anaesthetise her to the situation. Ian chipped in occasionally, though the two girls did most of the talking. Emma seemed not to notice when he stood up and crossed to the window, opened it to allow fresh air into the room. The tension and the smoke necessitated his taking two long blasts on his inhaler. His face hurt, as if blood had been drawn to his bruises and was pounding behind them like battering rams.

'When I came home from Uni yesterday,' Emma said, 'Cat and Nev were gone. I found this note on the table.' She crossed to the mantelpiece where an envelope addressed to 'Julie and Emma' was propped up behind a blue vase.

She handed the envelope to Annie, who unfolded and read the note inside. 'What's it say?' asked Ian. Annie handed the note to him. He read:

Dear J'n E,
Nev and I have decided to go away for a bit to escape the atmosphere in the house. This thing with Dan is getting us

both down. I have a friend in Wales; we may go there. Don't worry if we're not back after the weekend. See you soon. Love to you both.
Cat

Ian brandished the note. 'Is this Cat's handwriting?' he said.

'Yeah,' said Emma, 'I think so. But ... I dunno ... it doesn't seem right to me. It's weird.'

'Weird? In what way?' asked Annie.

'Well, for a start, I don't think Cat and Nev would go off together, and especially not when Dan was in any sort of trouble. I mean, last term Dan and Cat had a thing going, you know. We were all pretty sure that when they came back after the summer they would start going out properly − boyfriend, girlfriend. Cat's been going on about helping Dan, trying to find out what's wrong with him. I'm pretty sure she wouldn't just leave him in the lurch like this. And another thing is lectures. I mean, neither of them is a saint, but it seems really weird that they would go off right at the start of a new term when no one's really settled in yet.' She raised her hands in the air, trailing a stream of cigarette smoke. 'Maybe I'm being paranoid. I just don't know what to think. I'm really confused.'

'What does your other house-mate say about this?' asked Annie. 'Julie, is it?'

Emma rolled her eyes. 'Oh, Julie just says she agrees with me to please me, but, well, to be blunt, she lives in a bloody dream-world. I mean, if there's ever any conflict, any unpleasantness around her, she just closes her mind to it, sweeps it under the carpet, pretends it doesn't exist. She's the sort of person who goes out of the room when they show Ethiopia on the telly. She never contributes to charities or anything because that'll mean admitting that there's a need for them. I've hardly seen her the last few days. She's been pubbing, sleeping at her boyfriend's place and going to lectures, and that's it. If you've ever got a crisis on your hands, then Julie's the last person to rely on.'

'So,' said Ian, 'what do *you* think's going on? Where do you think Cat and Nev really are?'

Emma looked at him then her gaze flitted away, as if eye-contact might compound some dreadful truth which she was neither willing nor able to face. She bent and ran a hand through her hair; her earrings, inverted triangles of red plastic, hung down over her pale cheekbones like neat bloody gashes.

'I don't know,' she said miserably. 'I just ... don't know. I'm like Julie in that sense. I don't like to think about it.'

'But do you think it's something to do with Dan? You think
something ... bad might have happened to them?'

Emma looked up at him, anguished, then abruptly burst into tears.
As Annie's arms slipped around her to comfort her, Ian saw that she
was almost crying too.

43

Lying in the bath on Saturday evening, Stu had to make a conscious
effort to think: What a slag. He should never have gone with that
bird last night, he told himself firmly, should at least have used a
condom, but he had been drunk and randy and she had been all
over him. I mean, what does a guy do in a situation like that? He
responds, and fuck the consequences. You don't kick a gift horse
in the teeth by farting around, pontificating about the whys and
wherefores. You go for it, grab the opportunity with both hands.
He'd done nothing wrong, had he? Just had some fun, that's all —
so why was he being made to suffer? Did the bird know there was
something wrong with her? Probably. But Stu doubted she gave a
shit. That's why she had disappeared when he had woken up that
morning, leaving only her black lace panties and the transference of
whatever infection she carried as souvenirs.

He lay back, feeling drowsy, the warm water enclosing his body.
The best thing was to remain absolutely still and not look at his
penis. Maybe then he could quash the strange feelings that were
lurking behind his surface outrage. It was looking at his penis that
gave him these unwanted emotions. Looking at it and feeling it
chafe against the inside of his boxer shorts.

He had felt so good that morning when he had finally drifted
awake at 10:45. Normal good: satiated, fulfilled, content. The bird
had done all that he'd wanted, and more. She had maintained
her mystique by refusing to remove her black wig and shades,
perpetuating Stu's fantasy that she had been created solely for
him, a sex-toy from God. She had been voracious, demanding, but
Stu believed he had more than satisfied her. As she'd gone down on

him for the fourth time, he had thought: This is too fucking good to be true.

Upon waking, it seemed he was right. It *had* been too good. Almost immediately he began paying the consequences. The first indication that all was not well had come when he'd rolled sleepily on to his stomach – still unaware that the temptress had vacated the bed – and had been scorched by a bolt of pain searing through his urethra.

More than anything else it was the unexpectedness of the pain, the sheer surprise of it, which had made him scream, his head snapping up, his back arching like a bow. Almost at once the pain began to recede by degrees, but the shock of it seemed to ring in Stu's head like the echo of an alarm bell, shattering his languid contentment. Carefully he rolled on to his back, pushing down the bedsheets, which, though crumpled and twisted, covered him from the waist down. He had been terrified of what he might see, had thought there may be blood or worse. The fact that there wasn't had eased his anxiety, albeit only a little.

His penis didn't look too bad. The worst that he could see were two small puncture-marks halfway up the shaft, the skin around them a little red and inflamed. He wondered what had caused them; perhaps the temptress (she'd been so eager they hadn't even exchanged names) had been wearing some item of jewellery, a ring perhaps, which had scratched him. Or maybe her fingernail had done the damage. Certainly the wounds were not teeth-marks, not unless she was a bloody vampire. Apart from the wounds, nothing else seemed amiss. His cock was a little dry and flaky, but surely that didn't mean anything. It was more than likely simple over-indulgence which had caused that.

He got up to piss, his penis a throbbing bulb of now thankfully dulling pain. He pulled on his boxer shorts with great care; walking in them felt like his genitals were being scoured with sandpaper. Passing urine was agony; he threw back his head, teeth gritted, almost weeping as liquid fire tore a passage from the furnace of his bladder. But the urine was just that; there was no blood, no discharge. 'Bitch,' muttered Stu as he washed his hands and splashed water into his sweating face, 'fucking filthy bitch'.

He returned to his room and tended himself with TCP ointment and moisturising cream. After an initial flare-up, which caused him to bite his lip, drawing blood, the combination seemed to ease the discomfort. He wore his baggiest pair of chinos and stepped carefully, abandoning his usual swagger. If anyone asked him he'd say it was his leg – a rugby injury or a legacy from last night's punch-up.

He spent most of the day in his room; the morning hours were passed propounding theories, some of which brought him out in a cold sweat before he could reason them away. What if the girl had AIDS? Or syphilis? He could die! He was almost sick with panic before reason assured him that neither illness manifested itself so swiftly.

What then? Something *worse* than AIDS? No, don't be daft. It was nothing, an infection, that's all. In a few days it would be gone and he would laugh about his anxieties.

But what if . . . what if she'd injected him with something? Some poison? What if she was a man-hater, one of these lesbo types, who thought the male population should be castrated en masse? Yeah, maybe that's why she'd kept the wig and the shades on − so Stu couldn't reveal her identity to the police.

Nah, what was he thinking? If she was like that, she wouldn't have gone to bed with him, would she? And besides, in Stu's opinion, women only became lesbos when they couldn't get a man. I mean, let's face it, who's ever seen a good-looking lesbian? It couldn't be coincidence that all the lesbos he'd ever seen looked like overfed bulldogs.

No, he'd contracted something pretty harmless, painful though it was. On Monday he'd have to swallow his embarrassment and go see the doc. A course of antibiotics and a tube of ointment would soon see him right. In the meantime he'd just have to make the best of the situation, not move about too much.

The early part of Saturday passed slowly, edgily. He spent the afternoon lying on his bed, the over-excited football commentary on the radio slipping in one ear and out the other. At intervals he examined his penis; it was gradually becoming more scaly, like snake-skin. Gently Stu rubbed cream on it and began to find, after a while, that he was perversely enjoying the sensation. And indeed, as the afternoon progressed, he found his attitude towards his condition slowly, almost imperceptibly, changing. His initial panic gave way to a curiosity, and further, an acceptance. This strengthened even more to the extent that when he stepped into the bath at 5:20 p.m., wincing then smiling as his genitals touched the water, the sub-text to his lambasting of the temptress was a positive view of himself which seemed so illicit that he tried to resist acknowledging it.

'Slag,' he said out loud, but the word was unconvincing on his tongue. He closed his eyes, let himself float on his own thoughts, and moments later found himself wondering idly whether he could still have sex − not *worrying* whether he could, but actually considering the viability of the act. If the temptress reappeared now and offered

256

him a repeat performance of last night, he wondered what his response would be. Astonished by his own thoughts, he had to admit that there was no question: pain or no pain, he would answer, 'Yes.'

The confession was like switching on a light, opening a door to a new philosophy. A philosophy of pain and sex, pleasure and suffering, in which the two were inextricably linked, Siamese twins, flip-sides of the same personality.

Stu looked down to see his penis rising involuntarily from the water. The pain was exquisite because the skin was now so dry and tight that it had to stretch and tear to accommodate the influx of blood into the organ. He shuddered, though not solely from the discomfort. Before he realised what he was doing, his hand had encircled his penis and he had started to masturbate.

The pain was unbelievable. His body was rigid with it, and yet he felt disinclined to stop. When it was over, and he had dried himself, he sat naked in his room, a towel draped across his shoulders, shivering like a dope-fiend without a fix.

He dressed slowly, and it was only as he was applying gel to what little there was of his hair, that he realised he was getting ready to socialise. His groin felt like a bonfire, but Stu now found he was actually revelling in his agony, felt a savage glee in his own torment.

'Hot stuff,' he told the mirror, and laughed. He felt light-headed, and wondered vaguely how much that was due to lack of food; he hadn't eaten all day. He tied his tie, smoothed his eyebrows, and moulded a few errant spikes of hair into place. That done, he informed himself, 'You're gonna knock 'em dead tonight, Stu, my boy.' He whistled as he vacated the room, switching the light off behind him. The condoms by his bed, which previously he had regretted not using, he flushed down the toilet on the way out.

257

44

For the rest of the weekend, Ian and Annie felt they were suspended in limbo. It had been deep twilight, the sky beginning to gain on its darker clouds and absorb them, when they finally left Cramer Road. Before they did so they extracted a promise from Emma that she would call them at Uni the moment Dan returned home. But Saturday night and the whole of Sunday passed uneventfully. There was no sign of Dan, nor of Steph. If The Crack was operational, then news of its activities reached neither Ian's nor Annie's ears.

This was not to say, however, that the weekend was without conflict. The main clash came in dissuading Neil from setting up camp in Dan Latcher's garden. Ian could understand Neil's desire to beat the truth from Dan the instant he showed his face, but he could not condone it. However much satisfaction it might give Neil, in the long run, Ian felt, such an approach might do more harm than good. Even now he still believed that tact and diplomacy would ultimately save the day. Bloodshed led only to more of the same. It was a last resort, not a solution.

In the end, Neil grudgingly agreed to a compromise. In return for a solemn vow not to jump in with fists flying, he was given Dan's address and phone number. He dialled the number immediately, only to be told by Emma that she had not seen Dan in almost two days. On Sunday he tried six more times, but met with a similar response. All day Sunday he was like a caged tiger, prowling from door to window to desk to chair in either his, Ian's or Annie's room, chewing his fingernails, scowling and snapping, unable to sit still. Inevitably the tension took its toll and tempers between the three of them became frayed. Neil was desperate for the phone-call that would prompt them to action, Annie dreading it. Ian felt as though he were caught in the middle, trying vainly to emphasise the need for calm.

'We're only going to speak to Dan, remember, nothing else,' he kept saying. 'We don't want to antagonise him.' The looks he received in reply were close enough to contempt for him to feel worried about the possible result should a confrontation occur.

In this atmosphere, his and Annie's relationship had little opportunity to flourish. They were both tense and irritable on Saturday night, a state which was not altered even when they acted on Ian's suggestion of a drink in the bar, which he had thought might relax them. Indeed, the jovial clamour they encountered served only to highlight the tension between them. In the end they gave up the pretence and returned to Ian's room, where he unpacked his old black and white TV from its polystyrene-filled box. They sat and watched a comedy film in glum silence, during which Annie fell asleep. After the film, Ian picked up a book, opened it and stared at the same page for almost an hour without reading a word. Looking at Annie stretched out on the bed, he wondered how they would sleep that night – dressed or undressed, beneath or on top of the covers.

In the end the question became irrelevant, for Ian fell asleep in the chair and did not wake until a well-aimed shaft of sunlight clawed his eyelids apart at 8:20 the next morning. The weather was to be the only bright thing about that day. He went to bed, alone, in a foul mood at 12:45 a.m. When he woke on Monday morning, he thought at first he had a hangover, then he remembered it was his battered face which was making his head throb. The internal artist who painted his bruises was now, it seemed, finding his creative feet. Certainly his colour combination was striking: blues and reds blending with dramatic purples, subtle yellows, sombre greens.

During the first lecture of the morning, at nine o'clock, Ian's re-arranged face was the main topic of conversation. His fellow students admired his injuries as if they were modifications of choice, like tattoos or a new haircut. Before Carmichael arrived, and made the class laugh by asking Ian to remove his Hallowe'en mask, Ian was able to exchange a few words with Annie, most of which were apologies for yesterday's belligerence. She, too, was in a repentant mood. They agreed that the situation was nobody's fault, that the last thing they should do was start bickering amongst themselves.

The lecture passed quickly. Carmichael, flying in the face of Monday morning blues, managed the impossible by getting his group enthusiastic about Solzhenitsyn's *Cancer Ward*. After the lecture he motioned that Ian and Annie should stay behind.

'A meeting with Dan Latcher has been fixed for tomorrow lunchtime,' he said. 'I shall attend, as will John Hunt, Dan's Head of Department. Primarily the meeting will be to ask Dan why he hasn't been attending lectures. We'll ask him if he has any problems he wants to talk about, and we'll confront him with the rumours currently rife in the University.'

Ian nodded. 'Great. Is there any chance that one of us could sit in?'

'No, I'm afraid not. At this stage we simply want to find out what Dan has to say, hear his side of the story. Ostensibly, as far

259

as we're concerned, Dan's only real misdemeanour is his failure to fulfil his course obligations. If more than that comes to light during the meeting, then all well and good. But we want to avoid a judge and jury situation. We'll bring up the question of The Crack, but we don't want to start throwing accusations around.'

Ian looked a little dissatisfied, but Annie said, 'That sounds fair enough. Doesn't it, Ian?'

He shrugged. 'Yeah, I suppose so. How did you get in touch with Dan? Have you seen him?'

'No,' Carmichael replied. 'We simply left a message in his pigeon hole.'

'So you don't know that he'll definitely turn up tomorrow?'

'That's up to him. The more he defies us, though, the more trouble he'll be in. Don't worry, we won't let this rest until we've reached a solution.'

Ian nodded, looking thoughtful. 'We tried to get in touch with him this weekend,' he told the tutor. 'Just to talk to him, you know.'

'Oh?' said Carmichael.

'Yeah.' Ian told him about their visit to Cramer Road. Carmichael made a note of Dan's address and phone number.

'Okay,' said Carmichael. 'Well, speak to me after our three-thirty lecture tomorrow, and I'll let you know how the meeting went.'

'Right,' said Ian, lifting his bag off the desk. 'Thanks for all your help again, sir.'

He and Annie turned to go. Carmichael said, 'Oh, Ian?'

Ian turned. 'Yes, sir?'

'I've been dying to know – just what *did* you do to your face?'

45

Where now? she wondered.

Holding the needle in her right hand, she rolled it between thumb and forefinger so that it spun, catching the light. She smiled, though the needles she had pushed through both her upper and lower lips made the expression a difficult one to form. Fresh trickles of blood ran down her chin and into her mouth, tasting of liquid copper. The needle between thumb and forefinger was a tiny shaft of dazzling light, a sliver of pure pain. She extended her left hand and stretched out the fingers as though admiring nail varnish. Then she placed the needle beneath the nail of her left index finger and pushed it deep into the cuticle.

Her entire body arched with the pain, and with the thrill of the pain. Her skin felt as though it were writhing, dancing; tears squeezed from her eyes and mingled with the blood on her cheeks. A black-red coil of electric sensation spiralled through her, producing a series of whimpering gasps and an orgasm which seemed to swell in her like an egg before shattering into climax. The high lasted for no more than seconds, as always. The after-pain, the second stage, kept her buzzing, but as each needle pierced the skin she felt herself striving ever more desperately for the apex, the Ultimate. She wanted to clutch Epiphany and hold on, not allow it to slip through her fingers like a greased star. There must be a way to attain the unattainable. There *must*. And she would find it. She would push herself further and further, higher and higher, until she and Epiphany were an unbreakable bond.

In less than two days she had shed her old life as a snake sheds unwanted skin. Now she had to think hard to recall even her name (Amanda), and as for her previous ambitions (good education; good job; nice husband; nice kids; nice house), she now saw them for what they truly were. A cover, a blanket, which she had woven to overlay the real issues, the essential philosophies. Philosophies which previously she had been too terrified to face. Philosophies such as life, death, pain, pleasure, sin and divinity. But 'sin' and 'pain' were again no more than convenient words, trite labels, a further attempt to trivialise the quintessence of Being. A flimsy approximation of each of these qualities could be found, after all, in the shamefully risible life-plan which Amanda had previously mapped out for herself. No, what she was striving for was the centre-point of each of these apparently conflicting paths, the essence, the place where they all converged and became one. Call it Eden or Hell; Satan or God; Epiphany or Damnation. That, Amanda knew, was the one place, the only place, where she would find peace, nirvana, bliss – whatever one wished to call it.

She picked up another needle and thought again: Where now? Her image in the mirror was breathtaking; it was the primitive and the evolutionary in one body. By changing her flesh she was changing her soul too. Each time her skin was broken, she altered her state, her chemical balance, ascended another step on the ladder. But how high *was* the ladder? She had no way of knowing; until she reached the top she would remain blind. She wondered whether Stu was there yet. Whether he would be waiting for her. She hoped so. There was so much she wanted to thank him for.

Before Saturday night she had given little thought to the idea of destiny; indeed had given little thought, she realised now, to anything much at all. But Stu had changed all that. He had come like a saviour, and during their love-making had passed not only his seed, but also knowledge, truth, vision, the potential to transcend. The initial pain, the anxiety, had been a small price to pay for such a gift, a gift which Amanda had felt compelled to share with others as Stu had shared it with her. Already last night's partner, a slim, timid boy called Julian, would be experiencing the urge to communicate his good fortune to others.

'I bring you tidings of great joy,' Amanda told her reflection, her voice mushy with blood, lips constricted by needles. Oh, but she was beautiful. The needles, threaded through her flesh, gave her a bristling sheen, which seen from a distance was like silver down, or a coat of sparks. She had needles between her toes, in the soles and insteps of her feet, in her ankles, her shins, her knees, her thighs, her hips. She had pierced her labia and her buttocks, her stomach and spine, had needles threaded through her breasts like unyielding stitches, protruding from her nipples which resembled the heads of skeletal knapweeds. She had pushed needles into the soft flesh of her throat, into her shoulders and arms, into her ears, her cheeks, her chin, her nose, her lips. She had even skewered her tongue in a dozen places, resulting in a constant seepage of blood into her mouth. And all this work in a single day! If nothing else, surely her dedication merited some reward?

But no. There was little point in thinking this way. There could be no cutting of corners, no easy solution. To achieve her objective she must strive, give her all; there was simply no alternative. She

262

regarded the needle. Where now? Another fingernail? No, she had a better idea.

Stu had given her vision. Inner vision. It therefore followed that she no longer had need of the physical. And this, surely, was laudable sacrifice, proof of her commitment.

Without hesitation she pushed the needle deep into the pupil of her left eye.

46

Jayne Trent found herself padding down the silent corridors of the University. It was clearly night, though there was enough light for her to see by. But it seemed a false light, and it appeared to have no source. It was the kind of light found in movie graveyard-scenes, a cold mortuary-white. Some doors and walls retained the light, gleaming like giant slabs of ice, whilst others were angular blocks of charcoal shadow. Jayne's naked feet made no sound as she walked. The air circulating around her body had, it appeared, found its optimum temperature, for she was aware of neither heat nor chill.

She had to concentrate hard to feel her feet on the floor. It seemed an ethereal contact, present though only barely, as if drugs were dulling her senses. She was unsurprised to find she was naked, though wondered how she had managed to arrive here without attracting attention, molestation or arrest. And *why* had she come? An unconscious desire to resurrect her old life? Certainly the glamour of this new one was no more. It had begun to tarnish the moment she had woken up beside the thuggish university student and realised what she'd done. The initial blaze of revelation had now receded to an ugly darkness. She felt used and abused by Stitch; mentally — ashamed and disgusted, physically — listless, sick, as if she'd picked up some bug. She was like a star which had blazed brightly for one mad, desperate moment, and, unable to replenish itself, was now dwindling and dying.

Was this, then, intended as a final pilgrimage? Perhaps instinct had brought her here one last time before she ... before she what?

263

Pulled herself together? Left town? Committed suicide? Mentally she felt so buffeted by recent events that she could not get her head around any of these possibilities. One step at a time, she told herself. Don't rush things. Take it slowly. Now what did she really want? A sense of equilibrium. So the first option was the one to work towards. Sanity and survival.

But how? What should she do? Keep walking? At least forward momentum suggested some sort of progression. No, surely the thing was to get her bearings, pin down her exact position, anchor herself. If she looked at the doors she was passing she could work out which floor she was on, make her way to the nearest telephone and call the police.

Thus reassured, she turned eagerly to the door looming on her right. It was unlabelled. The next one, then. But that too was blank. Frustrated, she twisted the handle, expecting the door to be locked. She was therefore surprised when the catch disengaged from its socket, and the door swung silently open.

She stood for a moment on the threshold, trying to adjust her eyes to the gauzy darkness within. But try as she might, she could not; the room, if room it was, seemed to defy even the stark polar light that gave definition to the corridor.

Should she enter? If she did she could cross to the window, ascertain her exact location from the view. And why not? she thought. A sixth sense told her she *should* enter. Unconsciously drawing in breath, as though about to plunge underwater, she stepped into the room.

Immediately upon doing so, she felt nervous. The darkness enshrouded her like mist, chilling her skin. She shivered, twisting her head this way and that, half-convinced that the light cold touches on her shoulders, back and buttocks were the fingers of someone standing just behind her.

Wrong decision, she told herself. Go back, this doesn't feel right. She turned to the door, hand stretching for the handle ... but there was no door. Only the cold darkness, wrapping itself about her like spider's silk.

She took a few steps back the way she had come, the beginnings of panic lying heavy in her gut. But there could be no mistake. The door was simply *not there*. She clutched her hands together, then crossed her arms across her breasts, feeling suddenly, awfully, vulnerable.

What did this mean? What should she do? Minutes seemed to pass as she dithered, her entire body skittishly alert for the slightest threat. If only there was some focus to work towards, something to

264

aim for, anything at all. And then, like a granted wish, she saw a glimmer of green dappled light some distance away, a shimmer of twinkling ever-changing shards, like the sun on a pond, constantly scattered by the wind's breath on the water's shivering skin.

This, then, was presumably her cue. It was a warm soothing image, unlike the clinging murk around her. She walked towards it, mind focused wholly on its almost mesmeric incandescence. At some stage she became half aware that the cold smooth floor had changed to a carpet of grass beneath her feet, that the dark was merging and clotting to become tree-boles, that green was suffusing her surroundings like an injection of chlorophyll.

But she did not become fully aware that she was in a forest, or a garden, or a wood, until she reached the river. It flowed leisurely, swirling over small rocks and around larger ones, shattered jewels of sunlight trapped forever in its lazy motion.

'Beautiful,' she breathed. She knelt on the river's edge and reached down to the water. It played over her hand, refreshingly cool, startlingly clear. She drew out her hand and licked the fingers, closing her eyes at the sweet taste.

She stood up and looked around her, filling her lungs with fresh air. She saw healthy trees and bushes, and flowers in full bloom, almost luminescent beneath a sky which was piercingly blue.

In truth, she supposed she should be afraid. Something was wrong here. The laws of reality were obviously fractured in some way; nothing was as it should be. But she was not afraid. This place radiated a goodness, a sense of peace, dizzied her with its impeccable perfume. She began strolling, following the course of the river, feeling a part of it, part of its flow, part of its tranquillity.

She walked for perhaps an hour, her limbs moving easily, muscles fluent as the river, which was her role model. Now and then she bent to pick flowers, which she wore in her hair. Clouds white as purity tailed her like a procession of chariots.

And then, in the distance, rounding a curve in the river's flow, she saw a man. He was naked like herself, slumped against a tree. This far away no details were visible; his features were dark smudges, his hair − both on head and genitals − grey dabs. His left arm was moving. He held something in his hand which he periodically brought up to his face. As Jayne drew closer she saw that he was eating an apple which had fallen from the tree. Closer still and his features came into focus. Jayne gasped.

It was her father. He looked as he had just before the stroke which had killed him in 1974. He had been sixty-two years old at the time, semi-retired, his face already deeply lined, the burden of life already beginning to shrink him. Jayne could not decide which was more shocking; seeing her father here at all, or seeing him naked. She could not help but stare at his penis. It was proudly erect as though flaunting the frail sagging body of which it was a part.

'Dad!' Jayne exclaimed. She sounded as though she were admonishing him for his lewdness. The old man paused in his eating and looked up at her. His penis swung stiffly, like a third eye on a stalk.

'Hello, Jayne,' he said as if he'd been expecting her. They stared at each other for a moment as though unsure what to do next. Then the old man was pushing himself painfully to his feet. 'Hungry?' he asked, proffering the apple.

'Er ... no,' Jayne replied. 'Dad, what are you doing here?'

The old man shrugged as if the answer were obvious. 'Sitting,' he said. 'Eating.'

'But ... you died, Dad. Years ago. So ... so what are you? A ghost? And what's this place? Where are we?'

The old man smiled in that superior way of his that had always made Jayne feel inadequate. Remembering, she shuddered. Such thoughts, tipped from her subconscious, were a little too close to home.

'Don't you know?' he said infuriatingly. 'Can't you guess?'

'No, I don't –' Jayne began, then stopped. A shocking theory had just presented itself to her. 'Are we *all* dead?' she asked. 'Is this Heaven? Is Mum here?'

The old man laughed, but didn't answer her question. Instead he dropped the apple and opened his arms. 'Welcome home, Jayne. Come and give your old dad a hug.'

Jayne would have done so immediately were it not for the obscenity rearing from his midriff, excessively oversized.

Glancing at that, she suddenly remembered that she too was naked. The shock of seeing her father, and her own familiarity with her nudity, had chased the realisation from her mind. Now her whole body seemed to burn with shame. Her muscles bunched and cringed as if trying to hide her behind herself. Her left arm stretched across her breasts, concealing what she could of them; her right hand cupped her pudenda.

Her father watched this attempt at modesty with a frankness she found intensely discomforting. 'You know, there's really no need for that any more,' he told her. 'It doesn't matter here.'

'It matters to me,' Jayne said. 'I'm not used to us seeing each other ... like this.'

'Without secrets, you mean? Without inhibitions? Without the

266

barriers we spend most of our lives constructing around ourselves?'

Jayne said nothing. Her father took a step towards her, reiterating
the outspread of his arms. 'Embrace me,' he said.

Jayne remained still a moment, agonised by indecision, cheeks
burning. Then slowly, reluctantly, she let her hands drop to her
sides.

'That's better,' her father said. 'This is a new start for us, Jayne.
A world without shame. Now.' He inclined his palms towards her,
stretching his fingers. Another short pause, then Jayne was walking
unsteadily towards him.

She wanted to tear herself free the moment his hands touched
her bare shoulders, but she forced herself to remain still. Then his
arms were sliding over her back, his cheek against her cheek, his
puckered, wire-haired chest pressing against her breasts. She bit her
lip, keeping the scream inside as his erect penis bumped against her
thigh, and over her stomach like an inquisitive snake. Her father
grunted and put one hand down between them. Jayne didn't realise
what he was doing until she felt the head of his penis attempting to
part her labia.

'*What are you doing?*' she screeched, and wrenched herself free
from his grasp. He came shuffling towards her, an eager smile on
his lined face.

'It's all right, Jayne. Nothing to panic about. We do as we feel
here. As we see fit.'

'Keep away from me!' she warned, backing round in a half-circle.
She was edging towards the tree. She wanted something solid between
her exposed body and this beast who called himself her father.

'It's really nothing to get excited over. A harmless game, that's
all. An amusing diversion.'

Jayne ran behind the tree, crying out as her toe stubbed on a fallen
apple. She picked up the apple and flung it at him. Distress impaired
her aim.

'Come on, Jayne, there's no need for this.' Her father placed a
hand on the tree trunk.

'*Get away from me!*' She yelled again, so harshly that it scoured
her throat. Her fingernails hooked a flap of loose bark. Instinctively
she wrenched it from the tree.

'Now look, Jayne,' said her father a little more sternly. He rounded
the tree, and as he did so she struck. He threw up an arm, but the
jagged hunk of bark passed beneath it and into his side. The bark
tore raggedly through the flesh, followed almost immediately by a
copious gout of blood.

Now the old man's assurance faltered. His face became a triangle of O's; a piercing scream rose from the largest, his mouth. He clapped his hands over his wound and lurched towards Jayne, though whether for revenge or mercy was a moot point. Jayne again reacted instinctively. She thrust the bark out towards him and felt a splash of heat over her hand as it slid easily into his throat. His screams became an incoherent gurgle. He toppled forward on to the ground. His twitching hands clawed at the bark for what seemed an interminably long time, but they had neither the strength nor the co-ordination to remove it.

At last his muscular spasms became less, and then stopped altogether. Blood covered his throat, chest, stomach, hands and the lower half of his face. It was shiny as plastic, its colour a livid testimony to her violence. For perhaps a minute Jayne stood, feeling nothing, stained with her father's blood. Then an inner shudder began, working its way up through her legs and into her stomach, preceding an eruption of horror, disgust, disbelief. Her legs buckled and she pitched forward on to her knees. She began to sob, her breath hitching and struggling in her throat, fighting a losing battle to assimilate her grief.

She covered her face with her hands, her entire upper body now slumping forward until her brow was resting on the ground. The grass smelt fresh, sappy, green; the silence pressed on her ears like the most profound deafness. Wrapped up tight, squeezed into her own private darkness, Jayne felt a modicum of comfort. She'd killed her father – but he'd already been dead for sixteen years, hadn't he? So, if not her father, who *was* that lying on the grass with a gouged throat? No one, she told herself. And where was *she?* She was nowhere, she replied. And why was she nowhere? Because she didn't exist, she assured herself. The spiral of thoughts was comforting, a loop into whose centre she could lose herself. She wanted to go back to the beginning, start again, pretend this had never happened.

She found herself walking barefoot down the silent corridors of the University. There was a strange icy glow which threw the angles of walls and ceilings and doors into extremes of light and shadow, like a giant surrealist chess-board. She was aware of neither heat nor chill. She could barely feel the floor beneath her feet. She was unsurprised to discover she was naked. She wondered how she had managed to arrive here without attracting attention, molestation or arrest . . .

47

Cross-legged and hunched forward on the bed, Mally stared at his reflection in the small mirror he held in his right hand. He had tried to make his face as slack as possible, mouth hanging open, eyes glazed, but he still wasn't satisfied. Even the white-grey make-up with which he had painstakingly coated his face and body, dabbing little touches of blue here and there to emphasise the coldness of the flesh, was not enough. The trouble was, he *knew* he was not dead; he could see life squirming beneath the skin. His eyes held the flame, his body ticked with pulses. The power inside him was too vibrant to achieve the stillness necessary.

Which was a shame, for sometimes Mally *wanted* to be dead. Death was peace and nobility; it was the ultimate artistic statement. And to view one's own death must surely be the most enriching experience a man could have.

But Mally's obsession lay not only in the aesthetic; he was also concerned with power, or more specifically omnipotence. Mally wanted *control* over Death. He wanted to get inside its skin, learn its secrets, become its master. He was the Unmaker, he was transcending, but he was afraid that his Art would simply not be enough, that his preparations for ascendancy would be insufficient for him to scale the heights to which he aspired. He wanted to hold God in one hand, Death in the other, and to squeeze them until they pleaded for mercy. Already he was a colossus among men, but he was afraid that there were higher influences, which, if they wished, could strip away his achievements and cast him down. Angrily he rubbed the side of a hand across his face, exposing the pink flesh. This was a sham, a waste of time. He was achieving nothing by this charade.

He hurled the mirror across the room, watching with satisfaction as it struck the wall and broke. He uncrossed his legs and slid off the bed, leaving greasy smears of white make-up on the sheets. As he opened his wardrobe door and plucked the white cloth from the storage jar within, he thought of Peter Daniel Simpson. Of course Simmsy's death had not been peaceful, but nevertheless he had still achieved that stillness, that ... totality, which Mally found fascinating and, yes, even desirable. It was ironic, Mally thought, that in unmaking Simmsy he had created something whole and beautiful. After Simmsy was dead, Mally had stripped the body and had altered it, then had lingered over his masterpiece, lightly kissing the cooling flesh, before finally, reluctantly, biting off the part that he wanted and taking his leave.

He smiled. It had been so easy. So easy. But then he had known it would be. He lifted the jar and carried it across to the bed. The contents shifted sluggishly, as if waking up.

Mally crossed his legs once more and held the jar in his cupped hands. Some of the blood had blackened and crusted; the rest looked to have congealed like left-over gravy. The organ, coated in this muck, looked no more than a shapeless hunk of discarded gristle. 'Wakey, wakey, rise and shine,' he said. He shook the jar vigorously in both hands until dots of sweat oozed from beneath the corpse-white pallor of his skin.

When he heard the voices scratching behind his eyeballs, he stopped. He placed the jar on the bed, panting slightly, and watched the faces of his former tormentors emerging from the flux with painstaking sloth. He enjoyed their struggle, their obvious misery, their pain, their degradation, their fear. He felt in control again, felt strength surging through him. His doubts, his anxieties, were assuaged simply by listening to their pathetic, babbling pleas and knowing that he was in charge.

'Having fun, little ones?' he murmured, a smile hooking his face. He watched the mewling, transforming features for a while, relishing his control, savagely delighting in the fact that he could deliberately ignore the itch of their desperation, could sit casually and watch them suffer. But he mustn't be idle, he must feed on this strength, use it.

'Tomorrow,' he confided to his captive audience. 'Tomorrow I will create another masterpiece.'

Their itching voices stopped. Their makeshift faces gaped in awe. Mally, like a God, swept up his world and its people, deciding it was time, once again, for darkness.

48

'Come in, Dan.'

'Thank you, Dr Hunt.'

Dan Latcher looked smoothly confident as he stepped through the door which John Hunt was holding open for him. He wore a white suit with shoulder-pads to rival an American footballer's, black shirt with gold-tipped collar, bootlace tie, and black and white brogues, immaculately polished. He nodded to Carmichael, the half smile on his face remaining just this side of mocking. John Hunt closed the door and wafted a hand towards an armchair with a thin wooden frame and leather-look cushions.

'Sit down, Dan,' he said, and did so himself behind his cluttered desk. Carmichael's seat was positioned at the side of the desk, angled towards Dan. The impression created was of an informal chat rather than a dressing down.

John Hunt meshed his meaty hands together and leaned forward on his elbows, peering at Dan. He was a bulbous-faced man with a body to match. Fast approaching sixty, he wore gritty tweed suits which always smelt rather cosily of tobacco smoke. His wiry hair and unkempt sideburns were ash-grey. The patches of bristle beneath his chin and the odd nick of dried blood on his cheeks suggested he was a careless shaver.

His office was primarily brown, lined with shelves stacked with dour-looking textbooks. The light from a large window fell across his desk, causing the top sheet of a pile of unmarked essays to glow like phosphorous.

'Well, Dan,' said Hunt, 'have you any idea why we called you in here today?'

Dan allowed a smidgeon of puzzlement to impinge on the tranquillity of his features. 'Not really, sir,' he admitted. 'I assumed it was something to do with my thesis on cult psychology – the Collective Mind.'

Hunt and Carmichael exchanged a glance. 'Ah ... no, Dan. Not really. I've called you in here to discuss your inattendance at lectures.'

'My what, sir?' asked Dan politely.

'Your failure to turn up for any lectures last week, despite the fact that certain sources assured me that you were on campus.'

'Sources, sir? What sources?'

'That doesn't matter. The fact is, you were on campus and yet you didn't come to lectures. I'd be very interested to know exactly why that was.'

Dan looked steadily at Hunt for a moment, then his gaze shifted to Carmichael. From his expression it seemed he was uncertain as to whether his Department Head's query was a serious one.

At last he said, 'I'm a fourth year, sir.'

'So? What has that to do with anything?'

'I was led to believe, sir, that lectures were optional, that our theses — private research, experimentation and so on — were all-important.'

Hunt sighed, rotated his thumbs, as if he'd heard all this before and was bored with it. 'Not so, Mr Latcher. Your thesis is important, yes, but so is your course work. What made you think that you didn't have to attend lectures?'

'I can't remember, sir. I must have misunderstood. I'm sorry.'

He smiled to seal the apology and crossed his left leg over his right. He rested his delicately tapered hands on the bony jut of his left knee. His movements suggested an almost rehearsed serenity, as if he had been instructed precisely how to behave.

'May I say something?' asked Carmichael.

Both Hunt and Latcher turned to look at him. For the barest instant Latcher's eyes seemed to flash with a disturbing yellow light.

'Of course, Paul,' replied Hunt. He sounded indulgent as a kindly uncle, though unintentionally so, Carmichael suspected.

'Well, it's just clarification really. Are you saying, Dan, that you simply didn't know you were supposed to attend lectures?'

'That's right,' replied Latcher. His voice was almost too calm. Curiously the slight Liverpool inflection made it a little eerie, instead of, as should have been the case, more human.

'But didn't your fellow group members tell you? Surely the topic was raised in conversation?'

Unflustered, Latcher said, 'No, I don't believe it was. Though to be fair, I rarely mix with my other course members. That probably explains my ignorance, even if it doesn't excuse it. Outside the classroom I have my own group of friends.'

'You don't seem particularly worried to learn that you've missed over a week's lectures,' Carmichael persisted.

Latcher's gaze was implacable. 'Should I be?' he asked.

'I would have thought so. The fourth year is a very intense one, there's no room for drifters. Once you start to fall behind, it can be very hard to catch up.'

'I'll photocopy the notes I've missed and read them today in my free periods. I'm a good little student.'

He flashed a smile that failed to reach his eyes. Carmichael said, 'Is ignorance the only reason that you've been neglecting your course work?'

Again that tiny deliberate frown. 'I don't understand, sir. I thought I'd made that point clear.'

'There are rumours, Dan, that you've founded some sort of ... group on campus, some kind of quasi-religious society.'

'The Crack, you mean?' replied Dan. He challenged Carmichael with his steady, open gaze.

'Yes,' Carmichael said. 'The Crack. I've heard some rather discomforting reports. Perhaps you'd like to explain them?'

'In what way discomforting?'

'Well,' Carmichael said, shrugging to show he wanted to keep this as casual as he could, 'this is only hearsay, but I've heard reports of brainwashing and the like. Apparently certain students, subjected to your ... ah ... influence, shall we say, have experienced severe disruptions in their everyday routines. Communication withdrawal; a refusal to eat, sleep and wash; inattendance at lectures; a propensity to become uncharacteristically violent when questioned by their friends. To be frank, Dan, some people are becoming rather concerned by the whole thing. But as I say, we're not accusing you of anything, you're not in the dock, as it were. We simply wanted to put this to you in the hope that you could set all our minds at rest, quash these — let's hope silly — rumours.'

There was a silence that lasted the length of a heartbeat, then abruptly Dan threw back his head and laughed. It was a harsh, braying sound. Dr Hunt winced and looked around as if afraid the vibrations might set the walls trembling and spill forth an avalanche of books.

'You find this amusing, Mr Latcher?' Hunt asked soberly.

Dan's laughter subsided. Grinning wolfishly he said, 'Excuse me, Dr Hunt, but yes I do. Where on earth did you hear these ridiculous stories, Mr Carmichael?'

Still trying to keep the exchange light, Carmichael airily waved a hand.

'As I say, much of it is rumour. Though having said that, the matter *was* brought to my attention by what I would consider a fairly reliable source: one of my students, whose room-mate, apparently, has become rather disturbed since she's been attending your group meetings.'

Dan's drill-like eyes adopted a thoughtful sheen. He steepled his fingers to his lips. 'Ah,' he said. 'Now, that wouldn't be Annie O'Donnell, would it?'

Thrown, Carmichael stammered, 'Er ... well ... I'm not really prepared to tell you that.'

'Of course not,' said Dan smoothly, though his smile showed that Carmichael's bluster had been as good as an affirmation. Uncrossing his legs he said, 'If it *was* Annie O'Donnell who came to you, then the reason for this whole line of questioning suddenly becomes much clearer.'

'Oh?' said Carmichael in a neutral voice. 'And why is that?'

'Because Stephanie ... Peele I think her name is, and Annie O'Donnell attended my first meeting a week ago. It was obvious to me then that Stephanie had ... problems, shall we say? It sounds dramatic to call her mentally disturbed, but she was obviously suffering from some form of neurosis. She was hyperactive, over-bearing; she appeared to be desperately searching for something – an identity, a niche in life maybe. My first meeting was intended as a light-hearted introduction. I performed some magic tricks, illusions; I thought it would be dramatic and interesting. Most people seemed to take it in the right spirit, but Annie objected to it for some reason – I don't think it was quite what she expected – and besides she was not well. Physically, I mean, not mentally.

'However, it was Stephanie's reaction that was most astonishing. She treated me as if I'd performed miracles, insisted that I was some kind of guru. I tried to dissuade her from these notions of course, but she was immovable. She began to follow me around, begging for guidance, worshipping me in a most embarrassing fashion. She disrupted Crack meetings. It was obvious she was neglecting herself physically. Her ramblings became more and more incoherent, her demands more and more outrageous. Eventually I became annoyed. I shouted at her, told her to pull herself together, seek help. That was four days ago. She went away and I haven't seen her since. If there are rumours circulating about The Crack, then it's probably she who's spreading them. Either her or her room-mate, Annie, in the mistaken belief that I've abducted Stephanie, or been responsible for her breakdown in some way.'

He ended his explanation with a small shrug. It had been related calmly and precisely, supplemented by neither hand nor body gestures. His quiet confidence suggested a lack of guile. If he lied, he did it very well. Hunt sat back with a sigh. Carmichael still sat hunched forward, looking intently at Dan. Eventually he said, 'If you knew that Stephanie was ill, why didn't you tell someone?

274

Why did you simply allow her to follow you around? Why did you ignore her worsening condition?'

Dan looked up at the window. He neither squinted nor even blinked as the sun suddenly shed its haze of clouds and masked his face with light. The pile of essays became luminous again. Dust writhed like infinitesimal floating larvae.

'Because it's easy to be wise after the event,' he said. 'I didn't immediately know the extent of her neurosis. I thought perhaps gentle persuasion would bring her round, then perhaps that anger expressed on my part would snap her out of it. I realise, as a psychology student, I should have given more thought to the situation. But putting theory into practice is not so easy when you find yourself the object of an obsession.'

'Where's this girl now, Paul?' asked Hunt. He was fiddling with a pipe which he had taken from his pocket.

Carmichael shrugged. 'No one knows. Apparently her room-mate hasn't seen her since Friday.'

Hunt looked thoughtful. He tapped the stem of the pipe against his teeth. The silence was broken by Dan who asked calmly, 'May I go now? I have work to do.'

Hunt seemed about to acquiesce, but Carmichael said quickly, 'Not just yet, Dan. Tell us about The Crack first.'

Dan spread his hands. 'There's nothing much *to* tell. It's a discussion and debating society. We have no sinister secrets.'

'So all these claims I've put to you concerning The Crack's activities are completely without foundation?'

'Absolutely. I can't really believe that anyone could seriously think otherwise.'

It was difficult to tell if the comment was intended snidely. Carmichael asked, 'And if I wanted a list of members, you'd give me one?'

'Of course,' said Dan. 'Better still, why don't you come to a meeting and see for yourself? You too, Dr Hunt. You'd be most welcome.'

Surprised by the offer, Hunt stammered, 'Well, I ... er ... I don't – '

'Thank you, Dan,' Carmichael interrupted. 'That would be most interesting. Wouldn't it, John?'

'Er ... yes ... yes, of course,' Hunt said heavily.

'That's settled then,' Carmichael replied. 'Just give us the time and the place, Dan. We'll be there.'

'Guinevere Hall, room forty-six. Tomorrow night, nine p.m.,' Dan replied without hesitation.

'Right,' said Carmichael. 'See you then.'

Latcher was allowed to leave. He did so unhurriedly.

'Well, John,' said Carmichael when the door had closed behind Latcher's gangly frame, 'what did you think?'

Hunt considered for a moment. 'It all sounded very convincing, didn't it? But ... ' He tailed off, grimacing to show he wasn't entirely happy.

Carmichael nodded. 'That's the way I felt too. He was very glib, very open, but he was ... I don't know ... too perfect, I suppose. He had an answer for everything. It was one rational explanation after another. There were times when I felt he was reciting lines like an actor in an audition.'

Now it was Hunt's turn to nod. 'I agree. His manner was a little peculiar. He was so ... so *still*. I haven't taught him that often, but I seem to remember him being a little more animated than that.'

Carmichael stretched as though he'd been dozing, and stood up. 'Ah well. Tomorrow night should be an enlightening one for us both.'

Hunt took a worn leather tobacco pouch from his pocket and began to fill his pipe. 'Ah, yes. Thank you, Paul, for roping me in on that one.'

Carmichael grinned. 'My pleasure.' He moved to the door, but paused with his hand on the handle. 'Apart from Dan's manner, did anything else strike you about him? I mean ... I don't know ... was there anything that made you feel uncomfortable? Anything at all?'

Hunt looked a little alarmed, as if he'd suddenly discovered that Carmichael had access to his secret thoughts. 'Well, yes,' he replied. 'As a matter of fact ... ' He snorted, gave a sharp unconvincing laugh and shook his head.

'What?' Carmichael prompted. He let go of the door handle and took a step back into the room. 'What were you going to say?'

Hunt looked more than a little embarrassed. 'It sounds rather silly. I'm probably mistaken.'

Carmichael shrugged. 'Tell me anyway. I won't laugh. You've roused my curiosity.'

'Well, I may be wrong about this, but I always thought Dan's colouring was dark. Dark hair, very dark brown eyes.'

'So?' said Carmichael.

'Well, didn't you notice? His eyes were still brown, but they were pale, very light. When the sun caught them they seemed almost yellow. Yellow as ... as a lizard's eyes. Yellow as a snake's.'

49

Smelling of ink and fresh paper, political fiction magazine, *Wargasm Words,* hit the news stands on Tuesday morning. Even as Dan Latcher was explaining his recent behaviour to Hunt and Carmichael, people were reading his story and being changed by it.

One such person, Warren Royle, would never have believed this was a day for revelation. When he crawled out of bed sometime between nine and ten, his mood and his life seemed as dreary as the slate roofs he could see from the window of his attic bedsit. The sky pressed down like a scowling bully, threatening to crush the egg-box houses and shoe-box tenements. People, either on foot or in cars, threaded through the grey maze of streets, living lives of directionless bustle.

Royle felt grotty – aching limbs, sour mouth, woolly head – and this without the dubious benefit of either tobacco or alcohol. It was life that was weighing him down, though not life per se; it was the constant rejections, each one like a separate pound of flesh, another knife-thrust, another bruise to his already bludgeoned ego. How long ago since he'd left drama school? Two years this month, wasn't it? Happy Anniversary. And how many parts had he auditioned for? Seventy? Eighty? And how many had he got? One: an extra in a four-week run of *Pirates of Penzance* in some draughty, smelly shithole in Romford.

Sometimes Royle felt like packing it all in, leaving London and going back to Manchester. He'd left drama school with a six-month target: to have earned his Equity card and at least something of a favourable reputation for himself. But so far he had achieved neither of these objectives; winning the pools seemed a more likely possibility. He'd give himself six more months, he decided (at eighteen months he'd said the same). Six more months. Make or break. If there was still nothing doing, he'd admit defeat, call it a day.

He took his time eating his breakfast. The radio filled his bedsit with desperate cheer. The bank statement he received through the post did not make pleasant reading; the glossy brochure announcing his eligibility for a !!GRAND PRIZE DRAW!! to win a trip to Bermuda if he spent a fortune on double-glazing was like a joke that someone was playing on him.

In the bathroom mirror he amused himself by pulling faces. He had a high forehead and narrow features. He would never play Rambo, but then who wanted to? Without his spectacles he could look like a student or even a schoolboy, he convinced himself; with them he could look like a scholar or a Nazi commandant.

'Warren Royle has a unique gift,' he announced to his reflection, using his toothbrush as a makeshift microphone. 'He is a man of many faces. He has the ability actually to *become* the characters he plays so that nothing of the actor remains. His portraits are chilling in their accuracy, thoroughly convincing. Royle is a prodigious talent, a giant, a role model for future generations.'

Twenty minutes later he was trudging through the grey rubbish-strewn streets of Tottenham, en route to his fortnightly obligation at the unemployment benefit office.

The place was as depressing as ever, full of the desperate and the deranged, the resigned and the resentful — and that was just the staff. Royle signed on the dotted line, startled the beleaguered girl behind the counter with a smile, and left, sidestepping a gaunt man with fuzzy blue tattoos on his neck and hands, who was sprawled on the steps outside, haranguing the world in a wet mumble.

Royle had a little under three pounds in his pocket (heady days indeed, he thought), which he intended to spend on food and literature. He did so; he bought a carton of milk, some soup, bread and cheese, a *Guardian* and a copy of *Wargasm Words,* whose fierce anti-Thatcher stand always cheered him up immensely.

Royle considered himself an optimist. True, he woke each morning feeling desperate, but deep in his heart he felt certain that his current situation could not last forever. The bad days were being peeled from the calendar one by one. If he could endure them he was certain that eventually, probably dramatically, his luck would change. He *would* be an actor because he couldn't see himself being anything else. His few friends supported him; his sister, Jo, was behind him all the way; but most of all, he sustained himself with a combination of pig-headed belief, unwavering hope, and a fierce, sometimes cruel humour which he kept from turning to bitterness by his ability to direct it inward, laugh at himself.

Back in his bedsit he put the kettle on, stuck Bach on the turntable and settled down to read his paper. He sipped lemon tea as he devoured the latest on Eastern Europe; the situation there had changed dramatically over the last twelve months and was still changing. After the politics he read the theatre, film and book reviews, then glanced at the letters page and the sports section. Manchester City had lost a cup match last night he noticed with a flicker of annoyance. As a boy he'd stood on a milk crate on the Maine Road terraces with his father beside him. They'd stopped going when the hooligan problem got bad. He supposed that was when he and his father had finally drifted away from each other. He tried to recall some of the things he and his father had talked about on the drive to and from the ground, some of the triumphs they'd shared when City had been at their height. He found that he couldn't; his only clear memory was of looking forward to the oxtail soup his father always brought in a thermos flask for half-time. Nowadays, on the rare occasions that he went home, his father's strained civility managed to last for approximately a day before he was provoking Royle with phrases like 'waster' and 'scrounger'.

He stretched his *Guardian*-reading and tea-drinking to lunchtime when he made himself a boiled egg on toast. He watched the news and *Neighbours* (his guilty secret), then ate a banana and opened the magazine he'd bought. He read the Editorial (the first 'i' was a mushroom cloud with a smiley face above it) which, as always, was hilariously biting. It was about the PM's visit to the *Coronation Street* set, which she believed would put her in touch with the man-in-the-street.

After the editorial he read the contents page, then flipped through until he came to a story entitled 'The Temptation' by someone he'd never heard of: Dan Latcher. He didn't know why he felt an urge to read this story first. The title, or the name, or something, had leaped out at him from the page, demanding attention. He began to read, and was instantly entranced. The story sucked him in as voraciously and unexpectedly as a sea monster rearing from a small boy's plastic bucket on a beach. *He* was the traveller in the story, drawing light to him. *He* was the only brightness in a dismal world. *He* was the core, the nucleus, the central spindle around which all else revolved.

He put the story aside, feeling something had changed irrevocably inside him. It was as if a rock or a lid had shifted somewhere and the real Warren Royle had emerged from underneath, a creature of light and knowledge and purpose. His life so far had been nothing but a pupal stage; the story he had just read had, with shocking suddenness, somehow stimulated the dormant part of him into wakefulness, had pulled him from the cage, or more specifically from the womb. Yes, that was what it felt like: a re-birth, a shedding of his old skin. He was a butterfly rising in splendour from the cocoon and spreading its wings; a Phoenix, golden and magnificent, ascending from the ashes.

He walked about the room and felt he was floating. This place, these things, no longer seemed part of him. He was equipped with a

279

knowledge and a direction which he knew instinctively only travel, putting moving miles behind him, could satisfy. He had somewhere to go. There was a place for him. When he got there he would know he was right.

He took little with him when he left: his stoutest shoes, his cheque book, rail card and bus pass. He shrugged into his leather jacket and away he went, and soon his long striding feet were eating the miles, taking him on a journey both certain and uncertain. The magazine stayed behind, pages open at 'The Temptation', like a man-trap poised to spring its jaws on an unwary ankle. Royle did not need the story, he knew it already. One reading and he could quote from it as surely as any religious man could quote the Holy Word.

50

After their three-thirty lecture, Ian and Annie stayed behind to talk to Carmichael again.

'Well?' Ian said, pulling up a chair and sitting down. 'How did you get on? Did he show up?'

'Yes,' Carmichael replied, 'he showed up. In fact we had quite a chat.'

'You mean you actually *spoke* to him? Face to face?' said Annie.

'Oh, yes.'

'What was he like? Weird? Did he try to hypnotise you or anything?'

Carmichael did not immediately reply. He leaned back in his chair and regarded Annie for a moment.

'No,' he said, 'he didn't try to hypnotise me, and I wouldn't really describe him as weird. He was . . . a little strange. A little unsettling. He answered our questions politely and confidently, though carefully too. He was quite open about The Crack.'

'*Really?*' Annie exclaimed. 'You mean he admitted everything? Where's Steph? Did he tell you?'

'Ah . . . well, actually, the account that he gave me was very different to the one that you gave me.' He told them what Latcher had said about The Crack being a debating society and about how Annie and Steph had over-reacted to him initially.

Annie looked at Ian, dumbfounded. Her mouth hung open, soundless, for a few moments, then she spluttered, 'But ... but that's rubbish! It's a pack of lies! You surely didn't believe him?'

Carmichael just looked at her

'You *did* believe him, didn't you?' Ian said. 'How could you believe a story like that? Annie's not a liar. And you said yourself that Latcher was a creep.'

'I don't think "creep" was quite the word I used, Ian.'

'Well, whatever ... '

'And as to who I believe, well, I'm doing my best to keep my options open. Admittedly Annie's story is harder to take because it's more ... let's say, fanciful.'

'Aw, you can't — '

'Please! Let me finish.' Carmichael lowered the hand he had raised only when he was satisfied they wouldn't interrupt him. 'That's better. Now, as I was saying, Annie's story was more way out, more far-fetched than Latcher's. However, my gut reaction is to believe her because she strikes me as being completely sincere. She's genuinely concerned about her friend and genuinely afraid of Latcher and his society. Now, unless this is all an act, which I'm fairly sure it's not, I believe her account of the situation, as she saw it, was truthful.

'Latcher, on the other hand, gave a more down-to-earth explanation, but he struck Dr Hunt and I as being rather glib, rather insincere. We both agreed he was like an actor who had learned his lines well but didn't quite carry the conviction to deliver them. His reactions were ... calculated. Nothing surprised him, nothing fazed him. However, having said that, he did not deflect our questions about The Crack. He seemed quite happy to provide us with a list of members and he even invited us to a meeting tomorrow night which both Dr Hunt and I will attend.' Carmichael spread his hands. 'And as far as I'm concerned, there the matter rests, at least until tomorrow. We can do no more than be vigilant. Latcher now knows that we are aware of him and that he and his group are under observation. Tutors will be instructed to keep an eye on "problem" students, and any who are exhibiting the same symptoms that Steph is showing will be investigated in relation to The Crack.'

There was silence for a few moments, during which Ian and Annie digested all this information. Ian did not look entirely happy. He

281

said, 'But what about Steph herself? Are there no plans to look for her?'

Carmichael shrugged. 'What sort of plans would you suggest?'

'Well ... I don't know. Call the police in, I suppose. Make Latcher tell them where she is.'

'But according to Latcher he doesn't know. He says he hasn't seen her for four days.'

'He's lying,' said Ian.

'We've got no evidence to support that.'

'We've seen Steph. We've heard from Annie what happened to her at that meeting. That's all the evidence *I* need.'

'Look,' Annie added, 'even if Latcher *is* telling the truth, which he isn't, shouldn't we still call the police? I mean, if Steph's had a breakdown and nobody knows where she is, she could be in danger, couldn't she? None of us has seen her for four days and even then she was in a real state. It was obvious she hadn't eaten, slept or washed for a while, and when she left she didn't take anything with her — no clothes, no belongings, I don't think she even had a coat. Given these circumstances, surely the matter is serious enough to bring the police in? In fact, I think we should have done it sooner. We've been putting it off too long.'

This was a long speech for her and when she subsided her face was a little flushed. Ian looked at her thoughtfully, fingering the bruised flesh around his eye.

'She's right,' he said to Carmichael, 'we should have called the police before. We're not getting anywhere trying to deal with this ourselves, and Steph could be in real danger.'

Carmichael considered for a moment, then nodded. 'Okay. The Chancellor won't like it — bad for the University's image and all that — but he doesn't have to know, does he?' He stood up. 'Come on, I'll run you down to Maybury. You don't have any more lectures today, do you?'

Ian and Annie both shook their heads. They looked pensive now that the oft-suggested police involvement was about to become reality.

'Could Neil Gardener come with us?' Ian asked as they walked along the corridor.

'Who?'

'Neil Gardener. He's Steph's boyfriend.'

'Certainly. I assume the police will want to speak to him too. Does he live in?'

'Yes. Mordred Hall.'

'Fine. We'll pick him up on the way.'

51

She must be quite a woman to keep Stu from rugby training, thought Freddy Marshall, reaching the penultimate floor of Mordred Hall. He examined himself critically in the glass door that led stairwell to corridor: he liked looking at himself because he considered himself a handsome bastard, the spitting image of Sidney Poitier in his younger days. He was known as Silks because of his penchant for wearing execrably loud silk shirts with ties to match. Tonight's ensemble consisted of an orange shirt with blue cufflinks complemented by a blue tie with orange pin.

Freddy, you're a Mean Machine, he told himself, then pushed open the glass door, his reflection swinging away from him. To his left an open door revealed a room in which a bunch of guys he knew were drinking beer and watching *Bilko*.

'Hey, Freddy!' one of them shouted in greeting.

Freddy clenched his fist in the air like a triumphant boxer.

'Nice shirt, Silks. You look like a satsuma,' someone else yelled.

'Fuck you, shithead,' Freddy responded, grinning, and turned right.

Stu's room was through a fire door and down two steps. The heavy door cut out eighty per cent of the sound from the *Bilko* mob. Freddy knocked on Stu's closed door. 'Hey, Stu, you there? You coming to this party or what?'

There was no reply. Freddy shrugged and turned away. He had put out his hand to the fire door again when a faint voice croaked, 'Who's that?'

Freddy turned back. 'It's fucking Santa Claus, who do you think? There's a bus in ten minutes. You coming?'

'No,' the voice rasped, 'no, I can't. You go, Fred. I'll ... I'll see you.'

Freddy lingered. Stu sounded funny. 'Hey, Stu, you okay?' he asked.

He heard a strange scraping noise. It made Freddy think of some heavy object being dragged across a carpet of sandpaper. Instinctively he took a step back from the door. Stu's voice came again.

'Yeah, yeah, I'll be fine,' he said. 'You'd better go, Fred. Fuck one for me, eh?'

'Sure thing,' Freddy said. 'What you got? 'Flu or something?'

This time he heard a stertorous wheeze, obviously intended as a laugh. 'Yeah, that's right, Fred. Just a touch of the fucking 'flu.'

That strange chitinous scraping again, this time moving away from the door. Freddy couldn't imagine anything that made a noise like that. Intrigued and disquieted, he knelt and put his eye to Stu's keyhole. He saw the corner of Stu's bed, a block of bilious carpet; then something bulky, milk-white, edging sluggishly into the frame and lowering itself on to the bed.

What the fuck *was* that thing? Freddy stared, but could make no sense of its physiology. Then it shifted a little, sat upright. The shiny white lump which he had taken to be some sort of sac or tumour was revealed as a head, now raised.

Freddy made a sound, somewhere between squeal, gasp and expletive. The thing, he realised, was Stu, but it was a Stu much changed from the one Freddy knew and loved. This Stu was naked and completely hairless — he didn't even have eyebrows. His skin, or suit, or whatever, was albino-white, a scaly bleached carapace. The flesh had split in several places, revealing pinky-red meat, but no blood. It didn't occur to Freddy that the wounds were self-inflicted until he saw Stu lower a piece of broken glass to his white stomach and slice it into a gaping salmon-pink flap.

Freddy fell against the door as his legs buckled under him. He shouted something before his own fear sucked the air from his throat. He could still see the thing in the room. Now it looked directly at the door — at *him* — and he saw that its eyes were flat and black with no whites whatsoever. It pushed itself slowly up from the bed, dropping the shard of glass, and began to shuffle across the floor towards him. It grew larger in his vision. Its new wound opened and closed like a flapping mouth, secreting a trickle of colourless ooze. Freddy fell away from the door, scrambled sideways like a crab and managed to get to his feet. He lost a cuff-link but didn't care. He hit the fire door as though thrown against it. Behind him the door to Stu's room rattled and began to open. As he ran for the stairs, Freddy heard the guys along the corridor laughing at *Bilko*.

52

Neil had been back from Maybury for no more than twenty minutes when he received a call from Emma to say that Dan was home. Now he was sitting on a number 44 bus, feeling a combination of shame, nervousness and cold anger. He stared beyond his jolting reflection in the grimy glass at a world which resembled Picasso's blue period. Fields, buildings, flowers, trees, even people, were painted by twilight. Here and there lighted windows punctured the gloom, phantom sitting rooms just discernible behind gauzy lace curtains. Neil felt as if both muscle and emotion were coiled in his body, threatening to erupt.

He wondered how much of his inner agitation was apparent to his fellow passengers. He looked around, but eyes were either staring fixedly ahead or flitting through columns of newsprint. Beside him a shapeless, dough-faced woman with a shopping trolley glared at the scaly pate of an old man. A couple in denim smooched and giggled; a small boy wearing a *Ghostbusters* t-shirt poked at the glass and asked, 'What's that, Mummy?' of a woman to whom it appeared he was invisible.

After a weekend and a day of frustrating inaction, it seemed to Neil that wheels had suddenly and thankfully begun to turn. First Ian, Annie and their English Lit. lecturer, Carmichael, had appeared with the news that they were finally going to the police with the story of Steph's disappearance. The drive to Maybury had been tense; no one had spoken much. At the station − a small cream-coloured building tucked rather cosily between the library and a pub called The Round Table − the four of them had spoken to a Chief Inspector Kaye.

Though Maybury was a sleepy, genteel market town, Kaye projected the persona of a hard-bitten, overburdened city cop. He was fiftyish, tall and broad-chested, a trifle overweight. There was little humour in the taut lines of his square face. His grey eyes stared at whoever was talking to him, be it victim or oppressor, with a disconcerting cynicism. His receding hair gleamed with Brylcream. He wore his shirt with the top button undone and his tie a little loose. Watching him in action, Neil surmised that he was an avid viewer of *Hill Street Blues* re-runs.

Kaye listened to their story in world-weary silence, his tongue probing at the gaps between his teeth like a mollusc looking for food. When they had done he dismissively suggested that Steph was visiting her parents or was staying with a boyfriend, a theory which Neil hotly refuted. Kaye seemed unimpressed by their protests, though in the end reluctantly agreed to send someone to the University in the morning 'to look into the matter'. His jotting down of personal details seemed perfunctory, a task performed merely to placate them. However Neil drew a little comfort from the fact that Kaye required a photograph of the '*allegedly* missing person'.

'We may need to circulate it should this enquiry lead anywhere,' he offered grudgingly.

'And what about Latcher?' Ian asked.

'The supposed *kidnapper*?' Kaye muttered, turning his discomforting stare on Ian. 'What about him?'

'Well . . . he'll need to be questioned too, won't he?'

'Will he indeed? Thank you for your invaluable advice.'

Ian shrugged, blushing furiously. 'Sorry,' he mumbled. His apology lingered, unacknowledged.

When they left the station, Neil was sweating, his stomach churning like a washing machine. His anger felt like bands of steel tightening around his intestines, his forehead, his throat.

That had been almost an hour ago, and still the anger remained. Neil was hoping he could use it to his advantage, turn it against Latcher, though for the moment it was still directed at Kaye. Who did that bastard think he was anyway? What right did he have to treat them like that? Jumped-up little nobody, he ought to be reported. Neil's silent rage barely smothered the shame which he felt for breaking his word, withholding from Ian and Annie the news that Dan was home.

Emma had tried ringing Ian first, she informed Neil, but the person who took the message had returned with the news that he was not in his room. Neil lied that he didn't know where Ian and Annie were, whereas in fact they had gone to the dining hall immediately upon returning whilst Neil had come straight to his room, too uptight to eat. Receiving Emma's phone call had tossed him on to the horns of a dilemma. He was itching to get at Dan, but he knew that if Ian was told the news he would recommend a cautious approach. He might even suggest they inform the police and let them deal with the situation.

Ashamed as he was of his own betrayal, Neil knew he could not allow that to happen. He *had* to see Dan. The thought of what that bastard was doing to Steph was twisting him up inside. He was not a violent person, though he never shied away from trouble, but these last few days he had felt like lashing out at everybody. He could feel his heart pounding as his contained rage and the prospect of

286

a showdown flooded his system with adrenalin. He leaned forward in his seat. The bus rattled unhurriedly along.

Following Emma's directions, Neil disembarked outside the Safeway supermarket in Royston and turned right. The glass-fronted supermarket showed him a dozen checkout queues peopled largely with twenty-year-olds, many of whom sported leather jackets and trendy haircuts – proof, if any were needed, that Royston was the town's student district. Neil passed a row of shops – a greengrocer's, video store, newsagent's, stationer's, drycleaner's, photographer's, baker's and bookshop. He waited at a pedestrian crossing for what seemed an age, then crossed to pass more shops – a clutch of takeaways, an optician's, a bank, a wholefood store and a chemist. After a couple of streets Royston's trading district gave way to more sombre surroundings – Victorian houses set back from the road, once rather grand but now converted into flats or, in one or two cases, old people's homes. It was in this maze of streets that Neil became lost and had to ask directions. Eventually he found Cramer Road, by which time the looming Victorian edifices had transmuted into back-to-back terraces, some lovingly maintained, others having fallen into dismal disrepair.

Number 42 was somewhere in between: obviously a student house, though owned by a landlord who, it seemed, was conscientious enough to renovate the place perhaps once every few years. Neil approached, sidestepping a Kentucky Fried Chicken box which the wind sent bowling towards him along the pavement. He could see lights on in the house. Upstairs the curtains were open and the room brightly lit. In the downstairs room, behind thick curtains drawn tight, he saw a glimmer of illumination, perhaps the suggestion of a lamp.

Crabs crawling and scuttling in his stomach, anger enclosing his throat like rubber, he strode to the front door and knocked. Emma answered it wide-eyed, as though just roused from sleep. She glanced beyond Neil, then asked, 'Is there only you? Where're Ian and Annie?'

'Couldn't find them. Sorry,' he said quickly, and stepped into the house. 'Is he still here?' He looked around as though half-inclined to believe that Dan was standing in the narrow hallway and he had somehow missed him.

'Yes,' Emma said. 'But, shhh. He's in there. That's his room.' She pointed to the door at the end of the hallway.

'Right,' said Neil, and started forward.

'What are you going to do?' Emma hissed, grabbing his arm.

'Speak to him, that's all. Don't worry.' Neil gently but firmly disengaged Emma's fingers.

Unaware that he and Emma were re-enacting a scene which a few days before had involved Nev and Catriona, Neil strode to Dan's door and knocked firmly.

'Latcher, are you in there?' he said. 'This is Neil Gardener, Steph Peele's boyfriend. I want to talk to you.'

Immediately a voice floated from beyond the door. 'Certainly,' it said. 'Come right in.'

Neil looked at Emma, the surprise plain on his face. At the very least he had expected evasiveness from Dan, if not outright resistance. For a few seconds he simply stood, not knowing what to do. He felt as though he had lost a little of his momentum, and struggled to regain it. He cleared his throat, muttered, 'Er ... right,' and shoved the door open a little too aggressively.

Immediately he turned his head aside, blinded by a desk lamp which shone full in his face. Emma put her hand on his shoulder, presumably to prevent him from backing into her. Neil blinked, but could not shift the after-image that the lamp's glare had caused, a green glowing stain on his retina. Emma said, 'Dan, do you mind?', a slight waver undermining the casual annoyance she was trying to instil into her voice.

Dan, wherever he was, did not respond. For a few moments the two of them simply stood there, Neil still trying to blink his sight back to normal, Emma just behind him, her hand on his shoulder. Gradually the green amoeba faded from Neil's vision and he raised his head, shielding his eyes as he peered in the direction of the lamp.

'Latcher, are you there?' he said. 'If you are, turn that fucking thing off so we can see you.'

Still no answer. Neil muttered, 'Arsehole,' then turned back to Emma and asked, 'Where's the light switch?'

By way of reply, she turned, stretched out an arm and pressed down on a switch by the door. Neil heard the click, but nothing happened. The bulb was dead — or Dan had removed it.

'Fuck,' Neil muttered and grabbed the edge of the door, intending to throw it open and allow light from the hallway to flood into the room. But to his astonishment the door did not move. And then it *did* begin to move, but the wrong way.

'Hey!' Neil shouted, both hands tight around the handle, straining backwards in an attempt to keep the door from closing. 'Hey, who's doing this? Let go!'

'What's wrong?' Emma asked, her voice rising in alarm.

'The bloody door. Someone's pulling it from the other side. I can't ... do anything ... to stop it.'

He dug his heels into the carpet, clenched his teeth and employed every muscle in his body, but still the door continued to close. It did so slowly, inexorably, as though hydraulically powered. Now it was open no more than twelve inches. Now ten. Now eight. Now six.

'Open it!' Emma screamed as though Neil was playing a joke on her.

'Help me then!' he yelled back. 'Grab my waist!'

Emma did so. They heaved together.

Four inches.

Two.

The door closed with a neat snap.

'Shit!' Neil said. He let go of the handle, his palms feeling bruised, his muscles quivering with effort. 'Shit, shit, shit!' He kicked the door, but it made no odds. It would have disturbed him to have learnt that four days previously, Nev's assault had left this self-same door splintered, the entire lock, handle and all, on the floor. Neil would have wondered how the door could now be so miraculously restored. He would not have found the answer acceptable.

He swung back to face the glare of the desk-lamp again. He did not know whether Dan was sitting behind it, but it was the only focus, the only thing to address.

'Who the fuck do you think you are?' he stormed. 'You don't scare me with your stupid games, you pathetic piece of shit!'

He strode across the room into the shadows. As he drew closer to the lamp he saw that there was indeed someone sitting behind it.

When he was near enough, he reached out, grabbed the lamp and turned it round. 'Let's see how you fucking like it,' he snarled.

In the instant before shock caused him to drop the lamp, he saw that the seated figure was not Dan Latcher after all. Emma, a few hesitant steps behind him, saw this too. Her screams were shrill and piercing. Neil heard her run towards the door, crash into something and fall, her screams degenerating into sobs both of panic and pain. He stumbled back towards her, his limbs like paper which was crumpling beneath the weight of his body. He found Emma, crouched down and put his arms around her. The desk-lamp lay on its side on the floor, its beam illuminating the scuffed boots of the seated figure.

Though he had never met him, Neil assumed that the figure was the missing Nev. He was quite spectacularly dead. His face was the most horrendous sight Neil had ever seen. His denim shirt had been soaked with blood, which was not surprising considering his injuries.

289

The bottom half of his face had been ripped from the bone, creating an undeniably misleading impression that he had enjoyed his demise. His teeth grinned wide and white through drooling red musculature. Furthermore his eyes had been removed and tightly crumpled balls of paper inserted into the sockets. As a final touch a name had been carved on his forehead, half-hidden by blood-sticky strands of hair. It was a name that meant nothing to Neil, though would soon enough.

The name was 'Larry'.

Emma was wriggling and mumbling and crying beneath Neil's embrace. He hugged her harder, as though he could smother her terror, douse it. 'Shh,' he said, 'shh. It's all right,' though he knew it was not. He wondered whether the madman who had butchered Nev was with them in the room, watching from the shadows, enjoying their panic. As his fragmented thoughts reassembled, he slowly made an awful connection: Nev, Latcher, Steph.

'Jesus, no,' he half-sobbed and squeezed his eyes tight shut as though that could crush the thought. But it would not go away. It gnawed at him like a tumour, eating him from the inside. He felt so desperate, so helpless; he thought the intensity of his anguish would cause his brain to burst. 'Come on,' he said to Emma, 'we've got to move.' He tried to drag her to her feet, but she frantically resisted, her impulse being to remain curled into a weeping foetal ball.

Deciding to leave her for the moment, Neil stood up and looked around. The lamp lay half-under the desk behind which Nev sat, its light mostly blocked by the desk's underside. Neil was thankful for that small mercy. He was afraid that a second look at that eyeless, falsely grinning face might snap the single thread of coherent thought to which he felt he was clinging. For the time being at least he could function; survival, anger and his desperate concern for Steph kept him going.

The lamp, shaded though it was, did however provide some illumination. It separated one shadow from the next, gave each its own shape, its own definition. This collection of shadows became recognisable as particular objects, albeit characterless ones. Here on Neil's left was a wardrobe, on the right a bed (it was the jut of the bedside table which Emma had tripped over). Directly before him was the desk, upon it a typewriter, Nev sitting behind it like a black paper cut-out wearing blue jeans and scuffed Doc Marten boots. Beside the desk was a waste-paper basket, balls of what looked like crumpled paper lying around it. Behind Nev's corpse was the window, discernible only by the slight undulation of the thick curtains and the minutest glimmer of orange soaking through

290

from the street lamps outside. At least, thought Neil, Nev's killer (he could only think it was Latcher) was not in the room. Or, if he was, he was hiding, in which case the bed and the wardrobe were the places to be wary of.

Loath though he was to approach the corpse again, Neil did so. He would have to stand right beside it, perhaps even push it out of the way, if they were going to escape via the window, which seemed to be their only alternative. But his trepidation was not centred wholly on the corpse. He eyed the dark bulks of bed and wardrobe, wondering which, if any, Latcher was using as a hiding place. If it was the wardrobe, then he might burst out of it as Neil passed by, murder weapon in hand. If it was the bed, what was to stop Latcher from slashing out at Neil's ankles? An axe could sever his feet if swung viciously enough. Even a small kitchen knife could slice through tendons.

Neil hovered for a moment, then moved forward, deciding to keep tight by the wardrobe. That way he could hold it closed, prevent Dan from surprising him. And if Dan *was* under the bed, he surely could not reach Neil from this distance. Neil was very aware of his body, sensitive to its heat, its life, its frailty, its potential for pain, as he inched towards the desk.

However he reached the desk without incident, his heart thumping. The room was silent save for Emma's sobs, though it seemed a silence pregnant with threat. Neil's glance shifted rapidly from corpse to bed to wardrobe. He tried to quell his paranoia, but felt it galloping through him like fever. He kept imagining glimpsed movement at the periphery of his vision, but whenever he swung towards it he saw only a collage of motionless shadow, black on grey on black. When he turned away from the corpse he felt certain it was coming stealthily to life. He sensed its head turning slowly towards him, its arm inching across the desk. Stop it, he urged himself, stop it. Nothing can hurt you in here. Normally pragmatic, he felt he was barely holding himself together, felt an urge to run in circles, flailing and screaming, to back into a corner and try to huddle himself out of existence.

Before rounding the desk he paused for a few moments and took some deep breaths. It didn't help much; indeed, it only served to plant another seed of paranoia in his mind. What if Dan was standing behind the curtains? In fact, now he came to think of it, it seemed a more likely hiding place than either wardrobe or bed. By having the door closed, Dan had left them only one possible escape route. It was inevitable that at some stage they would try the window. The corpse of Nev may have been placed there so that Neil would be distracted by its proximity. Neil pictured himself pulling the curtain aside whilst eyeing the corpse, Dan stepping from behind it, axe raised, and then ... WHACK! Diced Gardener.

He shuddered.

So what, he thought, can we do? He felt trapped, hemmed in by his own imagination. If he had a stick or something he could open the curtains from afar *and* he would have a weapon in his hand. He looked around but nothing presented itself. If this was his own room, back in Starmouth, there would be a snooker cue standing in the corner.

Never in his life had Neil felt so incapable. He simply stood, clueless as to his next move. In the centre of the floor, Emma still sobbed, hunched body heaving. Neil frowned. She seemed somehow ... different from before, and indeed, now he looked around, the entire room seemed to have changed subtly. For a moment he couldn't work out what it was that had altered. He put his hand out to the edge of the desk as though afraid he might faint. However the desk-top was higher than he remembered it; it was parallel with his navel, and not his thigh as he had thought. He looked at Emma again. She appeared to be on an upward slope; he no longer had to lower his gaze to see her. Mystified, he looked down at his feet. They were below the floor which appeared insubstantial. He was sinking, as though in quicksand, though there was no sensation of doing so. He saw the floor as a faint line, like a projected film image, reaching just below his knees.

Panic-stricken he tried to wade forward, but found he could not. The room had become a ghost, and he was being squeezed from it like a chunk of foreign matter. But still there was no impression of sinking. The floor-level continued to rise up his body like water flooding a punctured ship. Now Emma was parallel with his head: the desk and Nev's corpse loomed above him to his left. The wardrobe was a cliff, the bed a high plateau. When the floor level reached his eyes he experienced an instant of blackness, then the room was above him.

He craned his neck as he watched it recede, feeling like a hot air balloonist left behind on the ground. For the moment he felt no real terror; he was too astounded by the impossibility of what he was witnessing to feel anything more than numb shock. The room was little more than postage-stamp size now, Emma's body a tiny insect on glass. Higher it went, higher; now it was a speck of soot drifting up the chimney. In the instant before it vanished, Neil reached up as though he could pluck it back − then it was gone. Silence pressed in, grey and cool and thick as death. Neil hugged himself and looked slowly around with moon-eyes, a sleepwalker awoken.

He was in ... Starmouth. His home town. He was standing on the promenade overlooking the sea. It was night and it was still, the sky clear, the stars bright. He could hear the waves lapping gently.

He turned, faced the wide promenade with its empty tram-lines, the row of seafront shops and amusement arcades. Hotels stood proudly, balconies glinting. Beyond them, Neil knew, were boarding houses and holiday homes, street upon street of them, an interlocking grid of pastel-painted terraces.

Starmouth. He felt a shudder pass through him. He was profoundly afraid, though it was a deep-seated fear, held at bay by confusion, wonder, a fractured sense of unreality. Part of him felt relieved that he was out of that shadow-room with its aura of threat, its taste of death. Part of him rejoiced at the salt-smell of the sea, the familiar surroundings.

Starmouth. He was home. But how? Had he somehow been so scared, so desperate, that he had displaced himself? Was that possible? He shook his head, amazed he could even consider such a thing. He had never been convinced by any aspect of paranormal phenomena, though two years ago some pretty weird stuff had apparently happened to his brother, Richard, and some of his friends.

Neil sighed. He had never got the full details on that. The *official* story was that Richard and his mates had tracked down a serial killer who had then come after them. One of Richard's friends had died as a result when he and the killer toppled from a hospital window. It was a subject the Gardeners never now mentioned, a skeleton which had been thrust into a closet, the door slammed and locked.

So, what to do? A faint fishy breeze blew in from the sea, ruffling his hair. He would do what he supposed ninety-nine per cent of people would do if they found themselves in his situation. He would do what E.T. and a million pigeons would do. He would go home.

He set off, legs weak, stomach feeling as though it had been scooped out. Despite its name, Beachside was quite a trek from the seafront. It would take him a good half an hour to walk there, in which case he could do some thinking along the way. But thirty-seven minutes later, when he turned on to Cedar Grove, he was forced to admit that he was still as baffled and disturbed as ever.

The closest he could come to a rational explanation was that, like Annie and Steph, Latcher had exposed him to some form of hallucinatory gas and he was now living out a series of illusions. As explanations go, it was less than feeble, but it was all he had to cling to. If this was a dream, or an illusion, then he had no choice but to see it through to the bitter end. This theory was not reassuring; indeed it was more alarming than the impossible prospect that he might truly be home. Hallucination suggested a lack of control, a surrendering of wits. Who knows what might be happening to him in the real world while he stumbled about in this cuckoo-land?

But his street and his house *looked* real enough, and he felt skittishly alert; there was no dream-quality whatsoever to any of this. He crossed to his gate, the trees that lined the road wearing shawls of shadow in their branches. He walked up the path to the front door, pressed his finger on the doorbell. The bell rang.

He waited for someone to come, half-thinking that no one would, that here the illusion ended. He felt sick with nerves. It took him back to when he was thirteen and he had asked Jacqueline Crawford out, his first real girlfriend. He had tried telephoning her three times first, but each time he had heard her voice on the phone saying hello, his entire mouth had turned to wood and he had replaced the receiver without saying anything. When he finally plucked up the courage and did it face-to-face his prepared speech emerged all garbled – but she had still gone out with him.

The door opened. A slim, studious-looking sixteen-year-old stood there, eyes wide behind his spectacles. His mouth opened and closed before it found speech. Then he said, 'Neil! What are you doing here?'

Neil couldn't help it; he started crying. He would never have believed that the sight of his kid brother could do that to him. A detached part of him felt surprised at his sudden outpouring of emotion. He thought he'd been holding himself together pretty well considering all that he'd been through.

He tried to speak but his voice was stifled. Instead he stepped forward and flung his arms around Richard, who managed to look astonished, concerned and alarmed.

'Neil,' Richard said, voice muffled beneath his brother's embrace, 'Neil, what's wrong?'

Like clumsy dance-partners, Neil and Richard entered the house. The tears were still pouring down Neil's face, but the wadding of emotion which had blocked his throat was now clearing.

'Is Dad in?' he managed to say.

'Yeah, Mum and Dad both. They're in the sitting room. What's this all about, Neil? Why are you home? Why aren't you at University?'

Neil broke the embrace but kept an arm draped around his brother's shoulders. 'Come on,' he said. He led Richard to the sitting room door. They went in. His parents, Derek and Eileen Gardener, were watching television. They both looked up as Neil entered, surprise on their faces.

'Neil!' Eileen exclaimed as Richard had done. She put aside the *Radio Times* she'd been browsing through. 'What are you doing home?'

He wiped his face, looking apologetic. He went into the room and sat down. 'To tell you the truth, I don't know,' he said. 'I don't know how I got here.'

'Don't know?' repeated Derek. He was a tall, straight-backed man with steel grey hair and a moustache. 'What do you mean "don't know"? You must know. How can you not know something like that?'

Neil looked around. This room which he had taken for granted for so many years suddenly appeared so wonderful. He grinned despite his father's irritation, and squeezed the chair-arm, relishing its solidity, the downy feel of material beneath his palm.

'I just *appeared* here,' he said. He leaned forward, clasped his hands together. 'I was in one place and then everything went ... strange. And suddenly I was here. Or rather on the promenade. I walked back from there.'

He shrugged, feeling awkward. How could he explain what had happened to him when he didn't know himself? He looked round at his family. They were looking back at him, bemused and perhaps a little fearful. Now was the time to ask. Looking at Richard he said, 'What really happened, Rich, two years ago, when that mate of yours died? You've never told me the full story.'

Richard seemed to cringe into himself. He glanced at his father for guidance.

'I think that's all best forgotten, Neil,' Derek said firmly. 'It's all in the past now.'

Neil threw up his hands in frustration. 'But why wasn't I ever told?' he said. 'I'm part of this family too. Haven't I got a right to know?'

Eileen's hands fluttered nervously over the magazine in her lap, smoothing its cover. 'Why drag it all up again now?' she said. 'It's over. Why re-open old wounds?'

'Because I think something very similar is happening to me,' said Neil.

There was silence for a moment. Richard bowed his head while Eileen sucked in a sharp breath, her hand rising to her chest as though to cross herself. Derek said nothing. He stared implacably at his son.

Finally, in a miserable voice, Richard mumbled, 'I always thought it would come back. Every day for the past two years I've been waiting for something like this to happen.'

'Richard!' snapped Eileen as though he'd uttered an obscenity or been rude to a guest. 'Be quiet!'

Richard looked up. His eyes were blurry with tears. 'We can't ignore it,' he said. 'It won't go away if we turn our backs. Don't you realise, it's going to be with us forever.'

'Do as your mother tells you, Richard, and *be quiet*,' Derek ordered curtly. He stood up. 'I've had enough of this nonsense.' He strode stiffly from the room.

Neil watched him go, incredulous. 'I don't believe this,' he said. He turned to Richard. 'What *did* happen, Rich? I think you'd better tell me.'

'Don't you dare, Richard,' Eileen warned before her youngest son could say anything. Neil was shocked by the dangerous sparkle in her eyes, the rigid tension of her body.

Richard flapped a hand in feeble protest. 'I've got to, Mum,' he said miserably. 'Don't you see? I've ... I've got to.'

Derek reappeared in the doorway. 'Oh no you don't,' he said. He raised the revolver he was holding in his right hand and shot Richard through the back of the head.

The retort of the gun rang in Neil's ears. He saw Richard thrown forward by the impact, his face slamming into the deep shag pile of which his mother was so proud. The back of Richard's skull was a red-black crater. Neil was spattered with his brother's blood. He smelt cordite in the air; his nostrils recoiled from its harshness. Richard's hand was open, arm extended, as though he were both prostrating himself and begging, an attitude of optimum humility. Neil could see the arm of Richard's spectacles still hooked behind his ear. Blood was fanning out slowly from the place where Richard's face met the carpet like something alive oozing from a crack between two boulders. The echo of the revolver seemed to hang in the air for as long as the smoke. Eileen Gardener was nodding, looking down at her dead son with an expression of wistful piety.

'I didn't want to do that,' Derek said apologetically, 'but he gave me no choice.'

Neil simply gaped, his mind trying to cope with the impossible enormity of what he had just witnessed. His head seemed too tiny to accommodate such a vast and unbelievable truth. He stood up, his limbs like liquid, his mouth wide open as though to release a scream that was jammed deep in his throat. Black sparks danced in his head, buzzed like wasps in his vision.

Quite clearly he thought: I'm going to faint. He fought against it.

His father lowered the gun. 'I had to do that,' he said. 'You do see, don't you? It was unavoidable.'

Neil's mouth moved, but his voice was still trapped in his throat.

Eileen Gardener slid from her place on the settee and knelt beside Richard's body. To Neil's horror she leaned forward and jabbed her right index finger into the mess of splintered skull like a child dipping into a bag of sherbet. After a moment she withdrew, her finger coated and dripping with blood. Standing up, she crossed to a bare patch of wall and began to write, using finger and blood as quill and ink. The message was short – a single word; a name, in fact. When she was done, Eileen stood back and to the side as though posing for a photograph. The name she had written was:

Now Neil found his voice, though could do no more than moan incoherently. He stumbled backwards and fell down, feeling a sharp hard pain in his coccyx. He tried to stand up again, but couldn't. He shuffled backwards, away from his altered family. His mother had a vapid smile on her face as though she was still waiting for someone to take that photograph.

'It's time for the fun to end,' Derek announced, and tossed the revolver on to the settee which Neil was attempting to shelter behind. He strolled across to his wife, who raised her head to him adoringly. Without hesitation, Derek reached for her neck with both hands and snapped it as easily as if it were a twig. He stepped away from her as she collapsed to the floor. Then he turned to Neil and began to peel away his face.

Still Neil couldn't scream properly, though the pressure inside him to do so seemed enormous. His head and stomach ached with it; he felt that if his terror should spill out it might possibly tear him apart. The face that his father was stripping away looked horribly real; no latex illusion, this. A second face swelled from beneath the first – bloated, hairless, multi-chinned. Neil had the impression of a grotesque body tumbling forth, as though released by the undoing of corsets. His father's face in pieces on the floor, Neil now looked at the man who had replaced him.

He was squat, rotund and perfectly bald. When he showed his filed teeth, as he was doing now, he looked like a plump shark. His eyes were ocean-green and seemed to spit sparks which danced an instant and were gone. Derek's long limbs and broad shoulders had become stubbier, as if a gentle but irresistible pressure had been applied to the feet and the head, squashing the same amount of flesh into a shorter frame. Like a jolly magician, the man asked, 'So what do you think? Isn't my Starmouth perfect in every detail? Do you not think I deserve an award?'

Vocally, Neil had relapsed. The man's appearance had relegated him to silence once more. Nonetheless his lips parted and twisted into appropriate shapes. The man held up a hand.

'Please, don't trouble yourself. I know what you're trying to ask. My name is Peregrine Stitch, and you, Neil Gardener, are one of my players. You're the gallant young knight come to rescue the fair damsel. But you came unprepared, didn't you? You didn't reckon on a little chicanery, and now you're in rather a fix.'

With a flourish Stitch presented Neil with his open palm, which he then turned around and passed slowly in front of his face. It was the same gesture a clown might use to alter his expression, calculated to enforce the idea that each emotion is a separate mask, that there is no leeway between happy and sad, spite and adoration.

But the game this time was not so simple, for the face that Stitch revealed was one in which rain fell. Neil could see it quite clearly, through pink flesh that was stretched balloon-thin. Rain. Sheets of it. And somewhere in the man's bizarre anatomy it impacted with hard ground, producing a sputter-tick-hiss of collision.

'I am the storm,' Stitch said. When he spoke lightning arced between his teeth. 'I am the flood and the pestilence and the plague. I am legend and destiny and temptation.' He moved closer to Neil, grinning. Neil saw something squeeze out from between the bars of his teeth. A tiny serpent. And then another. And another. They fell like the rain in his face: albino-white, fanged, their tongues forked and flickering.

They zigzagged towards Neil en masse, many passing over the dead and bleeding body of his brother's simulacrum. They began spilling from Stitch's mouth dozens at a time, their squirming bodies gradually obliterating the colour of the carpet. Sick with his own helpless fear, Neil saw one last chance for salvation. Lunging forward he snatched the revolver from the settee and fired four shots at the advancing bald man.

Two went wild, one shattering glass, the other punching a hole in the wall, but the remaining two found their mark. Neil saw holes open in Stitch's stomach and in the centre of his chest, just below the flesh-cushioned throat. The bullets didn't even slow Stitch down. His advance continued, remorseless. As Neil dropped the gun the first of the serpents slithered over his foot and twined around his leg.

Twin spurts of fire pierced Neil's thigh. He screamed and swatted at the reptile, but it was immovable. A second serpent sunk its fangs into his ankle, a third into his wrist, a fourth into his back. Neil screamed and rolled and spun, trying to dislodge or crush Stitch's familiars, but his attempts were less than hopeless. With each bite he felt as though acid was being injected into his skin, and before long all he could do was curl up, cover his face, and wash the world of pain with his tears.

53

The lorry driver with whom Warren Royle had been travelling for the last sixty miles was his idea of how an old sea-dog should be. His bushy, grizzled beard lapped over the collar of his greasy black sweater. His forearms were discoloured by tattoos, their definition aged by time and a wiry growth of hair. He chainsmoked cigarettes, the butts of which he flicked expertly through the half open window. He and Royle didn't speak much. The sound of the engine battled for supremacy with a tinny radio that played Golden Oldies like a stubborn busker.

Staring out of the window, Royle felt hypnotised by the constant repetition of the motorway lights. There was no wonder motorists fell asleep at the wheels of their cars; the monotony was mesmeric as a swinging watch. He closed his eyes, and immediately he was drifting into a doze. Free from outside distractions, his body relaxing, he conversely felt his mind becoming sharper. He analysed himself, considered his actions, his motives. Why was he sitting here in this smoky cab, travelling to God-knows-where?

Examined coldly, logically, it seemed that what he was doing was crazy. There was no sense to any of this. His actions were those of a madman. But deep down, instinctively, he knew that he had embarked upon the most positive and important journey of his life. His soul burned with the *rightness* of it. He felt stripped clean, burning with purpose.

But from where had this faith, this sense of destiny, come? He knew it had been the story in the magazine, but again, in practical terms, the notion was ludicrous. A story was simply a story, after all. Words on paper. It had no mystical significance unless one was already pre-disposed to its message. At least that was what Royle had always believed – that sudden enlightenment, such as he had experienced, sprang from despair and a need for direction. In his opinion such individuals were lonely, inadequate, desperate. They were people who would clutch at straws in their search for some kind of meaning.

The idea alarmed him. Surely *he* was not such an individual? He was dissatisfied with his life, yes, but not to the extent that he would embark on irrational quests merely on a whim. No. His journey had a destination, he was certain of it. Waiting for him was Truth, or at least a variation of same. How did he know this? He just did, that was all. Somehow, by reading that story, he had unlocked a secret, perhaps divine, part of himself. The story had been merely the key, the combination. It was a fortuitous and startling coincidence that the words had just happened to fall into place at that particular time. What he was doing was so pure, so unfettered, that he was operating purely on instinct, relying solely on faith.

At that moment, as though shaken roughly awake, his eyes blinked open. They had left the motorway and were on an A-road. The headlamps extended overlapping cones of light into the darkness.

'Stop!' Royle cried, sitting upright. 'Stop here!'

The driver looked at him, bushy eyebrows raised. 'What's a matter?' he growled. 'You need a piss? Or you just dreaming?'

Royle shook his head. Each second the lorry moved forward, his sense of panic increased. 'No.' he said, 'I . . . I want to get out here. This is . . . this is as far as I want to come.'

'But there's nothing 'ere,' the driver said. 'Take a look around. It's all fields and stuff.'

'I want to get out,' Royle repeated. 'I have a friend. He lives over there. On a farm.' He pointed randomly to the left.

'You sure it's 'ere?' the driver said, frowning. 'How can you tell? All these fields look the bloody same.'

It was true. The only lights now came from headlamps on occasional vehicles and glittering cat's eyes. To left and right of the road were fields so black they resembled starless space; even the night sky was lighter. Twisted silhouettes of trees clawed into the horizon line like imperfections in glass.

Nevertheless Royle reached for the door handle. 'It's here,' he said. 'I've been loads of times. I know this place like the back of my hand.'

Still the lorry driver did not look happy. 'But you been asleep for the last twenty minutes,' he said. 'How can you be sure this is the place?'

'Trust me,' said Royle. 'Besides, I wasn't asleep, I was just dozing and thinking. I knew where we were.'

He was met with another dubious frown. The man's face was all hair and dark eyes and a bulbous nose that seemed to glow gently.

'Don't worry about me,' Royle said. 'Like I said, I've done this before. Anyway, as soon as I get down from this cab, I'm not your problem, am I? And if I am wrong, which I'm not, I can always cadge another lift.'

The lorry driver shrugged his huge shoulders. 'It's your neck,' he said. He pulled into the side of the road. Even before the lorry had stopped, Royle had opened the door and jumped down on to the grass verge.

The grass was wet and the night was cold. Nonetheless the spark in Royle's stomach suddenly ignited into flame. He could almost smell the anticipation in the air, as though the night was waiting for him. 'Thanks for the lift,' he shouted and slammed the cab door on the driver's gesture of acknowledgement.

He watched the lorry drive away, then turned and faced the fields. He could see nothing, and yet he felt irresistibly drawn to them. Excitement fluttered in his stomach and his throat. He began to walk forward. As though his progress was being guided, he jumped to clear a ditch he couldn't see, found a place in the fence where the hedge was thin and the rusted barbed wire had snapped.

The field beneath his feet was springy, a little squelchy in places. Though uneven, Royle traversed it with confidence, as if it were a route he followed every day. Before him was nothing but blackness; distant clumps of woodland wrestled with the night sky. With nothing to focus upon, Royle felt a little dizzy, though he wondered how much of that was due to his own mounting excitement.

It took him perhaps ten minutes to reach the far side of the field. He paused for breath and looked back at the road. Only the twin pinpoints of headlights distinguished it from the surrounding darkness. Car engines were like the soft growls of dogs; they seemed pitiful, insignificant. Unerringly Royle followed the thicket-entwined fence until he came to a padlocked gate. He climbed over the gate and dropped into the next field.

Now, looking to the left, he could see the byre. It was nestled close to the fence, shadowed by an oak tree and a particularly dense patch of thicket. From the road it would have been invisible, the oak tree spread before it like a protective father shielding his offspring from the prying eyes of motorists. Royle began to walk towards the byre, his heart beating fast. His limbs ached with urgency as if desperate to break into a run. However he resisted the temptation, forcing himself to walk slowly, cautiously.

He was close enough to smell the byre, a shit-straw-bovine aroma, when the figure emerged from it. It was a scarecrow, gangly and ragged. A moment later he smiled, realising it wasn't a scarecrow, after all, but a young man about the same age as himself. The man approached, extending a hand. He wore black leather fingerless gloves, a canvas jacket, jeans, boots and a black knitted cap. It was too dark to see what he was doing with his face, but his voice sounded friendly enough.

'Hi,' he said. 'I'm Nick. Who are you?'

'Er ... Warren,' said Royle. 'Are there ... er ... I mean ... is this where it's happening?'

'This is where it starts, I think. There are twenty-six of us so far, and more to come. No one knows exactly how many, but we'll know once everyone has arrived.'

Yes. It all sounded so good, so *right*. Warren grinned and took the proffered hand, which he shook with enthusiasm. He couldn't see, but he sensed that Nick was grinning back at him.

'Come on, I'll introduce you to the others,' Nick said.

54

The blades were singing again, their hymn embracing Mally, raising his spirit aloft. He sat in the serene darkness, feeling the power dormant within him, thrumming softly through meat and bone, through muscle, nerve and sinew. He could feel it gorging each artery, each vein, each needle-thin capillary. He looked at his hands, expecting them to ripple and change, to break open, unable to contain the Glory within the flimsy envelope of his flesh.

Tonight the Artist was abroad. He sat in his parked car on a dark country lane, waiting for the canvas on which to create. His materials were beside him, singing of their hunger, their need. The wind whispered through treetops like a secret ally. Shadows bobbed across the car's bonnet as though in solemn approval of his intentions. He was as motionless and as watchful as any predator, his mind fixed wholly on his mission, his senses acute, his patience and composure total.

He had no doubt that tonight the masterpiece would flow from his fingers. He had come here because this was where destiny had brought him. He could feel the heart beating inside him, slowly, leisurely. His breath was shallow, his skin cool. There was no outward sign of his coming transcendance. The rest of them, the offal, were deaf to his exultation, blind to his true face. He moved amongst them each day, living their lives, sharing their concerns as if they were important.

As if they were important? He frowned a little, for the phrase did not sit easily with him. Sometimes, during the day, he had to admit that their concerns did in fact *seem* important. Sometimes, incredibly, he actually forgot about this part of himself. It was as though dream and reality had crossed over and blanked his mind, for wasn't it the case that in dreams we often forget the truly important things in our lives? Misery can be erased by dreams – illness, death, grievances, anxieties. They can be discarded, simply put away and forgotten like items of trivia. And sometimes we forget the good things too. We dream we are in trouble, only to find, upon waking, that we are not. And so it was with Mally. Two lives, black and white, each carefully selective, each (in his opinion) perfectly balanced and controlled.

The lane in which he had parked — tree-lined, unlit, the road uneven — connected two busier roads, one at each end. From the road before him, some three or four hundred yards away, he heard

303

a rumbling sound, glimpsed a red metal wall inlaid with lighted squares through the gaps between the trees. The night-bus. Last bus of the evening. Students from the University who had been out on the town would disembark here and walk up this lane to reach the road at the far end. Across *that* road, and through an always open gate between two concrete pillars, lay a drive leading to the main University buildings, a cluster of Halls of Residence, sports fields and the rest of the campus.

Silently, calmly, Mally collected up the tools from the seat beside him and slipped them, one by one, into the deep inside pocket of his overcoat. He got out of the car, closed the door with a minimum of noise and locked it. At the far end of the lane the bus growled and pulled away. Mally saw a flicker of movement far off in the shadows as whoever had alighted from the vehicle began to walk towards him. One person only, it seemed. He nodded: Destiny. He crossed the lane and slipped behind a tree, stooping briefly to pick up a chunk of stone.

The energy inside him seemed to crackle and flicker like flame. Nevertheless he remained as still as the trees around him, his breathing deep, even and silent. His palms were dry. The rock felt snug in his hand. He felt no desire to squeeze it nervously or to shuffle his feet. He remained perfectly still even when the figure walked briskly into view, hands thrust into jacket pockets. The student's head was hunched into his upturned collar as though he was already anticipating his fate and had accepted it.

Mally allowed the figure to pass his hiding place, then he stepped out of the trees. Taking careful aim, he threw the rock, which landed to the right of the student, in a clump of bushes, making a noise like an animal or a person moving suddenly. The student jumped and instinctively stepped sideways, away from the bushes. In the brief seconds during which he paused and looked down to his right, Mally slipped up behind him, reached into his overcoat, produced a screwdriver and thrust it into the side of the student's exposed neck.

The tool was plucked from his hand as the student fell forward. He hit the ground wriggling, making a horrible squealing noise, his hands groping at the screwdriver's wooden handle. Moving quickly, though with the utmost composure, Mally kicked the student in the side of the head to stun him. He squatted by the almost unconscious body and rolled it on to its back. There was blood and saliva on the student's chin. His eyes were open; Mally saw the gleam of the moon reflected in their moisture. Reaching into his overcoat again he produced a cut-throat razor.

304

He opened it carefully, then used it to sever the windpipe and the jugular vein.

He jumped back as blood fountained into the air. The first spray arced high over his shoulder, speckling his overcoat like black rain. He tutted and stood up, watching dispassionately as the student's jerking limbs and rolling eyes became feebler, more spasmodic. Eventually they stopped; the student was dead, or as good as. Mally squatted by the body again, reached into his overcoat and laid his tools, one by one, on the ground. That done, he stroked the student's hair, then leaned forward and kissed his cooling forehead.

'Thank you,' he whispered. 'There's no more pain now. Don't worry. I'm going to make you beautiful.'

With steady fingers he untied the student's laces and removed the first of his shoes.

55

Even as a child, autumn had been Douglas Parks' favourite season. His friends, such as they were, had thought his predilection weird. Autumn for them meant rain and dingy days and a new school year. Winter was great — snowball fights and Christmas Day — and summer was sheer Heaven. But autumn? Nah, you could keep it. Hallowe'en and Bonfire Night were the only sparks of excitement in an otherwise dismal three months.

But for Douglas it was different. The heat of the summer he found oppressive; it made him feel faint and tired and sometimes nauseous. Besides which he was a weedy boy and he burned easily and he couldn't swim; the prospect of stripping to his underpants and leaping into a glittering lake or reservoir filled him with dread.

Winter, too, was a time of foreboding. Oh, Christmas was fine, but the cold was unbearable; it had a knack of seeping into his bones. Snowballs were vile things, and sledging a moronic pastime. It seemed to him merely a reckless way of breaking limbs.

Autumn, though, that was just right. For one thing the colours were beautiful — the reds and yellows and russet-browns. They were warm colours, restful, somehow comforting. And the temperature, too, was perfect — neither too hot nor too cold. And, though he never admitted it to anyone, Douglas loved school, positively relished the resumption of his studies. For him the act of learning was the great joy of his childhood. It was a pursuit he found noble, fascinating and worthwhile.

Which was why, he supposed, he had remained within the education system. It had simply seemed a natural progression, what he'd been born for. He had worked his way steadily up the ladder, until now, at the age of fifty-one, here he was, Chancellor of an English university. That, for him, was the pinnacle, the ultimate achievement. He felt like a lord overlooking his kingdom. The lecturers were his servants, handing out knowledge to the minions as if it were daily bread.

A knock on the door interrupted his musings. He turned from the window of his office, which offered a restful view of farmlands and clumps of trees cloaked in autumnal colours. 'Come in,' he called.

The door opened. Paul Carmichael entered, looking quizzical. 'You wanted to see me, Douglas?'

'Ah, yes. Come in, Paul. Sit down.' Parks gestured to the chair facing his desk.

Carmichael closed the door, crossed the room and sat. Leaning back and folding his arms he asked, 'What can I do for you, Douglas?'

Not until Carmichael was seated did Parks follow suit. He felt uncomfortable looking up at people, especially his subordinates. He leaned forward, elbows on desk, hands clasped together. 'I want you to do something for me,' he said. 'It may turn out to be rather a delicate mission.'

Carmichael raised his eyebrows. 'I'm intrigued,' he said. 'Go on.'

'It's about Howard Duffy. I understand that you're quite friendly with him.'

'Well ...' said Carmichael hesitantly, 'I wouldn't exactly say *friendly*. We chat in the staff room sometimes. I drove him to the hospital when his mother was taken ill.'

'You know she's since died, don't you?'

'No,' said Carmichael, surprised, 'I didn't.' He shook his head. 'Oh dear. Poor Howard. How's he taking it? Do you know?'

'Well ... no. We don't. That's the problem, you see.' He paused.

'Problem?' Carmichael prompted.

'Hmm. The thing is, Paul, Howard's not been in touch with anyone since he left the hospital after his mother died.' He leaned back in his chair, fingering the handlebar moustache that had earned him the nickname 'Walrus'. He had grown the moustache over twenty years ago, believing it gave his sallow, rather sulky face a kind of fierce military distinction.

'The hospital rang up this morning,' he continued. 'They've been trying to get in touch with Howard, but he's not answering his phone. As far as they're aware, he's made no effort to contact an undertaker with regard to his mother's funeral arrangements. They were rather hoping that they might find him here, immersing himself in his work, as it were, but I had to tell them he'd gone AWOL. I wondered whether perhaps you'd seen him, Paul, or spoken to him? I was led to understand that he might have confided in you.'

Carmichael spread his hands apologetically. 'Sorry, Douglas, but we're really not that close.'

'Ah,' said Parks, disappointed. He glanced at his watch. 'I don't suppose . . .' he began.

'Yes?'

'I don't suppose you'd like to pop round to his house anyway? See if he's there? Make sure he's all right?'

Carmichael pulled a face. 'I was afraid you were going to ask that.' He, too, looked at his watch. 'I'm teaching in fifty minutes,' he said.

'Just time then, if you're quick,' said the Chancellor. He stood up and walked to the window. Facing the view he said, 'I would appreciate it, Paul. I'd go myself if I didn't have so much work to do.'

A short, loaded silence made it evident what Carmichael thought of that excuse. He stood up, pushing back his chair, and said resignedly, 'Okay. I don't suppose I'd be able to concentrate anyway if I didn't go.'

'Good man,' said Parks, turning back, beaming through his moustache. 'I'll remember this, Paul, rest assured.'

'Hmm,' said Carmichael. He crossed the room and pulled open the door. 'I'll let you know as soon as I have any news.'

'Please do. I'm rather concerned, I must admit.'

Carmichael exited. Parks turned back to the window, but was interrupted almost immediately by another knock on the door. He sighed, and snapped, 'Yes?' The door jerked open. A student entered, looking distraught.

'Yes, what is it?' Parks asked tersely, irritated that his secretary, Miss Nightingale, had not dealt with the matter, whatever it was.

'Sir . . .' the student began, but the rest of his sentence was overtaken by rapid, stressful breathing. He clung to the door handle as though fearful of falling if he let go.

'What is it, boy? Speak up.' Parks had never quite made the jump from secondary school to university in terms of how he addressed his students.

'Sir ... it's ... someone's dead. It's awful, sir. I think it's murder.'

Parks went cold, though counteracted this by speaking even more harshly. 'Murder? What are you talking about? What do you mean? Is this a joke?'

'No, sir,' the student said. He was trembling as though from exposure. 'Someone's been killed ... It's ... it's awful, sir ... One of the students is dead. I ... I think you'd better come.'

56

Ian could not work out why the alarm clock was banging instead of ringing. He reluctantly extended an arm from the warmth of the duvet, his fingers groping at empty air until they closed around the cold metal casing. He pulled the clock into the bed and squinted at the luminous letters: 9:26. Shit, he was late for work! Immediately he re-evaluated: no, he wasn't, he was at University and this was Wednesday morning. His first lecture wasn't until eleven o'clock.

'Ian! Are you in there? Can you hear me?'

The voice outside the door belonged to Annie and it sounded close to panic.

'Er ... yeah,' Ian replied. He sat up, the duvet falling away from him. 'I'm in bed. What's the matter?'

'Something awful's happened, Ian. I need to talk to you.'

'Hang on,' he said, throwing aside the duvet and exposing his body to the cold. He felt horrible: Annie's ominous statement had been like a hand clutching his uncomfortably full bladder. Sleep still clung to his thoughts like clods of confusion, disorienting him. His bruised face ached; his breath wheezed. He crossed to the wardrobe, goosebumps bristling on his back and arms, and pulled it open.

Grabbing a pair of boxer shorts from one of the shelves inside, he pulled them on.

'Come on, Ian. What are you doing?'

'Just a minute,' he said irritably. 'I'm getting dressed. I won't be a sec.'

He heard Annie sigh and wondered what she would say if he opened the door naked and ushered her in. Perhaps he ought to try it. But he was tugging his jeans on now, which felt as though they'd been stored in a freezer overnight. Grabbing the jumper slung over the back of his armchair he padded barefoot across the room. No sooner had he turned the key in the lock than Annie had pushed the door open and was inside.

She appeared not even to notice his semi-nakedness. She was pale and looked jittery. Ian's bladder stabbed again.

'Oh, Ian,' she said, 'it's really terrible.' She crossed the room and slumped on to the bed.

'What is?' he demanded. His trepidation, his rude awakening and his physical discomfort made him snappish.

However Annie's next words swept away his irritability like a tissue in a hurricane. 'Someone's dead, Ian. It's all round the university. One of the students has been murdered.'

Ian almost pissed himself with shock. 'Christ,' he said in a strangled voice. 'Hang on ... I need ...' He rushed from the room.

When he returned a minute later, Annie was standing by the window, the sun marbling her face, lighting fires in her hair. It was a cold sun, like a dazzling ball of snow. As though he'd never left the room, she said, 'they found the body in one of the big dustbins behind the kitchens. One of the dinner ladies found it. They don't know who it is yet, but they reckon it's a first year ...' She sobbed suddenly and pressed a hand to her face. Ian was beside her in seconds, pulling her trembling body into his embrace. They stood silently, Ian resting his chin on Annie's head, gazing out of the window. He couldn't think of anything to say. Telling her not to cry would have been pointless and inappropriate.

It was she who spoke first. 'I've been so scared,' she said. 'I keep thinking: What if it's Steph? We've just stood by and ... and let that happen to her.'

'Hey,' Ian said gently, 'come on. It won't be Steph. Why should it be?'

Annie looked up at him. Her eyes were raw. 'Because she's been missing for five days. Because she's been with Latcher. Because ... because she can't look after herself any more.'

'You think that Latcher has something to do with this then?'

309

Annie pulled away from him as if he'd insulted her. 'Of course he has,' she declared, suddenly angry. 'It's obvious, isn't it? It's Latcher or one of his ... his followers who's done this. He's evil, Ian. I told you he was.'

'But you can't be *sure* he's involved,' he said. 'You're just jumping to conclusions. You don't know the facts.'

Annie glared at him, making him feel ashamed in spite of himself, as though he'd betrayed her. 'Of course he's involved,' she retorted, then bowed her head and sighed deeply.

There was silence for a few moments. It was so quiet that Ian could hear the timid ticking of his clock from across the room. Normally the building was full of noise. There was almost always music playing, muffled chat and laughter, slamming doors, feet pounding up and down stairs, someone singing in the shower. But this morning the silence was eerie. It was as if he and Annie were the only survivors of some mass abduction. When next she spoke, her voice was both terse and conciliatory.

'I know you're right,' she admitted. 'I know I'm jumping to conclusions. But all the same I've got a gut feeling about this. I know that somehow this ... this death, this *murder*, is something to do with The Crack.' She frowned and pressed a hand to her stomach as though suffering from indigestion. 'It's ... instinctive,' she tried to explain. 'It's something to do with all that stuff I was telling you before, when I spoke to Heather and I felt something click, as if I'd unlocked a door to a truth that had been buried for a long time.' She broke off, looking confused and dissatisfied with her attempted explanation.

'You mean all that white magic stuff?' Ian said.

'Yeah,' Annie replied reluctantly. She looked now as if she regretted having used that particular phrase.

Ian crossed to the wardrobe and took clean socks from the shelf below which he kept his underwear. He sat down and pulled them over his icy feet whilst Annie stared out of the window, like a caged bird longing for freedom. Ian had a question he wanted to ask, but which stuck in his throat, dreading the response it might provoke. At last, whilst lacing a pair of black Hush Puppies, he blurted it out.

'How did the ... person die?'

Annie remained stock-still at the window. Perhaps her shoulders hunched a little ... or perhaps that was Ian's imagination.

'I don't know,' she replied in a flat voice. 'There are all sorts of rumours. Some say stabbed, some say strangled.' She shrugged. 'Nobody really knows.'

Ian stood up. 'Come on then,' he said. 'Let's go and see what we can find out.'

He waited for Annie to cross to him, then slipped an arm around her shoulders. 'I love you,' he told her.

She blinked at him, though of the two of them Ian was perhaps the most surprised. He hadn't known he was going to say that, it had simply slipped out, impromptu. Was it true? He supposed so, for it had come from the heart rather than the brain. Now that he had said it, he was glad he had. There were tears in Annie's eyes.

'I love you too,' she whispered.

They kissed. Ian found himself wishing he'd brushed his teeth and quashed the thought. This felt so unreal, kissing in readiness for a murder scene. When they broke apart it was almost with embarrassment, as if both were aware that their display of affection was somewhat crass given the circumstances. Annie moved towards the door. 'Hang on,' said Ian. He splashed water into his face at the sink, dragged a comb through his hair, then joined her.

Even descending the stairs, the impression that they were alone in the Hall persisted. Doors were closed, corridors deserted. And the place seemed gloomier than normal, as if shadows had congregated, attracted by the sense of desertion.

Once outside, however, they were relieved to see parked cars, people moving behind windows which resembled the grainy frames of old, silent movies. One of the cars was white with a yellow band down the centre and the word 'POLICE' in block letters on the door. Annie looked nervous, her face pinched and pale. She rubbed the palms of her hands together as if trying to create warmth from which she could derive comfort. The cold air pressed on Ian's bruises, making them ache. The tightness in his chest was loosening a little, though each breath was like gulping crushed ice which scraped harshly. 'The kitchens are this way,' he said, pointing to steps on the right. He began to move towards them. Annie quickly stepped forward and placed a hand on his wrist.

Ian stopped and looked at her. 'What's the matter?' he asked.

'I . . . I don't want to see the body,' she replied. 'I just want to know who it is, that's all.'

Ian expelled a plume of breath and nodded. 'Same here,' he said. 'I doubt we'd be able to see it anyway, even if we wanted to . The police wouldn't let us.'

Annie looked relieved, though not much. They descended the steps hand in hand.

To reach the kitchens they had to enter a glass corridor which led to the dining hall and then leave it again via a parallel door. This took them on to a covered walkway, the long low building, like a barracks, that housed the kitchens to their immediate right, steps leading to the entrance of Mordred Hall directly in front of them. They ascended these, then crossed the patch of concrete in front of the Hall entrance and descended a further set of steps on the other side. Now they could see the area at the back of the kitchens. It was enclosed within a high wooden fence, presumably to deter animals enticed by the smell of refuse.

There were a great many people milling around here — students, lecturers, policemen and kitchen staff in their white overalls. A uniformed policeman was standing guard by the half open door in the wooden fence. Two police cars were parked askew just behind the crowd as if the drivers had entered the area at speed and then slammed on the brakes, eager to leap out and chase someone. A woman in white was sitting on a low wall, hands clasped around a mug from which steam rose. A large man with a knuckly face appeared to be coaxing answers from her; he continually smoothed his tie down over his chest and stomach as if afraid it might rear up like a cobra. Ian saw lots of wide eyes in shocked faces. There was chatter, but it was hushed, respectful, as if this was a chapel of rest and not merely the place where the slops were thrown. He squeezed Annie's hand and they walked down to join the throng. When they were close enough, Ian asked, 'Who is it? Have they said?'

A girl turned to them. She had close-cropped ginger hair, owlish spectacles and chapped lips. 'No,' she said, 'they haven't told us anything.' She sounded resentful, as if she'd bought raffle tickets to a draw that was being kept secret.

Ian and Annie weaved further into the crowd, asking occasional questions. There was plenty of conjecture but no concrete facts. Even the lecturers didn't know anything. Frustrated, Ian stomped up to the nearest policeman, who was leaning against a wall, arms folded, trying not to look pensive.

'When are we going to be told what's going on?' he demanded.

The policeman didn't change his position, but his body seemed to tense, as if readying itself for action. His expression hardened, masking any hint of vulnerability.

'Don't ask me, pal,' he said. 'It's not up to me.'

Ian expelled an exasperated sigh. 'but someone *has* been killed, haven't they?'

The policeman's face remained disconcertingly blank. Only his mouth moved. 'I'm sure there'll be an announcement when investigations are complete,' he said.

'But ... but can't you give us any clue?' appealed Ian. 'Was the victim male or female?' He sounded like a player in a macabre parlour game.

'An announcement will be made in due course,' the policeman repeated with stubborn calm.

Ian turned away. 'Oh, this is ridiculous,' he said. He glared his frustration at Annie, inviting her to share it.

'Perhaps we ought to tell Mr Carmichael,' she suggested. 'He might be able to do something.'

Ian looked doubtful, but nodded. 'Yeah, I suppose so. It's better than hanging around here anyway.'

They turned to head for the main building. Ian gestured up at Mordred Hall. From the majority of windows, faces peered down like caged rabbits. 'I'm surprised Neil isn't out here,' he said. 'Perhaps we ought to call on him, tell him what's going on.'

Annie wrinkled her nose. 'Yeah, I suppose so.'

'What's the matter?' said Ian, surprised. 'You like Neil, don't you?'

'Oh, yes, I like him, but you must admit he's a bit of a bull in a china shop. He'll probably come down here and cause a scene and get himself arrested.'

'No he won't,' Ian said. 'He's not as bad as that. He'll behave if I explain the situation to him. He's not stupid.'

Annie simply shrugged.

Ian said, 'Shall I get him then, or not?'

'If you like,' said Annie. 'I'll wait here.' She sat on a low wall, pressing her hands together between her knees. She looked tired and a little frail. Ian kissed the top of her head.

'I won't be long,' he said. He bounded up the steps and into the Hall. He was back within five minutes.

'Not there,' he said. 'He must be in a lecture or something. Come on, let's go and see Paul Carmichael.' He took Annie's hand and helped her to her feet. They left the apprehensive crowd behind.

But Paul Carmichael was not there either. They tried his office, each English Lit. lecture room, and the staff common room, all without success. Nobody knew where he was, though one or two of the staff had seen him earlier that morning.

'Oh, this is really annoying,' Ian muttered as they descended the staircase. 'I don't think God likes us today.'

'What shall we do now?' said Annie. 'Go back to the kitchens?'

Ian pulled a face. 'I suppose so. Maybe if we wait long enough, they'll tell us something definite.' He turned round on the stairs and laid a hand gently against Annie's cheek. 'How are you feeling?' he asked.

'Not too good. Tense. Scared. My muscles are so clenched up it's giving me stomach ache.'

'Do you want to sit down for ten minutes, have a coffee, something to eat?'

'No, I'd rather be doing something positive, even if it is just waiting around for the police to make an announcement.'

They returned to the murder scene. The crowd had not diminished. Nothing seemed changed. 'Any news?' Ian asked the ginger-haired girl who was still standing in the same place as before. She shook her head disgustedly. Ian sighed and the two of them made their way to the middle of the crowd. 'I heard his head was missing,' a pudgy girl in a voluminous pink jumper confided to her friend.

'He? Is it a he then?' Ian said, startling the girls. The pudgy one turned to him, and immediately Ian had an image of this girl twenty years from now — bloated, bored, hanging over the garden fence and exchanging delicious malice with an equally under-stimulated confidante.

'That's what *I* heard,' she said importantly.

'Who told you? Where did you hear it?' asked Annie.

Now the girl's self-confidence wavered a little. 'Er ... in the coffee bar. Someone in the coffee bar said it. I think they heard it from one of the chefs before the police arrived.'

Ian surreptitiously raised his eyebrows at Annie. At the same moment a ripple of anticipation passed through the crowd and a voice said, 'Hey, someone's coming out.' Ian twisted his head to see the door in the fence opening. A pause, and then two figures emerged, one of whom wore a drizzle-grey overcoat which flapped around his knees.

Ian's eyes were drawn to this man. He barely noticed the other. 'Hey, Annie, that's Chief Inspector Kaye. Come on.' He began to push his way through the crowd towards the policeman, who was now striding towards one of the police cars, deep in conversation with his colleague.

'Sir! Excuse me!' Ian shouted, raising a hand. Kaye, seemingly oblivious to his clamour, stooped to close his hand around the car's door handle.

'Chief Inspector Kaye, please hang on a minute. It's me, Ian Raven. I spoke to you yesterday about a missing person.'

Now Kaye looked up, though it was barely a glance. The expression on his face was not encouraging. He yanked the door open as though he had a grudge against it. In desperation Ian shouted, 'I know who the murderer is.'

Silence fell like an axe. There was not one head that did not

314

swivel in his direction. Kaye remained stooped though motionless for a moment, then he slowly straightened up. He glared at Ian with a face full of furious thunder.

57

It was not until he was about to admit defeat that it occurred to Paul Carmichael to try the door handle. He'd been standing here outside Howard Duffy's house for perhaps five minutes, banging on the door and ringing the bell, cupping his hands around his face to peer through the stippled glass panel. He could see nothing but blocks of colour – the wall and carpet presumably – splintered and merging at the edges, shifting like the patterns in a child's kaleidoscope when he moved his head. In truth, though, he was simply going through the motions. There was sufficient evidence here to suggest that Howard had gone away.

His car was missing for a start, though as Paul had never been to Duffy's house before he couldn't be sure his colleague didn't keep it somewhere else, in a lock-up garage perhaps. But there was also a newspaper still jutting from the letterbox and an accumulation of milk bottles on the step. The sight of all the milk irritated Carmichael. Was the milkman stupid or simply uncaring? If milk was left on the doorstep for longer than a day, surely the matter merited investigation?

But no, apparently not. Even coupled with the fact that all the curtains in the house were closed, the milkman had simply added, each day, to his previous deliveries. Carmichael sighed and turned away. Then he turned back as an after-thought and tried the door. It opened.

He stood for a moment, surprised. Howard must have been so distraught that he had forgotten to lock up when he left. He glanced around, then realised how suspicious that must make him appear. Pushing the door wider, his efforts somewhat impeded by the clutter of mail on the mat, he stepped boldly into the house.

'Howard?' he called. There was no reply. 'Howard, where are you?'

He looked around the hall. The decor and furnishings obviously reflected the old lady's personality. Chintzy, chintzy cheeriness, he thought, recalling a line from a poem by Betjeman. The large pink roses on the wallpaper contrasted sharply with the not-quite-sickening smell.

'Howard,' he shouted again, even though he was certain now that he was alone in the house. The gloom, the silence and the smell were somehow ominous, thickening like smoke. Carmichael hoped that his voice and his deliberately loud progress up the corridor would dispel it. He opened the front door wide. An inquisitive neighbour would not be unwelcome.

Further along, the hallway narrowed to half its width to accommodate the stairs down which Mrs Duffy had fallen. Carmichael peered briefly up them, seeing closed doors and shadows, then turned to the door on his right. He opened it and entered. It was the sitting room and it was empty. In one corner of the room a screen had been constructed from thick, faded curtains. He walked towards it, feet crunching on the shattered remnants of a china figurine whose severed head smiled its cherubic smile from beneath the side board. He reached the screen and pulled back the curtains. A commode displayed its porcelain throat.

He left the room and went back into the hall, where the sickly odour was more pronounced. There was something alarming about this smell. It was more than simply the mustiness of a house that has been sealed for too long. It set off warning bells inside Carmichael. Only something organic could smell so putrid. Bracing himself, he walked to the door at the end of the corridor and threw it open.

It hit him then, making him gag. But even as his gorge rose he began to chuckle with relief. He crossed to the kitchen windows and opened them, then to the door and opened that too. He walked on his tiptoes, trying not to step in the milk that was making the place stink.

Milk. That was all it was. From the broken glass lying amid the white pool he deduced that there were two pints here, filling the house with its curdled stench. He wondered whether he ought to clean it up. The prospect was not appealing. Then he thought of the police. Perhaps they should be informed of Howard's disappearance, in which case nothing should be touched.

He vacated the kitchen, pulling the door closed behind him. The fresh air blowing through the house was welcome, though the reek of souring milk was persistent. He stood at the bottom of the stairs, shouted, 'Howard?' before ascending. He opened each closed door on the upper landing and found each room empty. He went back downstairs.

In the hallway he picked up the telephone and dialled the University, only to be told by an annoyingly obtuse secretary that Parks was not available. He hesitated for a moment, then picked up the receiver again.

'I'd like to report a missing person,' he said when his call was answered.

58

Anger.

That was his protection. He wore his tight steel-grey fury like a suit of armour, the visor firmly down, concealing his eyes.

In his thirty-two years in the police force, Kaye had learned many bitter lessons. Trust no one. Do not give an inch. Do not accept anything until the evidence is irrefutable. People, he had learned, were cheats and liars, inherently spiteful. Petty, vicious, selfish morons, most of them. Even among the cultured and the educated he often found similar characteristics, festering beneath their frippery like gangrene beneath a spotless bandage. Kaye did not like people, and on the whole people did not like Kaye. Which was fine as far as he was concerned. It meant he could live his life exactly as he chose, with no interference.

Take that student at the University, for instance. A liar. Claiming he knew who the murderer was simply to gain attention. Well, he'd got that all right, and more besides. Kaye had given him a right bollocking, had made him feel about two inches tall, when he realised that the boy's so-called knowledge was nothing but a wild accusation, an hysterical stab-in-the-back, evidently encouraged by his personal dislike for the individual he had named. 'Check out Dan Latcher,' he had insisted, 'he'll know something about this.' When Kaye asked for evidence, the boy blustered and looked at his girlfriend. Their friend had gone missing, she'd said. Steph Peele. Remember, we told you about her?

So? Kaye had countered. What had that got to do with this?

Well ... well, they'd stammered; if there had been a corner to back into they would have been doing so.

And that was when Kaye had laid into them, telling them how dangerous and harmful it could be to jump to conclusions in matters such as this. Didn't they realise the seriousness of their accusation? And didn't they realise how idiotic they had been to shout out their suspicions in front of a large crowd of people?

They had looked suitably chagrined, though the boy had not been able to resist delivering a parting shot. 'Just check him out, Chief Inspector,' he had said. If Kaye had not been so encumbered with worries he would have insisted there and then that the boy be brought down to the station for intensive questioning to justify his allegations.

And yet, in the squad car on the short drive into Maybury, Kaye had taken his notebook from his pocket and had jotted down the name: Dan Latcher. He *would* have the man investigated, if only to be thorough. He'd been going to anyway, with regard to the alleged missing persons claim filed yesterday. He still believed the girl, Steph Peele, had simply gone off somewhere without telling her friends, though in light of current events it was better to be safe than sorry.

He sat now in his office, a collection of photographs spread before him, displaying the depths of depravity to which man could sink. For the moment he was looking not at the pictures but at his tropical fish, drifting lazily in the aquarium atop his filing cabinet like vivid, shimmering dreams, ineffable in their grace. It was not yet ten o'clock and already his normally tranquil manor had erupted into incident. First the hippies, now this. He wondered if there was a connection between the two events.

The hippies had arrived early that morning, a crowd perhaps sixty-strong, striding into Maybury as if they owned the bloody place. Where they had come from, Kaye had no idea. He had not been forewarned of any such group in the area. What was unusual about them was the fact that they were all on foot: there was not one van, not one motorbike, nor even a pushbike between them. They were not comprised of family units and did not appear politically motivated. They seemed simply a disparate band of young people, their intentions, for the moment, mysterious.

There had been no specific complaints about them as yet; only people ringing to express concern over their appearance and their number. His men had made four arrests for marijuana possession. The arrests had not precipitated any hostile reaction from the others, and even those arrested had come quietly. But despite their apparent docility, Kaye wanted them out of the way as soon as possible. They created tensions and anxieties amongst the townsfolk, which Kaye knew would escalate to hysteria once news of the killing became public. If it wasn't for the killing he would simply have ordered his men to round 'em up and ship 'em out. But now, he knew, they all had to be questioned. The problem was: how could that be done with the maximum efficiency and the minimum fuss?

He looked at the photographs again. They made his heart sink. The victim, eighteen-year-old John Pedder, first year philosophy student at Maybury University, was unrecognisable. Grotesquely his shoes and socks had been found in a rutted lane, some three or four hundred yards from the dustbin into which he had been dumped, though of his other clothes there was no sign. The killer had despatched John in the lane and then had apparently lifted the corpse into his car and driven it on to the University campus and round to the back of the kitchens where he had mutilated it.

The killer had left clues a-plenty. The tyre-tracks of his car had made a clear impression in the mud of the lane, as had the soles of his size seven Reebok running shoes. Furthermore there were some beautiful fingerprints on the victim's shoes and on the dustbin into which the body had been dumped. And on the body itself there were bite-marks, which meant that even if the murderer could not be traced through dental records, at least his blood-type could be ascertained from saliva samples. Kaye held one of the photographs up close to his face and stared intently at it as if daring himself to do so.

He pondered on the killer's state of mind. The actual murder had been so methodical, so coldly executed, that he couldn't believe the clues were the result of carelessness. In which case two options suggested themselves: either the killer was supremely arrogant and believed himself above the law, or he desperately wanted to be caught. Either way they would nail him soon. They had to. This was his second murder within a week. The one in Newcastle last Friday had yielded an equally spectacular glut of immediate evidence. Further information supplied by their forensic department included the man's hair colour − dark brown − and the fact that he had worn a black cotton garment, possibly a jacket, whilst carrying out the crime.

Kaye sighed, picked up the sheet of paper by his right hand and read it for the umpteenth time. This was the police surgeon's immediate appraisal upon examining the body; a more thorough examination

319

would result in a detailed report later today. But the surgeon's terse, scrawled notes contained the full horror which a report, dense with technical minutiae, would dilute. Kaye's stomach seemed to grind as he read the report, as though his anger was solidifying inside him, creating a poisonous pearl in his belly.

Estimated time of death: 1-2 a.m. (?)

Cause of death: not specifically known.

Injuries to body –

Stomach cut open, intestines removed and looped round victim's neck.

Fingers and toes severed and placed in stomach cavity

Throat cut, windpipe and jugular vein severed (possible cause of death).

Eyes removed. Sockets filled with gravel (eyes missing).

Flesh from bottom half of face (jaw) removed (ripped, peeled or cut away). Flesh missing.

The word 'Larry' carved on victim's forehead, probably with scalpel or similar implement.

Multiple lacerations over body, suggesting employment of multiple weapons (I'd guess at least six).

Many bite-marks on body, especially on legs, back, buttocks.

Penis and testacles removed, possibly bitten off (these, too, are missing).

Kaye tossed the sheet away from him, watching it see-saw through the air before settling on his desk. He rubbed his hands over his face. The body had only been discovered three hours ago, but already he felt under pressure. He knew that within these walls and outside

320

them the investigation was already in full swing. He was certain the man would be traced soon, whether it be through his fingerprints, dental records or car. But it galled Kaye to know that out there, at this actual moment, was a free man capable of absolute atrocity. No, he'd re-phrase that: we are all *capable* of such actions, but here was a man who had crossed the border and had found that he liked what was on the other side.

Kaye breathed deeply. He would have to control his anger for the press conference in less than half an hour. People do not like to see emotion in a policeman; it makes them uneasy, suggests a lack of control. He hoped that slime-ball Withers from the *Evening Post* wouldn't be there, though there was little chance of that. Give him a whiff of sensation and he appeared like a vulture wheeling above carrion, a grin on his face, his tongue hanging to his waist.

A knock on the door. Kaye looked up, his gaze sliding across a photograph of a hand with no fingers. 'Yes?' he said. The door opened and Constable Daley entered.

'Sir, I think you'd better come to the front desk,' he said.

'Why? What is it?' snapped Kaye, his face falling into its customary scowl.

'There's a man at the desk, sir ... well, no more than a boy really. He says he's Larry, sir.'

'What?' Kaye stood up as though launched and was half-way across the room before the constable could even raise his eyebrows. Daley flinched as his superior swept past him, then pulled Kaye's office door closed and scampered after him down the corridor.

There was, as Daley had said, a boy standing at the front desk. He was in his late teens, dark-haired, bedraggled, his eyes wide and staring as if he'd sleepwalked here and just woken up. His right arm was held in front of him, the fist tightly clenched.

'Right then, son, what can we do for you?' Kaye said.

The boy looked at him. Kaye was nagged by recognition. He'd seen this boy before. He'd been in the station within the last couple of days. But in connection with what? Then it clicked. He'd been one of that quartet from the university. He was the boyfriend of the girl they'd reported missing.

The boy spoke. His voice was quiet. 'I'm Larry,' he said. 'I'm the one you're looking for.' He opened his fist and let the object inside roll onto the desk-top. It was a human finger, the nail painted red. 'I'll take you to the rest of her,' he told Kaye.

Part Four

Parting the Red Sleaze

'I want to master life and death ...
What's one less person on the face
of the earth, anyway?'

Theodore Bundy

59

There was no sexual thing. Chaz wasn't a homo or nothing. Yet all the same Bernie knew that Chaz loved him and admired him and worshipped him. It was a phase he had never grown out of, a schoolboy crush which had endured and indeed strengthened as the two of them entered, and then waved goodbye to, their teens.

It was a joke, to be truthful. Chaz was Bernie's little lap-dog. He came when he was called and fucked off when Bernie told him to go. He was, to all intents and purposes, Bernie's slave, and Bernie treated him as such. He watched now as Chaz came lolloping across from old Mrs Manning's with a fresh bucket of water, the sweat standing out on his forehead, the muscles standing out on his arms, and the front of his jeans dark with spillage, making it look as though he'd pissed himself.

'Cheers, Chaz,' Bernie said, taking the new bucket from him and handing him the one full of dirty water. Even such a simple, and virtually meaningless, expression of gratitude such as this caused Chaz's eyes to light up as if Bernie had paid him the highest possible compliment.

'That's okay, Bernie. I'll ... er ... I'll get you another bucket of clean, shall I?'

'You do that, Chaz, old son,' said Bernie. He re-positioned the ladder until it was resting on the rim of an upper-floor window (the bedroom window, he reminded himself, eternally hopeful), then turned his back on Chaz, effectively dismissing him.

Nevertheless he was aware of Chaz lingering for a few seconds as though he couldn't bear to tear himself away. He could almost feel Chaz's gaze on his back, like hot coins being pressed to his sweaty flesh. Bernie was used to this and either revelled in it or became irritated by it, depending on his mood. Today he was feeling indulgent; let Chaz stare all he liked. Bernie knew he could do no wrong in Chaz's eyes; everything he did, or had ever done, Chaz held in awe. Bernie was the person that Chaz wished he was brave enough and confident enough and skilful enough to be. Bernie knew that Chaz admired his toughness, his arrogance, his success with women, the decisiveness with which he had left home and got his own flat and set up his window-cleaning business.

But there was even more to it than that. There were a million and one trivial things which he could do, or had done, and which Chaz held in reverence. There was his ability to juggle a football with his feet or his head for as long as he liked; there was the fact that he could toss peanuts into the air and catch them in his mouth; there was his drinking capacity (unlike Chaz, he could down six pints of lager without falling over); there was his skill at shooting pool, and his ability to shuffle and deal cards, and the way he could wear his baseball cap back to front and not look like a geek. And there was his appearance: Chaz was forever wishing he could pluck up the courage to have an earring like Bernie's, or a tattoo like Bernie's, or a trendy haircut with streaked highlights like Bernie's. But Bernie knew Chaz would never do any of these things − he was too scared of his mother. Bernie's mother had hit the roof too at first, but Bernie had simply drawled, 'Aw, fuck off, Ma,' which was another reason Chaz admired him.

All of which made Bernie, as he ascended his ladder, feel very superior. But not superior enough that he had yet plucked up the courage to make a pass at the Trent woman. Almost a year he had been cleaning her windows and in all that time he had exchanged maybe a dozen words with her. And he wanted her, he really did. It was her tightness, her prudery, that attracted him. So many of his conquests were like taking candy from a baby. There was no thrill in it, no edge, no challenge. But the Trent woman ... If Bernie could get inside her knickers, he reckoned he could get inside anyone's. He had this image of her turning to face him, tugging a single strategic pin from her school ma'amish hair, and seeing it tumble magically about her shoulders as she pouted her lips in a come-on.

Normally Bernie tried to time his visits so that he was here on a weekend when she was home. Saturday morning was a good time. From experience, Bernie had learned that this was a favourite time among females to take a bath. But Bernie had never seen Jayne Trent either bathing or undressing or in bed. He had heard water running once, but the bathroom blind and her bedroom curtains had been firmly closed.

He was not really expecting any action today, though, which was why he had allowed Chaz to come along. Today was Wednesday. The Trent woman would be at work, teaching or whatever. Bernie had hoped to arrange his schedule so that he could have been here at the weekend, but sometimes financial considerations had to take precedence over libidinous desires. He climbed the ladder, his upper torso bare despite the cold day, steaming bucket held carefully away from him, shammy leather sticking out of the back pocket of his jeans.

At the top he balanced the bucket carefully on the highest rung and tugged the shammy from his pocket. Only then did he glance through the window into the room. Immediately his heart leaped. 'Fucking hell,' he muttered. There was a figure sprawled on the unmade bed, undeniably naked. He flipped the shammy on to his shoulder, made the bucket secure by jamming it between his thigh, the rung of the ladder and the wall of the house, then arched his hands around his eyes and rested them against the glass.

He peered into the room, believing that his prayers had finally been answered. It took precisely two seconds for that supposition to be squashed flat. The woman on the bed *was* Jayne Trent, all right, and she *was* naked. But considering what else Bernie could see, it was more a nightmare than a dream come true.

She was dead. He could see that plainly. He didn't need to go in there and check her pulse to make certain. Her mouth yawned open, her eyes glared with a kind of appalled emptiness. Her body was horribly malformed, bulging with shiny scaly growths as if she'd been turning into the Elephant Man or something at the time of her death. Some of her hair had gone, absorbed by the chitinous shell, and her skin was almost as white as the sheet on which she lay. Bernie's immediate thought was that she had died from some sort of hideous disease, something he might very well catch himself if he hung around here much longer. He released the bucket from its precarious perch on top of the ladder, heard it hit the ground, the water exploding outwards like soft glass. He descended the ladder too quickly, searing his hands on the metal, his ankle turning with a jolt of pain as it impacted with the ground. He hobbled away, trembling with reaction, hissing his agony with each step. 'Chaz!' he yelled. 'Chaz!' And for the first time in all his years of using the name, there was a real, urgent need in his voice.

60

'The natives are restless, sir. I think you'd better go straight in.'

'Just give me five minutes first, Sergeant,' Kaye said, both looking and sounding exhausted.

'But, sir, I don't − ' Sergeant Wilson began, then flinched as his superior suddenly turned on him, energised by anger.

'I *said* five minutes, Sergeant. It won't make any difference. They've waited an hour already.' Kaye stomped into his office, slamming the door behind him.

The echo of his rage retreated, leaving a silence that seemed to collapse on to his shoulders, weighing him down. Kaye was a martyr to headaches, though normally he managed to keep them at bay while working. He had one now, though. It pressed against the front of his skull like ice against a nerve. Squinting to reduce the light streaming into his eyes, he shuffled to his desk and sat down.

He lowered his head into his hands, covering his eyes with his palms, his cool fingers resting against the pain, soothing it. He'd have liked to have stayed there indefinitely, but his presence was required by three dozen journalists and a bunch of TV people, whose mood, because of the delay, was ugly and turning uglier. The press conference had originally been scheduled for ten-thirty; it was now eleven thirty-six: lunchtime deadlines were looming. Not that such considerations mattered to Kaye, but the more you mucked these people about the more obnoxious they became. Journalists, in his experience, were sleaze-balls to a man (and woman); they possessed the moral sensibilities of sewer rats. He was getting annoyed just thinking about them, which was unwise for it merely made his head hurt all the more. But if they had seen what he had just seen ... He snorted mirthlessly. More than likely one or two of them − that crud, Withers, for example − would have whooped with delight at the extent of such carnage. Wankers like him gorged themselves on death and scandal and misery. A lurid murder or two was manna from Heaven as far as they were concerned.

Crash. Crash. The knocking on the door was like the pounding of a fist on flesh already bruised. Kaye grimaced and muttered discouragingly. The door opened to reveal Constable Daley, clearly nervous.

'Sir, I have a message from Sergeant Wilson,' Daley said. 'He says that it's been five minutes, sir.'

Kaye grunted and waved him away. Daley exited, clearly relieved that he had escaped without a tongue-lashing.

Kaye scooped up the photographs still scattered across his desk, admonishing himself for the unprofessional way he had left them exposed. Any Tom, Dick or Harry might have stumbled across them. It was just one indication of the stress he was under. He wouldn't have put it past Withers to have crept in here and pocketed a few. Plenty of masturbation material here, eh, Scumball, he thought savagely. He put the photographs into a brown envelope and put the envelope into the top right-hand drawer of his desk, which he locked.

He crunched two Aspirin, which tasted of bitter chalk, and hoped that they would work quickly − like in the time it took for him to walk down the corridor. On the way to the conference room, he passed a grey door behind which, he knew, were featureless white walls, a table and a chair. Four people would be in that room: a constable standing guard at the door, Detective Inspector Jacks, Detective Constable Bowen, and the boy who claimed to be Larry. There was little that unsettled Kaye, but he felt a shudder slither down his back as he recalled the boy's expression when he had shown them round the house on Cramer Road. Despite the almost unbelievable atrocities perpetrated in two of the bedrooms, the boy's eyes had remained dull, his voice matter-of-fact. 'I did this one first,' he had told them, pointing to what had once been a girl as if she were a painting or a piece of sculpture. Downstairs he had said, 'That finger I showed you belongs to this one.' And pointing again: 'I used that hammer and chisel there to get the fingers off.'

Kaye clenched his fists, as if to protect his own fingers from such treatment. More than anything the murders depressed him; they were like a sickening burden, embodying in their senseless and casual ferocity all that was dark and wrong in the world. His head still thumped. He was *not* in the mood to face journalists. He opened a door and was facing them. The immediate clamour of questions and grievances was like a solid wall, a barrier of treacle through which he had to wade.

He didn't speak until he had sat down behind a white table on which was focused the indifferent eyes of multifarious cameras. 'One at a time please, gentlemen,' he said then, holding up a hand like Canute defying the sea's approach. His use of the masculine provoked a sharp glare accompanied by an obvious 'ahem' from Angela Ridge of the *Coxley Standard* or *Guardian* or whatever it was called. Kaye ignored her. If these vultures wanted etiquette they could fuck off. He would tell them what they were entitled to know and no more.

329

At last they got the hint that Kaye would remain tight-lipped unless the uproar abated, and so grudgingly lowered their cacophony to a dissenting murmur. Kaye looked around, blinking at the flash bulbs, trying to conceal his discomfort and so deprive them of the photograph they wanted – a policeman under pressure. He saw Withers to his right. The man resembled a grotesque baby – corpulent, his skin pink and smooth as if he had never shaved, a domed forehead framed by fluffy blond hair. But there was nothing innocent about Withers' expression. His thick lips gleamed as if he was salivating at the smell of blood. His eyes, forget-me-not blue and ever watchful, glittered behind spectacles whose small, round, steel frames did not suit his pudgy face.

'To save time for all of us,' Kaye said, 'I'll first of all make a statement. If, consequently, you have any queries concerning that statement, I'll do my best to answer them.'

He saw journalists raise eyebrows at each other. Some pulled faces. However Kaye knew this was mostly affectation. They knew the form. They couldn't have expected anything else. As soon as he began his statement, the place became as hushed as a cathedral. Heads lowered as if in prayer. Pens scribbled.

'Early this morning,' he said, 'a body was discovered in the grounds of Maybury University. It was the body of a young man who had clearly been murdered some hours before. Due to the manner of the killing it was concluded that this murder could be linked to one that took place in Newcastle late on Friday evening.'

'Peter Simpson,' someone said.

'Yes, that's right. Certain ... characteristics indicated that both murders were committed by the same man.'

'What characteristics?' a voice asked.

Simultaneously someone said, 'So the murderer's a man, then? How do you know?'

Kaye held up his hand. 'Please. If you'll all be quiet I'll explain.' The buzz of speculation died down. 'Thank you,' Kaye said. He paused, then continued.

'At ten-thirty this morning, the time at which this press conference was originally due to begin, that was all the information we had. There was then a rather startling development in the inquiry. Someone actually walked into the station claiming to be the killer. He gave us certain information which led us to believe that he might be telling the truth. Subsequently Detective Inspector Jacks, Detective Constable Bowen and myself accompanied the man to a house in the Royston district of Maybury. In the house were three more bodies, all murdered. The man is currently helping us with our enquiries.'

330

Not surprisingly there was uproar at the conclusion of Kaye's statement. Everyone began to speak (or rather shout) at once; questions scrambled on top of one another, seeking ascendancy. The noise was like a drill in Kaye's head. Hoping that no one was taking a picture at that moment, he closed his eyes briefly and pressed a hand to his brow. Then he took a deep breath and jumped up, almost knocking his chair over. 'Please, could we have a little order!' he shouted. 'Otherwise we shall have to consider this press conference at an end.'

The room quietened, though only slowly and very grudgingly. 'That's better,' Kaye said, glaring around like a teacher with a class of unruly pupils. He sat down. 'Now,' he said, 'let's conduct ourselves in a civilised manner, shall we? Would those of you with questions please raise your hands.' A forest of hands shot up. Kaye sensed and saw resentment among the crowd facing him, and felt considerably cheered to know that, for the moment at least, he held the upper hand. He possessed information so desperately sought after that he could probably make this lot turn cartwheels for it if he wanted to. He looked around, savouring the moment. Then he nodded his permission for the questions to begin.

For the next half-hour Kaye was engaged in verbal fencing. However he was an old hand at the sport and did not allow his guard to drop even for a moment. He parried questions with ease, even those surprise thrusts that might have had a lesser man floundering. Sometimes hesitation in a policeman could be very telling indeed, but Kaye did not hesitate. The closest he came to doing so was, predictably, when confronted with the only question that Withers asked him.

How were the victims killed? What are their names? Is the man you've arrested local? Is he from the Newcastle area? Enquiries such as these were easy meat to Kaye. Most were tossed aside with a bland 'No comment' or 'I'm sorry, but I can't answer that for obvious reasons.' He was congratulating himself on a job well done, and even his headache was beginning to fade, when Withers asked, 'Is the man you're holding a student at the University?'

Withers always spoke in a quiet, apparently bored voice, and yet his words seemed to carry, as if he had the ability to pitch his questions straight into a listener's ear. The beat of silence that followed was only a fraction of a pause. How the hell ...? thought Kaye, then immediately told himself: lucky guess. He did not allow his surprise to show on his face. He stared at Withers with steady indifference. 'No comment,' he said and was pleased at how brisk and strong his voice sounded. Withers smiled and wrote down something. The moment passed.

Kaye knew it was time to wind up the proceedings when the wheel of questions began to turn full circle. Queries he'd already dismissed were served up again in a different guise, but Kaye was no fool; he dismissed them again, and quickly. He glanced at his watch and stood up. A last desperate barrage of questions assailed him. Kaye smiled as if he'd heard none of them and said, 'Well, that's all for now, gentlemen.' Angela Ridge scowled at him again. Kaye ignored her again. 'If you'll excuse me?' He didn't give a toss whether they would excuse him or not. He left anyway. Questions hit the closing door behind him like a rain of arrows.

The Aspirin had almost put paid to Kaye's headache. He strolled back towards his office, rather pleased with himself. He had managed to feed the vultures without getting his fingers snapped off. 'Sir,' said a voice. He turned to see Sergeant Wilson hurrying towards him.

'Ah, Sergeant. And where have I *got* to be this time?' he said, his voice low and icy.

Wilson squirmed uncomfortably.

'Don't you *dare* ever send a constable with a message like that again,' Kaye told him.

'Sorry, sir,' replied Wilson, crimson with embarrassment. 'It's just that those press boys were giving our lot a bit of a hard time.'

'Oh dear. What were they doing, stealing your dollies? For Christ's sake, Wilson, don't be so bloody pathetic!'

'No, sir,' said Wilson. He stared straight ahead as if fascinated by something hovering in the middle distance.

Kaye allowed the silence between them to lengthen until he saw a bead of sweat ooze from Wilson's forehead and trickle down his face, then he asked tersely, 'Well? What is it you wanted to see me about?'

'We've got the names of the five students who lived at Cramer Road, sir. The three dead ones are Neville William Walton, Catriona Elizabeth Peters and Emma May Chettle. None of them have been *positively* identified yet, sir, but we're virtually certain it's them. We still haven't traced the other two, sir, and ... er ... *Larry* apparently isn't saying anything. Their names are ... let's see ... Daniel Steven Latcher and Julie Emmott.'

Wilson looked up from his clipboard to see Kaye staring at him as if he'd suddenly grown two heads. Wilson did not like Kaye. He considered him unpredictable, possibly unstable, and this appeared borne out now in the expression on his superior's face. Nervously

332

Wilson asked, 'Er ... is something the matter, sir? Can I ... er ... can I do anything?'

'Read that name again,' Kaye said quietly.

'Er ... which one, sir?'

'Daniel ... something.'

'Daniel Steven Latcher, sir,' Wilson said, wondering if he was about to be bawled out for pronouncing it wrongly or some equally minuscule misdemeanour.

'Daniel. Steven. Latcher,' Kaye repeated, leaving a sizeable gap between each word. The preoccupied expression still on his face he said, 'I'd very much like to speak to this Daniel Steven Latcher, Wilson. In fact, there are quite a number of people I would very much like to speak to. I want you to arrange something for me, Wilson, something very important. Come into my office and I'll tell you all about it.'

61

Dan Latcher seemed to bound weightlessly up the stairs of Guinevere Hall like an astronaut on the surface of the moon. His eyes were fire-brands in his waxen face, his grin stretched into a glowing crescent. His body seemed leaner, more elongated than ever, bony wrists and long-fingered hands jutting from the sleeves of his glittering blue suit. Though Dan remained elusive, his appearance yelled: Look at me! Look at me! In more ways than one, he was a paradox, a conundrum, an enigma. Despite his crackling energy and voracious smile he exuded the aura of something wasted and desperate.

No one passed him on the stairs. No one even so much as glimpsed his ascent. It was as if he threw out a soundless warning to anyone nearby: don't cross my path or I'll turn you to stone. When Dan reached the top he stretched out a hand to the fire door that led to the corridor. It opened before he could touch it. Seemingly unsurprised, he stepped through. He stood in the silence, a shimmering blue-white form, like a cold star that has fallen to earth. His eyes by contrast were burning, sweeping the cream-coloured walls and stout closed doors with the hungry fire of his gaze.

Here were rooms 43 to 48. Dan strode purposefully to room 45 and again opened the door simply by threatening to do so. Inside was gloom and the slow rise and fall of synchronised breathing. Dan's teeth were like lozenges of phosphorous, touching on gleams of moisture in many pairs of staring eyes, causing them to twinkle with crumbs of light.

It had been easy to conceal The Crack here. All those who lived on this floor were members, and all were first years which meant that they had not had time to form lasting friendships. Few suspicions had therefore been raised among the student body; a smattering of voices crying in the wilderness, nothing to worry about. Even the cleaning ladies who clattered around for an hour every morning were no problem. They didn't find it strange that there was always one room on the floor they couldn't gain access to. After all, students were always sleeping late, nursing hangovers or just being lazy. There had been no evidence of drugs or anything sinister that needed reporting. It was a pretty quiet floor as far as they were concerned. A quick dust and hoover round and that was that.

'Children,' Dan said warmly as he entered. There was a stirring, a rustling, a creaking of bodies easing slowly into life. The Crack numbered thirty-six, and all of them were here in this one room, shoulder to shoulder like a store-room full of mannequins. They slept standing up, like horses, though in truth it was not really sleep but simply a block on thought, a closing down of free will, emotion, motivation. None of The Crack had eaten for days, nor had they washed. As a result they looked haggard and grubby and they smelled bad. But none of them complained – their facility to do so had been taken away. Their only thoughts, implanted by Dan, were a confused mush of doctrines and beliefs, a maze of gibberish at the centre of which was the promise of Ultimate Glory.

'Children,' he said again as fingers reached out timidly to touch him. He was surrounded by shuffling forms, by the ravenous, adoring gaze of many eyes. He placed his hands on the unwashed heads that bowed before him. 'Mine is the kingdom,' he murmured, and they moaned at the words as though pierced, exalted by his profundity. 'Soon,' he told them. 'Soon it will be time.'

He grinned ferociously, desperately, into the gloom, a scimitar of clenched teeth that might have concealed a scream.

62

It had been a morning spent on tenterhooks for Ian and Annie. The minutes had passed horrendously slowly, so much so that the thought of sixty of them slotting together to form an hour seemed like a lifetime. After their embarrassing débâcle with Kaye they had retreated to the coffee bar where they had sipped tepid tea and been driven crazy by the rumours which flew about the room like manic birds. They hadn't talked much. They held hands tightly and smiled uncertain assurance at each other now and again. They had gravitated between the coffee bar, the murder scene, Ian's room and Annie's, restless and anxious, their thirst for facts unassuaged. All lectures for that day had been cancelled, which in a way simply made things worse because it contributed to the feeling of stasis, the impression that the entire place was caught in a limbo of shock and that nothing constructive was being done. They both knew that this was not the case, that a massive police investigation was already underway, but being excluded from it made it seem distant, inconsequential, something which they could neither relate to nor become involved in.

The morning's only crumb of comfort had come, obliquely, from their confrontation with the Chief Inspector. The murder victim can't be Steph, Annie had reasoned, because Kaye had reacted all wrongly when they had mentioned her name. He had looked at them blankly and said, 'So? What has that got to do with this?' If it *had* been Steph lying there among the rubbish, he would have hauled them in for questioning straight away, would not have gone on about wild accusations and all that other stuff.

Ian had nodded, though had not appeared entirely convinced. His view was they had gone about it all wrong, challenging Kaye like that. They should have realised it was obvious the Chief Inspector was not going to give anything away in front of such a large crowd. 'Maybe we ought to go down to the station,' he said, 'or to whoever's in charge of that Portakabin in the car park.'

The arrival of the Portakabin had been perhaps the most exciting development of the morning. It had arrived around eleven o'clock on the back of a lorry and was at least one large, visible, noisy indication that the police inquiry was progressing. Police officers had been going in and out of the temporary incident room all morning. But still their only response to the fluctuating crowd now held at bay behind a cordon of yellow plastic ribbon was stubborn silence.

The two of them had made their way back to the murder scene for perhaps the fourth or fifth time that morning. They had spoken to a Sergeant Craig, repeating what they had told Kaye the day before, but they had found out precisely nothing in return. Ian felt as though they were feeding money into a giant fruit machine which sucked in the coins and never gave anything back. Even his direct question, '*Is* Steph Peele the one who's been killed?' had been answered with an apologetic shrug and a bland, 'I'm sorry but I'm not at liberty to divulge such information.'

It was now midday, the time when they would normally make their way to the dining hall, but neither of them felt like eating. They were in Annie's room, she lying on the bed, sighing occasionally, Ian sitting on a chair by the window, elbows on the sill, looking out. From where he sat he could see the main entrance, all the comings and goings, both vehicular and pedestrian. He didn't know what he was hoping to see — the return of Kaye, he supposed.

'Let's go somewhere else,' said Annie after a silence which had stretched into minutes.

Ian looked up. 'Why? Where? We only got here about quarter of an hour ago.'

'I know, but . . . I don't like it in here now. It makes me feel creepy seeing all Steph's stuff.'

'Why does it?'

'Because . . . well . . . because what if it *is* her lying there behind the kitchens? This is all her personality in this room, all her happiness. It's like her ghost is haunting the place.'

'I thought we'd decided that it wasn't Steph because of what Kaye said.'

'Yes, I know, but why didn't that sergeant just tell us it wasn't her if it wasn't? Why did he have to be so secretive? It wouldn't have hurt him just to say, "No, don't worry, it's not your friend."'

Ian shrugged. 'Aw, you know what coppers are like. They're not renowned for their tact or initiative. They daren't wipe their arses unless someone tells them they're allowed to.'

Annie was silent for a moment. Then she said, 'All the same, I don't feel comfortable here any more. I don't want to be on my own at night, Ian, not now this has happened. Can't I move in with you?'

Ian smiled. 'Yeah, course you can. In fact, if you hadn't asked I'd probably have insisted. I'm not leaving you alone now. We'll stick together all the time, okay?'

Annie nodded and smiled back at him, then abruptly her face crumpled into tears. She sat up and wept, the tears dripping off the end of her nose, her hands limp by her sides as if she didn't have the strength to raise them.

Ian went over to her, hugged her tight. He didn't have to ask why she was crying. The entire situation was sickening, distressing, and having Steph's things around her − her books, her knick-knacks, her posters, her clothes, even her make-up − exaggerated the ache, was a constant reminder of the way Steph *had* been. Even if it wasn't Steph who'd been killed, it did little to ease the tragedy of the situation. The fact was, *someone* was dead out there, and Steph was still lost to them, both physically and mentally.

Ian held Annie until her tears had run their course. He didn't say anything, simply cuddled her, feeling empty inside, wondering if there would ever come a time when things would be normal again, when they could simply enjoy the love they had for each other. Part of him felt angry − at the murderer, at Latcher, at The Crack, even at Steph for the way their burgeoning relationship was being spoiled, its impetus forced into unnatural and unpleasant directions. Some love, it was true, blossomed because of hardship; it was the adversity which stimulated the seed to flower. But his and Annie's relationship had been developing in happier times before all this Crack stuff had begun to happen.

'Sorry,' Annie said when she could speak. 'This isn't doing much good, is it?'

'Don't apologise,' said Ian. 'It's doing *you* some good. You've got to open the pressure valve every now and again or else you'll explode.'

Annie wiped her face, then puffed out a deep breath. In a decisive voice she said, 'Right, I'll put some stuff in a bag and we'll take that round to your place. Then we'll go and get something to eat, whether we want it or not. Then we'll go and see if we can find Mr Carmichael again. Then we'll go down to Maybury and see if they'll let us speak to Kaye.'

'All right,' Ian said. It might not get them anywhere but at least it would feel purposeful. He re-took his seat by the window while Annie wandered around, collecting clothes, toiletries and lecture notes and packing them into a holdall.

A red Ford Escort pulled in through the gates of the University. Even from this distance Ian recognised the moustached face behind the wheel. 'Annie, there's Carmichael,' he said, jumping up. 'He's driving through the gates now. If we're quick we can catch him before he gets out of the car.' While Annie was digesting this, Ian ran out of the room and started pounding down the stairs.

Abandoning her packing for the time being, Annie went after him.

337

She caught up with him in the car park, breathlessly attempting to explain all that had happened to a bemused Carmichael, who was trying to lock his car door and listen to Ian at the same time.

'Hang on,' Carmichael said. 'Are you telling me someone's actually been *killed*? One of the students?'

'Yes, sir. Well, we're not sure who it is yet, but someone's definitely dead. One of the dinner ladies found the body stuffed in a dustbin this morning behind the kitchens. There've been police everywhere. Chief Inspector Kaye's been here, but he wouldn't speak to us. Me and Annie were hoping that maybe he'd take us seriously if you were with us.'

Carmichael looked shocked and confused. He pressed the fingers of his right hand to his forehead as if to still the thoughts that were rattling in his skull. 'Look,' he said, 'perhaps you'd better come up to my room and tell me all this from the beginning. Funnily enough I've been with the police myself, but I had no idea any of this was going on.'

The three of them entered the main building and ascended three flights of stairs to Carmichael's book-lined office. Once there, Ian and Annie told him everything that had happened that morning. Carmichael listened with a frown of disbelief crinkling his forehead. When they had finished he shook his head slowly from side to side.

'This is awful,' he said. 'I can't believe it's happened.' He rubbed his eyes as if he were suddenly very tired. Ian and Annie said nothing. They sat patiently and looked at him. Carmichael stopped rubbing his eyes and blinked at them. 'I think I'd better go and see all this for myself,' he said.

Five minutes later Ian and Annie found themselves at the murder scene once again. The crowd had diminished since the last time they were here, but it was still fairly sizeable. 'What's going on?' Ian asked someone, and was told, 'Nothing much.' Carmichael pushed his way to the barrier of yellow ribbon and began speaking to a constable, his manner earnest, urgent, authoritative.

Eventually he turned and made his way back to where Ian and Annie were standing. 'Any luck?' asked Ian, nodding in the direction of the policeman.

Carmichael pointed at the Portakabin. 'They're expecting some kind of announcement any minute now. Apparently the sergeant has just had a phone call from Kaye.'

Sure enough moments later the door of the Portakabin opened and Sergeant Craig emerged. He stood on the top step, holding up his hands to quell the murmur of expectation, pinched features bland beneath the brim of his cap. When there was sufficient silence he said, 'I've just been asked to inform you that Chief Inspector Kaye, who is leading this inquiry, will address a meeting in the University auditorium in approximately half an hour's time. Everyone is invited to attend, and we would be grateful if you could spread the word. If you have any queries about this investigation, then hopefully Mr Kaye will be able to answer them. That's all. Thank you very much.' He stepped quickly back into the Portakabin and closed the door.

The murmur rose again, became a speculative babble. People began to drift away to tell their friends. Ian looked at Annie and saw the trepidation on her face. 'Half an hour,' he said, looking at his watch. 'That makes it one-thirty. What shall we do in the meantime?'

'You heard the man,' said Carmichael. 'Spread the word. Praise the Lord.' He began to move away. 'I'll round up some of the staff. See you at half-past.'

63

Word of mouth and two dozen posters scrawled hastily in lime green marker pen ensured that Kaye's meeting, half an hour later, was well attended. Ian and Annie arrived almost ten minutes early with the auditorium around a quarter full, and took their seats three rows from the front. By the time one-thirty arrived there was standing room only and people were still filing in. Ian saw Carmichael arrive with two other members of staff. The English lecturer scanned the rows of seats but, despite Ian's frantic waving, didn't see them.

'I wonder where Neil is,' Annie said, speaking for the first time in minutes, 'I hope he's all right.'

'Yeah,' replied Ian. 'It's strange, isn't it? You'd have thought he'd have wanted to be here.'

In fact, Ian was more worried than he was letting on. If Neil had found something out about Latcher and gone to confront him without telling them . . . Ian tried not to think of the possible consequences. He clung instead to the hope that Neil had rushed to the police station, demanding answers, as soon as he had heard about the murder that morning.

The audience was growing restless when Kaye finally appeared almost fifteen minutes late. There was an ironic cheer from the back row and a smattering of applause. Kaye cast a slow, baleful glance in that direction. He strode to the lectern in the middle of the room, clipboard dwarfed in his large hand. Grey-suited, square-set, grim-faced, he looked every inch the policeman.

Before speaking he looked slowly around the room, as if to locate potential trouble-makers, then he grudgingly introduced himself, explaining that he was head of the investigation into 'certain very serious incidents' which had occurred in Maybury over the past twenty-four hours. Ian almost laughed at his gruff coyness, but in light of what Kaye was about to tell them the policeman's initial reticence was understandable. When Kaye mentioned the word 'murder', Annie reached for Ian's hand and gripped it hard. The audience shuffled uneasily as if collectively bracing itself. But Kaye did not provide them with the one piece of information which they were both longing and dreading to hear: the victim's name.

'I'm sorry,' he said as if he wasn't when certain sections of the assembly began to make disgruntled noises, 'but I really can't reveal such information until relatives have been informed and the body positively identified. However, what I *can* tell you is that the victim is male, in his late teens, and is believed to be a first year student at this University. He was subjected to a particularly savage attack, not actually on the University campus but on a dirt-track across the road from the main entrance. However, this is not all I came here today to tell you. Since this morning's discovery there have been certain very major developments in this inquiry.'

As soon as Kaye told them that the victim was male, Annie let out a long sobbing breath, clutched Ian's hand even harder, and slumped forward in her seat like a puppet whose strings have been cut. Ian, however, felt a cold, sharp contraction in his stomach, and immediately thought: Just where the fuck *is* Neil?

However neither of them had time to dwell on this revelation because there were more to come, and these more startling and horrifying than ever. In a steady neutral voice Kaye told them that the bodies of three more University students had been found slain in the house they shared in the Royston district of Maybury, and that the man who had led them to the house was now being held for questioning.

As in the press conference earlier there was uproar at this disclosure, but in this instance it was more intense, more desperate, motivated by personal anxieties, fears for friends, rather than simply a desire to eke out the juiciest, kinkyest, goriest details for public consumption.

Students stood on seats, yelling at Kaye. 'We have a right to know!' shouted a guy in a combat jacket whose dreadlocks sprouted from his head like a woolly Yucca plant. Kaye waited out the clamour stoically, eyes half-closed, mouth set in a terse line, body still and upright and grey as a granite statue. Arguments broke out among the crowd. 'Shut up, let him speak,' boomed a bear-sized student whose beard and spectacles made it impossible to discern his age, and quickly his plea was taken up as a chant by the majority: 'Let him speak! Let him speak! Let him speak!'

When only the chant filled the hall it faded quickly. Now Kaye roused himself, giving a small nod as if he had just witnessed something mildly interesting. 'I came here to give you as much information as I'm able to,' he said in a voice that managed to sound both indifferent and admonishing, 'but I can walk out here and now if you'd rather. It makes no odds to me.'

'We just want some names,' came a voice from the back. 'We've all got friends we're worried about. We just want to know who's dead.'

Kaye swung towards the voice, lips drawn back as though to snarl. 'You think *you've* got a right to know before the relatives, do you? Perhaps we ought to let the parents find out from the Nine O'Clock News?'

The silence which followed his sharp response was heavy with both shame and resentment. There were whispers, mutterings, but no one it seemed was either courageous or foolhardy enough to engage the Chief Inspector in open debate. Ian had tried it once and had been made to feel approximately the size of a bug. He had already decided that as soon as the meeting was over he would rush down to the front and request a private word with Kaye before he made his exit.

Already it seemed that the policeman was anxious to wind up the proceedings. He appealed for patience and co-operation as if he'd learned the lines by rote, and urged people − simply as a precaution − to make sure they had someone with them at night, a request which raised a round of giggles and a boorish cheer. Kaye reddened with anger at the unwitting innuendo. However he made no comment. He reached for the clipboard which he'd placed on the lectern and had thus far made no reference to.

'Before we go,' he said, 'I have some names here of people I'd like to talk to, people who I believe may be able to provide us with information to further this inquiry. If any of these people are in the audience could they please stay behind: Julie Emmott, Daniel Steven Latcher, Ian Raven and Annie Katherine O'Donnell. If, in the meantime, any of you feel you have information which may prove useful to the investigation, there is a Portakabin in the car park behind Mordred Hall which is being used as a temporary incident room. It will be manned twenty-four hours a day until this investigation is complete.'

Ian and Annie, after the shock of having their names read out, felt rather like lepers. They were stared at and whispered about. Ian wanted to declare, 'We're innocent. We had nothing to do with it, honest.' Annie sat and stared at the floor, hands clasped together in her lap. The impression she gave of praying was consolidated when Ian heard her mutter miserably, 'Oh God, let this all be over soon.' He put his arm around her and kissed her ear. Amen to that, he thought.

64

Jacks and Bowen, the two policemen who were questioning Neil, had known for some time that he was not the killer. The evidence was just about as irrefutable as it could be. There had been no fingerprints found at Cramer Road, but those found at last night's murder scene and in Newcastle had not been Neil's. Also the killer had small feet for a man; he took size seven Reeboks. Neil's shoes were size ten. Neil did not drive a car, whereas the murderer did. Neil could tell them nothing of the murder in Newcastle: he fell into a preoccupied silence whenever they asked him to describe the victim, the locale, the route he had taken, details of the killing itself. Jacks and Bowen were even willing to bet that Neil had been seen around the University on Friday night by plenty of witnesses when the Newcastle murder was taking place. Soon they would know for sure. Kaye was talking to a couple of his friends now. It was confidently expected that they would unwittingly provide him with an alibi.

Exonerating Neil did not make them particularly happy. In fact it dismayed them to have to admit he was innocent. It meant the killer was still out there and had to be caught bloody quickly. Anyone who killed five people in as many days did not warrant a leisurely approach.

Jacks, a tall sandy-haired man with a disarmingly boyish expression, looked at Neil with a mixture of frustration and sympathy. They sat facing each other, a formica table-top separating them. Bowen, bulky, bald and moustached, leaned against the wall, gulping the latest of innumerable cups of coffee. Neil was staring blankly at the index finger of his right hand, which, had it been a pencil, would have been drawing a complex pattern of spirals and swirls. It was obvious he was disturbed, and as such communication with him had been tortuous. At times Jacks had felt like slapping him, but had refrained from doing so.

They were currently plodding a much-trod path. 'Neil, *why* do you think you're Larry?' It was a question Jacks had asked so many times that it was beginning to lose its meaning, to sound alien, like a word repeated over and over.

Neil's finger continued to doodle; his eyes continued to watch it. 'Because I killed them all,' he mumbled through barely moving lips.

Jacks sighed. 'No, you didn't, Neil. You didn't kill anyone. We *know* you didn't. Why do you say you did?'

'I killed them. I'm Larry. I killed them because they had to be killed.'

'Why did they have to be killed, Neil?'

'They were alive. I had to kill them.'

'But that's no excuse is it, Neil? That won't convince us. Why are you lying to us, Neil? Why are you pretending?'

No answer. Doodling finger. Blank eyes.

'I'll tell you, shall I, Neil? I'll tell you what really happened. You went along to Cramer Road this morning to see a friend or a girlfriend, am I right? You arrived there and perhaps you found the front door open. You went inside. Upstairs you found Catriona, or maybe you found the other two first and Catriona afterwards. It was such a terrible shock that your mind reacted in a funny way, sent all your thoughts haywire. It took in all the details. You saw all the weapons and all the injuries and immediately you knew what had been used to do what. And because of this, because of the way your mind was working, you thought that *you* had done it all. You felt guilty at this and horribly ashamed, and you decided that the only way you could put things right was to confess what you'd done. And that's what you're doing now isn't it, Neil? You're confessing to something you haven't done to try to restore some sense of order.'

Neil didn't reply. Bowen whistled and murmured, 'Tonight, Sigmund Freud, this is your life.'

Jacks turned to Bowen with a scowl. Bowen raised a hand in apology. Turning back to Neil, Jacks ordered, 'Neil, look at me.'

343

He did not do so immediately. His finger stopped tracing circles and he became very still. For a moment the four of them in the room seemed frozen into a tableau. Then slowly Neil raised his head and stared straight into Jacks' eyes.

He's out of it, thought Jacks. Though Neil's gaze seemed intense there was emptiness there, as if he wore opaque contact lenses, saw only the pictures in his own mind. Very clearly and very loudly Jacks said, 'Your name is Neil Gardener. What is your name?'

The mask stared blankly back. Then the lips moved almost imperceptibly and a rumble of sound, barely words, emerged. 'I'm Larry.'

'No,' said Jacks patiently. 'You're not Larry. Look'. He held up a card in a transparent plastic case. It was green with the initials NUS printed in white across the top. There was an over-exposed station booth photograph of Neil on the left, personal details on the right. Jacks held the card in Neil's line of vision but saw no indication of his pupils altering to accommodate this fresh visual input.

'See?' said Jacks, hoping that Neil did. 'You're not Larry. You're Neil Gardener. Remember? Neil Gardener. This is you here.' He wiggled his finger above the photograph. 'You didn't kill anyone did you, Neil? You've made a mistake. Your friends *were* killed, but not by you. Who really did it, Neil? Do you know?'

Neil seemed to be studying the card intently, his face stiff with concentration. However appearances, Jacks knew, were deceptive. It was just as likely that he was sinking even deeper into himself, hiding beneath mental blankets to avoid coping with the truth. His lips moved again, but at first no sound came out. When he finally spoke the word was predictable: 'Larry.'

'*No!*' shouted Jacks. He slammed his hand down hard on the table top, making Bowen and the constable by the door jump. Neil, however, didn't move. The sudden shock could not penetrate the deeper trauma which he wore like armour plating.

Jacks closed his eyes briefly, took a couple of deep breaths. The cracks in his patience papered over, he began speaking quietly again.

'Neil, you are *not* Larry. You didn't kill anyone. But if you think hard you might be able to give us some clue as to who the real Larry is. You could help us that way.'

Neil's stare was that of a foreigner listening politely to gobble-degook.

Bowen said, 'With all due respect, guv, I think we're wasting our time. The kid needs a bloody shrink, not a policeman.'

Jacks sat back with a sigh, looking at Neil with a weary expression.

344

'You're probably right, Doug. Do us a favour, will you? Go and ask Kaye if we can take the kid to hospital.'

Bowen curled his lip, making his moustache bristle. 'Do I have to, guv? You know Kaye doesn't like me.'

'He doesn't like anyone, Doug. Ask at the desk for a crucifix and some holy water. You'll be safe enough then.'

Grumbling, Bowen exited. He was back before he should have been.

'That was quick,' said Jacks suspiciously.

'Message from Lucifer himself, guv. Can I see you outside a moment please?'

Jacks glanced at Neil and stood up. In the corridor he asked, 'Well, what is it?'

'Kaye says we have to hold the boy for another twenty-four hours. Bang him up in a cell. On no account is he to be allowed out of the station.'

Jacks rolled his eyes. 'What's the point? We know Gardener's innocent.'

'You know, guv, and I know, but according to the Big Chief although we have enough evidence to know he killed neither Simpson nor Pedder, he's all we've got for the other three murders at the moment, and as there were no prints at Cramer Road the boy is still the prime suspect.'

'Aw, that's bollocks,' said Jacks. 'It's obvious all five murders were by the same bloke and it wasn't Neil Gardener. What's he playing at?'

'I think it's a little game called 'face-saving', guv. If we let Gardener go now after what Kaye told the press it'll make him look stupid and bring a whole lot of shit down on our heads.'

Jacks made an exasperated sound and raked a hand through his hair. 'What about taking the kid to hospital? I reckon he needs someone professional to talk to.'

Bowen shrugged. 'Don't ask me, ask Kaye. But I can guess what his answer'll be ...' Adopting a tough Kaye-like voice he barked, 'Tomorrow, when the fuss has died down a bit. The lad's all right. He's had a bit of a shock, that's all. He'll get over it.'

'Wanker,' Jacks said, directing the remark in the general direction of Kaye's office.

'Permission to agree with you, sir?' Bowen requested, straight-faced.

'Granted,' said Jacks.

'Wanker,' said Bowen.

65

It was obviously a very big mistake. The prospect that it might be true was inconceivable. Neil a murderer? No way. But Kaye believed it, and Kaye was the law, and in the final reckoning it was the law who made the decisions.

But perhaps, Ian thought, he was jumping to conclusions. After all, Kaye had not said in so many words that Neil was their suspect. But Neil was certainly involved, and if he wasn't a victim what else could he be? Ian tried to quell the thoughts buzzing madly inside his head, tried to calm himself so he could just think clearly for a moment.

When Kaye had called out his, Annie's, Julie Emmott's and Dan Latcher's names in the auditorium, Ian's initial reaction had been: Neil's dead! Latcher's killed him! But quickly he realised that that couldn't be the case. Kaye had said that a suspect was already being held for the murders, which meant that it wasn't Latcher, otherwise why had Kaye expressed a desire to speak to him? Ian, Annie and Julie Emmott had remained silent as they had been driven to Maybury police station by Kaye himself. Julie looked confused and frightened. Questions pounded in Ian's head, but Kaye's expression, even grimmer than usual, discouraged him from voicing them.

At the station, much to their dismay, they had been peremptorily split up. 'I'll speak to you first if I may, Miss Emmott?' Kaye said. Polite though the request seemed, the tone of it made it clear her choice was negligible. Julie had been led unhappily away, whilst Ian and Annie had been shown to seats that seemed moulded from iron and licquorice, where they sat fidgeting, glancing around, barely speaking, as if afraid hidden cameras might be observing their movements.

It was over half an hour before someone came for Annie. They did not see Julie leave, and though Ian supposed they were being kept apart to avoid any prospect of collusion, the fact was nevertheless unsettling. He wished that Annie hadn't cast a miserable, pleading glance back at him just as she'd turned the corner. There was nothing he could do to prevent what was happening and yet he felt guilty just sitting there. He spent the next forty-five minutes trying to calm his nerves by thinking up as many words as possible using the letters from the poster headline on the opposite wall: 'Be a Crimebuster.'

'Crater,' he whispered just as a dark blur at the end of the corridor made him look up.

'Chief Inspector Kaye's ready for you now, Mister Raven,' said the constable.

Ian felt his chest tightening as he followed the policeman along the corridor. Discreetly he took a blast on his inhaler. The first thing he noticed in Kaye's office were the tropical fish. A telephone line crossed the white sky outside the window like a visible join.

'Sit down, Ian,' said Kaye. He looked massive behind his desk, like an adult using school furniture. Nervously Ian sat. Kaye continued, 'I asked you here today so that we could go over a few things.'

'Where's Annie?' Ian asked, and immediately felt annoyed at how reedy his voice sounded.

'Drinking tea by now, I should think. Don't worry, son, you'll see her soon enough.'

'Is Steph all right?' Ian said quickly. 'Is Dan Latcher the murderer? Have you arrested him yet?'

Kaye's last comment had seemed almost genial and had encouraged Ian to blurt out his questions. Now, though, the Chief Inspector's face clouded over. His eyes adopted the blankly menacing sheen which was so unnerving.

Quietly Kaye said, 'I think it would be a much better idea if *I* asked the questions, don't you?'

Ian said nothing. He cleared his throat and stared at his hands to avoid eye-contact with Kaye. Nevertheless his bruises began to throb and he felt himself sweating, as if Kaye's presence was a wave of heat, enclosing and stifling him.

'I want you to tell me all that you told me before,' Kaye said, 'when you came in to report Stephanie Peele's disappearance.'

Ian told him, wishing he knew why Kaye wanted to hear all this again, but not daring to ask. When he had done, Kaye began to ask him questions.

'How would you describe Neil Gardener? What sort of temperament does he have? Would you say he was an open person, a private person or what?'

Puzzled Ian replied, 'Er ... I don't know. I suppose he's a pretty normal bloke. Got a bit of a temper, I suppose.'

'A temper?'

'Yeah, you know. When something annoys him he has a tendency to rush straight in without thinking things through.'

'Would you say he has a propensity for violence?'

'Er ... I don't know. How do you mean?'

'Did you ever see him lose his temper and hit anyone, or

347

even threaten anyone? Did he ever strike Stephanie Peele, for example?'

'Oh no, he'd never hit Steph. I think he might have knocked Dan Latcher about a bit, given half a chance.'

'Did he ever threaten to kill Latcher?'

'Um ... I don't think so. Not seriously anyway. Why are you asking all these questions about Neil?'

Ignoring the enquiry, Kaye went on, 'Did Neil know anyone who lived with Dan Latcher in Cramer Road?'

'Er ... yeah. He knows Emma. Emma Chettle.'

'What was his relationship with Miss Chettle?'

'What do you mean?'

'Was he a good friend? An acquaintance? Were they sleeping together?'

'Oh no, nothing like that. Like I say, he's been going out with Steph. No, they're ... acquaintances, I suppose. He doesn't know her very well.'

'Was he round at Cramer Road very often?'

'No. In fact I don't think he's ever been there.' Something about this conversation was making Ian very uneasy.

'When was the last time you saw Neil Gardener?'

Ian suddenly realised what it was. He said, 'Why are you referring to Neil in the past tense? He's dead, isn't he? Latcher *has* killed him?'

Kaye was silent for a few moments, his deep breathing like that of a large animal, a lion or a bear. His face was deadpan, his eyes divulging nothing. Finally he repeated, 'When was the last time you saw Neil Gardener?'

Ian's hands gripped the chair-arms as though to push himself up. However he remained seated, sweat gluing his body to his clothes, his heart thumping. He was terrified, partly of his own audacity in standing up to the ogre, but mostly of the knowledge which he knew Kaye was concealing behind his stony façade. Shrilly Ian said, 'I'm not answering any more questions until you tell me what's going on. I have a right to know whether my friends are okay.'

Very deliberately the Chief Inspector placed his hands palm down on the desk and pushed himself to his feet. For a moment Ian thought he was about to be lifted by his hair and thrown against the wall. The way Kaye was looking at him he seemed to be seriously considering this. Then he strode stiffly across to his aquarium and stared at the fish describing lazy patterns of gleaming colour behind the glass.

Ian hated the silence, but he couldn't pluck up the courage to repeat his outburst. He could hear distant, busy sounds and his own harsh breathing. He took his inhaler from his pocket just as Kaye began speaking.

'Your friends are fine,' the policeman said. 'Or at least Neil Gardener is fine. Stephanie Peele has yet to be found. I have a number of officers trying to track her down at this moment.'

'Then ... neither of them is dead?' Ian experienced such a wash of relief that he felt like laughing.

'No', said Kaye. 'As far as I am aware, neither of them is dead.'

'Then why all these questions about Neil and Emma Chettle? Where's Neil now? Do you know?'

Kaye turned from the aquarium and looked at him. 'There's only so much information I can give,' he said. 'Surely you can appreciate that most of our findings must remain confidential until the inquiry is complete?'

The policeman was speaking to him reasonably now, almost with compassion, though Ian guessed this was largely because he wanted information from him. He couldn't yet quite work out where Kaye's inquiries were leading. Perhaps he would find the solutions between the lines of the Chief Inspector's questions.

'Okay,' he said, feeling calmer, more in control now that he knew his friends were safe. 'I'm sorry to be obstructive. I was worried, that's all. I'll answer any other questions you want to ask.'

'When was the last time you saw Neil Gardener?' Kaye responded immediately.

Ian thought hard. 'It was ... yesterday. About half-six, seven. Just after we came back from the station, in fact, after we'd told you about Steph.'

Kaye nodded. He seemed to have been expecting this. 'What were you doing on Friday night?' he asked then.

For a few moments Ian was at a loss, thrown by the unexpectedness of the question. Then, remembering, he said, 'Oh, yeah, it was the night of the Freshers' Ball. It was fancy dress. I went as Dracula. There was a band and a disco, but I never got to either of those.'

'Oh? And why was that?'

'Aw, I went into the bar and there was this yob pestering Annie, virtually pinning her against the wall. I went across and there was a bit of a barney. I got knocked about, hence the black eye and stuff. I went back to Annie's room to clean myself up.'

'Did you see Neil Gardener at all on this particular evening?'

'Yeah, it was Neil and a couple of his mates who dragged the gorilla off me.'

'And what time would this have been?'

349

'I dunno. Half-seven, eight o'clock, something like that.'

'And did you see Neil Gardener again that night?'

'No, not until the next day. The next evening, in fact.'

'I see. What would you say was the nature of the relationship between Neil Gardener and Daniel Latcher?'

'Er ... there isn't one.'

'Not even one of antagonism?'

'Well, like I say, Neil's sort of talked about what he's going to do to Latcher when he catches up with him, but as far as I know they haven't met face to face yet.'

'Would Neil have any reason to hold a grudge against any of Daniel Latcher's house-mates?'

'No, I don't think so.'

'He had no reason to believe, then, that they might be withholding information about Stephanie?'

Ian shook his head. 'No. In fact, Emma was frightened of Dan. She said he'd changed this term, become really weird.'

'She told Neil Gardener this?'

'No, me and Annie. We told Neil later.'

'And what of Neil's relationship with the others in the house, Neville Walton and Catriona Peters, for example? Was he acquainted with either of these people?'

'Not as far as I know. I don't get it. What has all this got to do with ...'

Ian tailed off, for all at once he *did* get it. Suddenly all the disparate components clicked together in his mind, one following another in logical sequence. His stomach dropped into a bottomless well that had opened somewhere beneath him. For a moment he couldn't speak; when he tried only a croak emerged. He gulped air so violently that it made him cough. After clearing his throat several times he finally found his voice.

'That's who's died, isn't it? It's Emma and ... and Neville and Catriona. And you think Neil did it. That's why we haven't seen him, because he's helping you with your enquiries.'

His hands were trembling badly. He clenched them into fists and drew them into his roiling stomach. All at once the room seemed flat, a cardboard sham, the light a harsh and vulgar approximation of daylight. Kaye was standing at the window now, looking out, perhaps so that Ian could not see the expression on his face. He appeared to be deep in thought, perhaps calculating how much it was wise to let Ian know. This seemed confirmed when at last he turned, having apparently reached a decision.

'What we're about to discuss,' Kaye said, 'must not – I repeat,

350

not – be repeated outside these four walls. Is that clear, Ian? I'm telling you now only because I believe it may help this inquiry.'

Ian nodded. 'Yes,' he said, 'of course.'

'Good. If I *do* find out you've disclosed information before I'm ready to have it known, you'll be back here so fast your feet won't touch the ground. Is that clear?'

Another nod. 'Yes,' he almost whispered.

'All right then.' Kaye crossed to his desk, opened a drawer and took out a photograph. 'What you've just guessed is all true. Emma Chettle, Neville Walton and Catriona Peters are dead. Murdered. Their bodies were discovered this morning. Your friend, Neil Gardener, is the prime suspect. He led us to the bodies, and furthermore confessed to the killings.'

Ian wanted to say something, to protest, but Kaye held up a hand before he could squeeze the words past his swollen throat. The policeman handed Ian the photograph he'd taken from his desk. Ian gazed at the unfamiliar likeness of a young bony-faced man with a broad forehead, short dark curly hair and a slightly lopsided grin.

'Who's this?' Ian managed to ask, his voice still little above a whisper.

'You don't recognise him?'

Ian shook his head.

'His name is John Pedder. He's a student at your University. It was his body that was found in the dustbin this morning.'

Ian felt a definite cold spasm ripple through his stomach at the news. He stared into John Pedder's dark eyes as though trying to read some inkling of the tragedy to come. He felt sick. He handed the photograph back to Kaye, who replaced it in his desk. Ian was glad to see the photograph disappear, though in itself it was innocuous enough. How long ago since Pedder had had it taken? he wondered. A few weeks? A few days?

'You're sure you've never seen him before?' Kaye was saying. 'You've never seen him in Neil Gardener's company?'

'No,' Ian croaked, 'definitely not. What course did he do?'

'Philosophy, I believe.'

Ian shook his head again. 'No, I haven't seen him. I met Neil on the first night at Uni. I'm pretty sure he didn't know the guy either.'

Kaye looked gravely at Ian for a moment, then crossed to the window again, sighing. There was silence in the room for a few moments whilst Ian plucked up the courage to speak.

'You've got it all wrong,' he said then. 'Neil's not a murderer.

351

He can't be.' His voice dried up as Kaye swung from the window, stiffly, as though afraid body language might betray him.

'I'm not prepared to discuss the whys and wherefores of the case,' he said. 'I've told you all you need to know for the time being. You do understand, don't you, Ian, that this inquiry will get nowhere if our every move is leaked to the public? I want to get to the truth, that's all. I won't have anyone jeopardising that aim, do you understand?'

Ian nodded dumbly, though he was unsure whether Kaye's clipped phrases were intended as an appeal, a warning or a threat. Kaye nodded, satisfied. 'Good, I think we understand each other. I won't keep you for much longer now. I just want to ask a few more questions.'

For the next quarter of an hour Kaye did just that. Ian felt a desire to save Neil somehow, vindicate him through his testimony, but he was only half aware of the queries which Kaye fired at him, and which he answered almost in a daze, his mind still whirling. As far as he could tell it was mostly trivial stuff, background information which might or might not prove useful. When he was done, Kaye said, 'Okay, that's all for now. I may want to speak to you again, so stay where I can find you.'

Annie was waiting for him at the front desk and they hugged like lovers after a long separation. There was no sign of Julie; Annie hadn't seen her. Secretly Ian hoped that she was not being asked to identify the corpses of her friends. The two of them walked into the centre of Maybury, talking with a feverishness born of shock, barely noticing the peculiarly high proportion of young people strolling through the streets or loitering in groups. Despite Kaye's warning to keep what had passed between them to himself, Annie had apparently been given the same information as Ian. Appalled, almost numbed, she kept murmuring, 'I can't believe it. We were only talking to Emma the other day. It's so awful.'

In the middle of the street Annie drew startled and disapproving stares by bursting into tears and clutching Ian around the waist. 'This is a nightmare,' she sobbed. 'I'm so scared, Ian. What are we going to do?'

He felt like crying too, but his tears had formed into an ice-block which had slid hard and unmelting into the pit of his stomach. He clutched Annie back, kissing her forehead but unable to reply. They stood like that for what seemed a very long time, oblivious of the attention they were attracting from passers by.

The walk back to University was long and undertaken mostly in silence. The day was pleasant, breezy but warm, yet the two of them felt so despondent that it seemed there was a blight over everything; the world seemed dark with poison and shadows. Their first sight of the University, a trio of red brick peaks craning over a screen of hills and trees, prompted Annie to speak, as if she wouldn't get the chance once she was back on campus. 'I'd go home now if I could,' she said, 'but I feel so involved. I feel as though I'm caught in the strands of a giant web.'

Ian nodded vaguely and squeezed her hand to show that he understood and sympathised. More red brick emerged from the ocean of grass as they plodded towards it, lean towers and squat boxes, some of which winked lewd sunlight from eyes of glass. They both averted their gaze from the lane where last night's murder had taken place, though the yellow plastic police ribbon stretched across its entrance snapped in the breeze as if to attract their attention.

'I feel ... drained,' Ian said. 'Utterly shattered. I feel as if all my energy, all my motivation, has been sucked out of me.'

'Let's go back to your room and sleep for a bit if we can,' said Annie. 'I think we both need to put this out of our heads for a while.'

Hand in hand they trudged back to Lancelot Hall and entered the lobby. It was dark and cool as a cave. A bumping sound from the corridor on their right preceded a figure carrying a suitcase so large and heavy that he was forced to half-drag it along the ground. The figure's face was ghostly white and cadaverously thin, the eyes smudges of sooty shadow. If the man had not been clean-shaven Ian and Annie might have recognised him earlier, but it was only when he spoke that they realised it was Duncan Westey.

'Hey, guys,' Westey said, 'give us a hand with this bitch, wouldya? I'll give myself a hernia.'

Ian and Annie rushed to oblige. Ian said, 'Going on your holidays, Duncan?'

Westey rubbed his hands together and snorted mirthlessly. 'Hardly,' he said. 'There won't be too much fun on this trip.'

'Why? Where *are* you going?' asked Annie.

Westey looked uncomfortable. 'Well, it's ... it's kinda personal, you know.'

Ian gestured vaguely. 'Is it because of all this?' When Westey looked blank he elaborated, 'The murders and everything? You're going away because of it?'

'Shit, no, though that's a good enough reason. No, it's ... well, to tell you the truth, guys, it's my son. He's dying, you see.'

'Your son?' Ian exclaimed. 'I never knew you had a son. I never even knew you were married or anything.'

353

'I'm not. Was though. Ellie and I got divorced in '86. We've got a kid, Rickie. He's seven now. He's ... er ... he's got spinal cancer, has had it for about six months. Ellie ... er, wouldn't let me see him, said it upset the little guy more than was good for him. I thought I wasn't going to be able to see him again before ... well, you know. But she's relented now, so I'm going. Hence the new clean-cut image. Don't want her to think I'm going to seed.' He stroked his chin, smiling rather forcedly. His voice had been light, chatty, but the strain and grief lurking just below the surface was not hard to detect.

Ian tried to say something but his own voice felt choked. He patted the hall warden awkwardly on the shoulder. Annie stepped forward and kissed him on the cheek, causing Westey to turn immediately away to hide the emotion that her tenderness had elicited. He made a big show of fiddling with the handle of his suitcase, then said in a muffled voice, 'Gotta go, guys. See ya around.' Annie held the entrance doors open as he bumped his way out of them. 'Good luck,' Ian managed at last, but Westey had already gone.

66

Walking to Maybury had taken Royle and the others over seven hours. At just after midnight last night a girl called Charley had arrived at the byre, at which point they had all immediately and instinctively known that she was the last, that the group was now complete and that they could move on. By this time the group had numbered over two hundred. They milled in and around the byre, sat cross-legged on the muddy grass or leaned against the stone wall, talking together in low voices. There was a certainty about the group, a sense of purpose, almost of destiny. No one questioned their gathering here, no one wondered how or why they had all managed to congregate in such an obscure location, no one wondered where they were going. Conversation was simply a socialising procedure: What's your name? Where are you from? How did you get here? A few of them discussed Dan Latcher's story, 'The Temptation', in hushed, reverential tones, though strangely they spoke of it as if it were something long-established and accepted in their lives, and not as a miraculous (and in some ways frightening) catalyst for that day's events.

When Charley arrived she was greeted warmly, and then they all began to stir, standing up and brushing themselves down, readying themselves for their journey. There was no rallying call, had been no earlier mutual agreement; they all simply *knew* it was time to leave. It was a knowledge that seemed natural and unremarkable, like knowing you had to chew food before swallowing, like knowing how to manipulate your hand to pick something up, like knowing how to walk, how to speak, how to breathe. Despite the late hour there were no indications of tiredness among the group, and neither would there be as the night progressed; they would maintain the same steady pace and arrive feeling as refreshed as when they had set off.

They kept to fields and woodland to avoid creating alarm, and although none of them knew what their final destination would be, they all knew exactly where they were going. There was no debate, no hesitation. There was only the strong, sure squelch and tramp of two hundred pairs of feet, the occasional light murmur of conversation complementing the night-rustle of leaves caressed by wind.

Peculiarly no injuries whatsoever were sustained on the journey. Despite the darkness, the uneven terrain, the large number of people, there was not a single scratch from an overhanging branch nor an ankle turning in an unseen divot. As he walked, Royle surmised that this, on top of everything else, would earlier have struck him as eerie, unnatural, but now he simply accepted this minor miracle as he had accepted all the others.

'This is it,' someone said to him at seven-thirty that morning as the group trooped across a final field, swarmed over a dry stone wall and emerged on to a country road that led downwards.

'I know,' said Royle, for suddenly he did. The market town spread below them was their destination. There was such a feeling of certainty and a sense of homecoming that the place may just as well have had a neon sign above it flashing 'Welcome'.

'That's where it'll happen,' said someone at Royle's shoulder. He turned, and instinctively embraced the person who had spoken, as if something momentous and hazardous had been achieved. All around he saw that others were embracing too, some weeping as if greeting loved ones back from some bloody and terrible war.

And indeed their march into town *was* like a homecoming. They laughed and acted the fool; a boy with long hair and a striped

355

jumper kicked up his legs and walked two hundred yards on his hands, earning a round of applause. When they came to a road sign reading: 'Maybury 2 miles', they all fell into an awed silence, staring at the name of the place, repeating it silently to themselves, touching the metal pole with their fingertips as they passed as though it were a totem which would keep them from harm.

Maybury. Despite himself, Royle was as enchanted as the rest by the word. He could not have been more so had the sign read 'Camelot' or 'Never-Never Land' or 'Oz'. There was a fire in his belly now, rapture in his veins. He felt buoyant and happy, almost divinely so. Each step was like a weightless bound, a fresh taste of freedom. Nothing mattered any more but Maybury and whatever they would find there.

They arrived, unperturbed by the attention they were attracting, by the long stares which were by turns disapproving, alarmed, hostile. Whatever happened now was meant to happen. Their destinies were unfolding before them. All they need do was wait for a sign.

And wait they did, throughout that long day, eternally patient, eternally hopeful. Despite the hassle they received from passers by, shop assistants, bus drivers, policemen, they remained polite and compliant, knowing that eventually 'it' would happen. They split into smaller groups, re-formed, split again — it was as if they were searching for the correct pattern, trying different combinations in the hope that it would act as some sort of key. They trudged the streets, tracing and re-tracing their steps; they sat in cafes and visited the library and browsed in shops until they were shooed out by the owners.

It was all part of the waiting, all part of what was meant to be. Not one of them begrudged the long hours spent kicking their heels. They were moved on time and again, forced to endure abuse and suspicion; they were even, in a few cases, arrested — and yet they accepted it all, knowing that it was right.

And now Warren Royle looked into the sky, an almost imperceptible haze informing him that twilight was approaching. The rush hour, such as it was here, was over. The shops were shut, a few premature street lamps blinking on. He should have felt frustrated and disillusioned at this aimless waste of a day, but he did not: serenity, well-being, contentment enclosed him like a mother's embrace. The expectation was delicious, curling and curling inside him. He felt like a child on Christmas Eve, but a thousand times better. Soon the reason for his entire life, the meaning behind his every action, would be revealed to him.

He was sitting on the wide stone steps outside the Sports Centre

356

with about fifteen others. He was neither cold nor tired nor hungry, yet for want of something better to do he stood up and announced, 'I'm going to get something to eat. Does anyone want anything?' Most people shook their heads, but a few gave him money, asking for chocolate or crisps. Royle wandered off to look for a corner shop that would still be open.

He was out of sight of the Sports Centre when he noticed a newsagent's door standing open, grimy front window dominated by a block of red and white sticky-backed plastic that was an advertisement for Coca-Cola. He entered a poky area which smelled of inky dust. Shelves were stacked high with an assortment of goods: magazines, stationery, greeting cards, sweets and cheap plastic toys. A large glass-fronted refrigerator full of canned drinks groaned and shivered in the corner as if it required a sick bed. A small bird-like woman peered at him across a wide counter, eyes dark and swimming behind spectacles from which depended twin loops of thin gold chain.

'Can I help you?' she warbled. Her grey hair seemed to tremble as she spoke, as if it were a nest balanced precariously on her head.

'Yes, I ... er ...' Royle selected chocolate bars and crisps from the confectionery display and carried them to the counter. 'I'll have these please.'

Her finger pecked off the price of each item on the ancient till. Royle clinked the money around in his trouser pocket and stared at the pile of newspapers on the counter. It was the local evening news, hot off the presses. Royle stared at the headline: 'BLOODBATH IN HORROR HOUSE'. On a sudden whim he lifted the topmost copy from the pile. 'I'll have this too, please,' he said.

The price was duly added to the total. The woman's finger pecked the money from Royle's hand and thrust change at him. He stuffed the snacks into his pockets, tucked the newspaper under his arm and walked out of the shop. Outside something − an almost irresistible urge − caused him to snatch the newspaper open, to devour the front page story with the lurid headline.

Three unnamed University students had been butchered in their house in Cramer Road, Royston, Maybury. Another had been murdered and dumped in a dustbin behind the University kitchens. Linked to this was a story focussing on the strange death of one of the University lecturers, a woman named Jayne Trent who had apparently been discovered by a window cleaner this morning. At this stage police were not disclosing how she had died, though speculation was rife that she was another murder victim, or perhaps a suicide.

The story appalled Royle, and yet simultaneously he felt a

357

mounting excitement, a sense of clouds clearing in his mind, of lights blazing forth, filling him with radiance. This was it! The sign they'd been waiting for! He didn't quite understand how or why, but he knew without doubt that the hideous events reported here were instrumental in the fulfilment of all their destinies.

'This is where it happens,' he whispered. He placed his finger on the grainy photograph of Maybury University. Folding the newspaper with trembling hands, he thrust it into his pocket. Then he broke into a shaky-legged run, the knowledge cutting like scissors inside his belly, eager to be shared with the others.

67

'No, Liam. Mummy said we weren't to go into the woods.'

'Aw, c'mon, Hannah, don't be a waz. That's when we're on our own. We're together now, and we've got Henry with us. He'll protect us, won't you, boy?'

Henry was a black labrador, still young enough at three for his musculature to ripple beneath the seal-black sleekness of his coat. Hearing his name he turned from the stile he'd been sniffing and lolloped towards Liam and his sister, wagging his hind-quarters. The two children stroked and patted their pet, sending him into tail-chasing ecstasies. Eventually the dog streaked over the stile and away up the track towards the first of the trees, then abruptly stopped and turned back to see if they were following.

'Look, he's smiling,' said Hannah, pointing at the dog's wide upturned jowls, his lolling pink tongue.

Liam was about to reply, 'Nah, he's just hot,' but bit back on the words. 'That's because he knows how nice it is in the woods,' he said. 'He wants us to go in there too.'

Seven-year-old Hannah pouted dubiously, but Liam, five years his sister's senior, pointed out, 'Dogs know when somewhere's safe. They can sense it.'

Hannah squinted up at him. 'Can they?'

'Oh yes,' said Liam pompously, 'they have these ... things built into their noses and ears like ... like radio transmitters.'

'Wow!' said Hannah. She'd never realised Henry was some kind of half-robot. 'Do they have them put there when they're puppies?'

'Well ... they're born with them,' explained Liam. 'All animals are. They hear and see and smell all kinds of stuff which we don't.'

Hannah dropped her voice to a whisper. 'Do you think Henry can hear what I'm saying now?'

Liam glanced at the dog, who was wandering back and forth along the track, sniffing the ground. 'Well ... maybe,' he said, then quickly added, 'but he's probably not paying much attention. He wants to go into the woods.'

Hannah considered a moment longer, then nodded decisively. 'Okay.'

The two children climbed over the stile, Liam gallantly helping his sister, Henry running up and bounding around them as if overjoyed they had indulged his whim.

The path into the woods was little more than a snake of dry earth through a field, compacted by the passage of many feet. A set of steps roughly-hewn from logs and dirt and rocks led down into the first of the trees, terminating in a shallow scoop of earthen valley like a dry river bed. Wooden posts painted with discreet arrows denoted that this was an official rambler's route. It was chilly in the woods; the leaves were on the turn. Shadows bobbed and wavered in a gentle lullaby motion, like the movements of old people conversing quietly.

'This way,' said Liam firmly, pointing in the opposite direction to the route the arrows recommended.

'Can't we follow the path?' said Hannah, her trepidation apparent in her subdued voice, her wide and solemn eyes.

But Liam, being twelve, was not prepared to compromise. 'Nah, that way's boring. This way's much better. Come on.'

The three of them - boy, girl and dog − set off, Hannah trudging with care behind her brother, who was kicking piles of leaves, throwing sticks for Henry, jumping up to slap at branches which craned above his head. They'd been walking for about ten minutes when a fluttering, squawking commotion erupted above them, causing the children to jump and Henry to prick up his ears and wuff indignantly.

'What's that?' cried Hannah, frightened. She had dropped to her knees and brought up her arms to protect herself.

Liam laughed shakily. 'Just birds. Look.' Magpies or rooks −

359

it was difficult to tell which through the trees — were flapping like rags, circling the dark clumps of their nests.

'I don't like it here,' wailed Hannah. 'I want to go home. I want Mummy.'

Sensing her distress Henry padded over and licked her face. 'We'll be home soon enough,' said Liam. 'Look, let's see if we can find some animal sticks, shall we?'

Hannah's collection of 'animal sticks' had started as a nature project at school, but had quickly swelled beyond these parameters. Their teacher, Miss Sheridan, had suggested a 'stick zoo', requesting that each of the children find and bring to school a stick or a piece of wood or even a rock which resembled some kind of animal. Hannah's contribution, a horse which daddy had helped her find, had been voted best in the class. Her success had encouraged her to continue her collection. Now she had seventeen stick animals, her favourite being a tiger which Liam had coloured in yellow and black stripes using his felt-tip pens.

Her face immediately brightened at the suggestion. 'Okay,' she said. 'I want a Nellie-the-elephant and a lion like Aslan with a big mane.'

'You look over that side, I'll look over this,' said Liam. 'And Henry, you bark if you see anything, okay?'

The dog wagged his tail briefly and wandered off, sticking his nose into every nook and cranny, occasionally cocking his leg to leave a spurt of urine on a tree. The children ranged about, looking at the ground. Liam picked up rocks and tossed them as if they were grenades, making explosive sounds and diving behind bushes when they landed. Hannah, completely engrossed, strolled through Liam's battlefield, miraculously unharmed by stray bullets, flying shrapnel and detonating landmines. She talked softly to herself, picking up pieces of wood, examining them, and then, dissatisfied, flinging them into the bushes.

'What about this?' said Liam, lifting a hunk of earth-clogged root and showing it to Hannah.

She screwed her face up critically. 'What is it?' she asked.

Liam turned it upside down. 'Well it's ... it's an octopus, isn't it? Or a jellyfish,' he added as an afterthought.

'Hmm, all right. Keep hold of it and I'll decide later.'

'Yes, Your Majesty,' said Liam. He stuffed as much of the root as he could into his pocket, sprinkling his shorts with dusty earth.

A few minutes later, while Liam was whirling Henry's lead above his head like a helicopter blade, chopping leaves from branches with the end of the chain, the dog started barking. Both children looked up. Hannah was holding a leafy length of branch which she had been trying to convince herself resembled a giraffe.

'Why's he barking?' she said. For the moment they couldn't see the dog. He sounded as if he were two or three hundred yards away.

'I dunno. Maybe he's found a stick animal. Or a real one,' Liam replied, making himself smile. 'Henry,' he shouted at the trees. 'Here, boy. Come on.'

But Henry didn't come on; he continued barking. 'Henry, you bad dog, come here,' Liam called, pushing through the foliage. He swung the lead to and fro in his hand, the chain rattling like a sack of bones. The first he saw of the car was the glare of sunlight on the windscreen, which dazzled him.

'Oh,' he said, squinting, raising an arm against the unexpected flare of light.

'What's the matter, Liam?' Hannah asked, clutching the leafy abstract giraffe instinctively to her chest.

Liam blinked and looked again. The sunlight, weak though it was, scampered like cold white fire across metal and glass. 'It's a car,' he said, pushing aside a springy bush to climb onto a rock. 'Come on, let's go and see.'

The children approached the car cautiously. It was a white Volkswagen Beetle, scabby with rust. Dents in the bodywork, a slew of tyre tracks, and mangled undergrowth suggested it had been driven carelessly, perhaps drunkenly, into the clearing in which it now sat.

'Who does it belong to?' Hannah asked, whispering as if the wreck might hear her.

Liam edged close enough to see that the car was empty. 'I don't know,' he said. 'Maybe big kids nicked it and left it here.'

Hannah shivered and glanced quickly around. 'Do you think they're still in the woods?' she said.

Liam shook his head, trying to look and sound more confident than he felt. 'Nah, they'll be long gone by now.'

'What's Henry barking at then?' Hannah whispered. Both children turned to look in the direction of the barking, which was now near enough for them to hear the dog's paws scuffing the ground.

'Let's go and see,' said Liam.

'Don't want to. Want to go home.'

'We'll go home as soon as we've had a look, I promise. Come on, we'll be all right.'

Hannah stayed rooted to the spot, looking sulky, hugging the piece of branch as if it were a doll.

'Okay, I'll go,' said Liam. 'You wait here.' He walked away and, as he expected, heard Hannah scampering after him a moment later.

The two of them stuck tightly together and made as little noise as possible as they edged around tree trunks and bushes towards Henry and the source of his commotion. 'There he is,' whispered Liam a minute later, pointing through the ragged gaps left by overlapping greenery at a shiny black shape bobbing and jumping.

'Henry,' warbled Hannah much to Liam's alarm, but the dog ignored them. They broke through a clump of bushes, rounded a final grey tree trunk, and there was Henry ... and the dead man.

Immediately Hannah began to scream and backed into a bush, which made her scream all the more. She fell down, dropping the giraffe, and covered her face with her soily hands. Liam could only gape, throat closing up, the inside of his stomach feeling as if it were being squeezed in a vice. He began to shake, suddenly cold. All the saliva in his mouth changed first to glue, then to sawdust.

The man had hung himself from a tree branch, which, despite its thickness, had sagged so much it seemed he were pirouetting grotesquely, his toes touching the ground. He was a fat man, hideously shapeless in death, his stomach like a vast balloon which seemed swollen with water, about to burst. Some animal had shredded one of his shoes with its teeth in an attempt to get to the flesh beneath the leather. The rope made his head crane back, the black-blue-purple face with its hideously bulging eyes gazing into the sky above the treetops as though in a last vain search for God.

'*Henry*!' screeched Liam hysterically, the word like gravel, scraping his throat. The dog was jumping up at the corpse, barking at it as if annoyed at its lack of response. His attentions were making the corpse sway, the tree-branch creak alarmingly, but at the raw panic in Liam's voice the dog turned, cowed and puzzled, and trotted over to his young master. 'Henry,' Liam said more quietly and slipped his arms around the dog's neck. He clung there, wanting the warmth, listening to his sister scream, the birds cry, the tree branch creaking gently.

68

As soon as the door closed behind Miss Nightingale, Douglas Parks – much-beleaguered Chancellor of Maybury University – felt his knees turn to sludge. He plumped heavily down in his chair, then slumped forward, elbows on desk, head in hands. He felt as if his world was collapsing around him, as if his precious domain was being singled out by some jealous and vindictive god. He couldn't help but regard all that had happened as a personal slur, for in the end it all came down to him. His was the responsibility, he made the decisions, and hence also carried the blame for mistakes. He had just spent the worst day of his life talking to policemen, students, journalists, education officials, parents and governors, all of whom were demanding and many of whom were angry, as if it were *he* who was personally responsible for the chaos which had swept like a snow storm across his University. What had they expected him to do, for God's sake? The murders had all happened outside the campus, and Jayne Trent had died in her own home. Why should he be the whipping boy, the focus for their rage? And yet he was, and despite the injustice of it all he couldn't help but feel guilty.

Now, for the first time in almost ten hours, he was grabbing a few minutes' peace. It was seven o'clock, twilight outside. Yesterday at this time Parks had been at home with his feet up, a glass of white wine by his elbow, a book of George Herbert's poetry open on his lap and Mozart on the turntable. Cynthia, his wife, had been busy in the kitchen, from which drifted the aroma of chicken in red pepper sauce and spiced basmati rice. Almost subconsciously Parks stuck out his tongue and licked the spiny hairs curling over his top lip as if the memory of the sauce's flavour on his moustache could take him back in time.

But how could he even think of eating after all he'd seen today? He'd kept his eyes averted from the body in the dustbin, but the blood and the smell (which may have been merely rotting food) had been enough to make him nauseous. And Jayne Trent whom he'd had to identify ... the sight of her corpse lying still and white on the slab behind that large glass window would stay with him forever. He hadn't realised a human being could look so ... so *changed*, so hideously alien. He'd heard of growths and tumours, of course, but he'd always thought them small, discreet, primarily disrupting the system from within, spreading their poison that way. He'd never

363

imagined there could be tumours that resembled giant fungi, whose effects were devastating enough to twist limbs, to obscure features, to bloat and re-structure flesh. Mortality had leered at him today, ugly and real and terrifying. Douglas knew that however long he lived, his life had now been tainted, and that the shadow, the mark, the stain, would never leave him; it would be a dark companion, as permanent as it was unwelcome.

He wanted to cry for his loss, but his body felt too numbed for the production of tears. For probably the first time ever he wished that he and Cynthia were closer, that he could confide in his wife, pour out his heart to her, expose his weaknesses and know that she would not recoil. But their marriage had been built on the foundations of a mutual reserve. What little passion may once have existed between them had dwindled and died over the years. Parks had never regarded this as a bereavement but now he did and he regretted it. By his right hand the phone suddenly rang, jangling his nerves. Oh God, what now? he thought. He picked up the receiver unwillingly.

'Hello?'

'Mr Douglas Parks?' The enquiry was made in a voice he didn't recognise.

'Yes?'

'Mr Parks, my name is Detective Inspector Chivers of Railsham CID, Surrey. I believe you have a lecturer at your University by the name of Howard Duffy?'

'Yes.'

'Could you tell me, sir, when was the last time you saw Mr Duffy?'

'Er ... last week sometime. His ... um ... mother died a few days ago. No one's seen him since.'

'Ah. That's what I thought, sir. I'm afraid I have some rather bad news for you.'

'Oh,' said Parks in a fading voice.

'Yes, sir. I'm afraid that Mr Duffy was found dead in an area of local woodland this afternoon by two children. It seems he committed suicide. There was no note but early indications would suggest this.'

'Oh,' said Parks again and put down the receiver before the policeman could say anything else. There was silence for a few moments, then the phone began ringing again. Parks stared at his hands and decided not to answer it.

69

Freddy Marshall was a party animal, but after his encounter with Stu the previous evening he had returned home, too shaken to carouse. Like many of Maybury's student population he lived in Royston, in an untidy house he shared with three other guys. When he arrived back they were all out. Still trembling from his experience, Freddy had patrolled the house with an umbrella, slapping on lights, throwing open cupboard doors and jabbing his makeshift weapon forward like a Musketeer. He knew he was being irrational but he couldn't help it. He could still hear that door in Mordred Hall dragging open behind him, could still picture the thing that had once been Stu with its unblinking black-bead eyes, its wounds that flapped obscenely like the mouths of madmen.

At last, satisfied that the house was empty, Freddy had locked the front door, helped himself to a six-pack of Carlsberg Special from the fridge (studiously ignoring the mutating cheddar) and had retreated to the sitting room where he had closed the curtains and switched the TV on loud to drown any noise from outside. If Stu was coming for him he didn't want to know. He'd rather be unconscious, too pissed to care, than have to face that thing again. Determinedly he had got as smashed as possible, finishing one six-pack and starting another, gulping so quickly that much of the beer ran down his chin and soaked the front of his orange silk shirt. At some stage he must have passed out and been put to bed, for when he awoke he was in darkness, wearing only his boxer shorts, his duvet wrapped around his sweating body like a boa constrictor.

He woke, in fact, gasping, his eyes opening so suddenly that his eyelids felt wrenched. He'd had a nightmare, the only part of which he could remember was the end, where Stu had lunged forward to smash his hairless white head against a table, causing the skull to split like an egg, releasing a mush of frothing black foam and a sticky ooze like placental fluid. Freddy's hands flapped at the stifling air in his room as though to shove the dream-images from him. His stomach and head felt clogged with nausea. He pushed aside the duvet and stood up, and immediately realised how pissed he still was. Staggering to the bathroom he threw up in the bath, his stomach expelling alcohol so violently that a stream of tears were squeezed simultaneously from his eyes. He remained there for a long time, hanging over the bath, retching up vomit and then bile and then nothing at all.

At last, exhausted, he returned to bed. But he couldn't sleep; he sat against the wall, the duvet bundled around him, and listened to the silence. Dawn opened a sleepy pink eye after a century of darkness, and then eons passed while the penumbral light remained constant. Eventually the birds awoke and began their chorus, encouraging the reluctant sun to show itself. It did so, prodding weak fingers at Freddy's curtains. A new day had dawned. He had survived the night.

He could work up little enthusiasm for his salvation however. He felt deflated and depressed, and, reluctant to draw attention to himself, abandoned his usual sartorial excess and opted for jeans and t-shirt. Of course, all the talk at Uni was about the murders, and so no one immediately noticed how subdued and preoccupied he was. Gradually, however, the questions began. At first it was: 'What's up with you, you miserable bastard?' Then: 'Why didn't you come to the party last night? Why did you stay home and get smashed?' And then finally: 'Hey, come on, Freddy, tell the lads what's wrong. We're all mates. We'll help you, whatever it is.'

For a while he shrugged off the questions. He told them, 'Aw, it's nothing, guys, forget it. Had a rough night, that's all. Woman trouble, you know how it is.' It wasn't until they were all in the bar later that evening, and Freddy was knocking back the juice once again, that the truth finally came out. He hadn't wanted to stay on campus, but the other guys had expressed a desire to stick around in case there was any more murder news. And so Freddy had resignedly bowed to majority opinion. It was seven-twenty and they had been in the bar almost two hours when Moxy said, 'Hey, we ought to go and get Stu. He's missing all the excitement.'

'*No*!' exclaimed Freddy, and realised immediately that his response had been far too extreme. Before he could cover up his faux pas the questions came flooding.

'Why not?'

'Wassamatter, Silks?'

'What's eating you, pal? You've been behaving funny all day.'

'It's something to do with Stu, isn't it?'

'How come no one *has* seen Stu since last Saturday?'

'Yeah, Freddy, how come?'

'Is it something to do with the murders?'

'Hey, Stu's not the one they found in the dustbin this morning, is he?'

Freddy stared down into his drink and tried to be evasive, but there was no way that his friends would let him wriggle free now. At last he raised his hands in resignation and said, 'Okay, okay, I'll tell ya. Just get off my back. But I warn you, guys, it's pretty weird.'

Self-consciously he began, his voice low, eyes gazing fixedly into his drink the whole time. He didn't really know why he'd kept his experience a secret for so long. Maybe because he was afraid of ridicule. Or maybe because he'd half thought that keeping it hidden would enable him to forget. Or perhaps he'd simply hoped that Stu's condition would become someone else's problem, which, if that were the case, meant he was a self-centred bastard, not much of a friend at all. Whatever the reason, he realised as he told the tale that he'd been wrong to keep it to himself. It felt good to share the burden. It made him feel less hopeless, less paranoid.

Only when he had finished his story did he look up from his drink. He saw a blend of emotions on the faces that regarded him: fear, awe, disgust, sympathy, disbelief.

'Are you having us on, Silks?' Rob asked, but his voice was quiet and serious.

Freddy shook his head. 'No way.'

'You sure Stu wasn't having *you* on?' said Moxy.

Freddy shook his head again. A murmur of dread, trepidation, travelled around the table.

'So,' said Freddy, 'what do you reckon, boys? What shall we do?'

Gav spoke up. He was small and foxy, hair like a toilet brush. 'I reckon we ought to go and see Stu,' he said, 'talk to him. I mean, he's still our mate, isn't he? He might need our help.'

A few heads nodded. Beer was gulped as though to salute the suggestion. However Rob, hunching forward over his pint, said, 'I dunno, guys. What if he's got something contagious? And what if he's fucking loopy? I mean, he must be pretty cracked to slice himself up like that.'

'All the more reason to help him then,' said Gav. He stood up. 'Come on, guys. Who's with me?'

All, it transpired, were with him, though a few — Freddy among them — left their warm seats with reluctance. Nine pairs of feet tramped up to the penultimate floor of Mordred Hall. Stu's corridor was ominously quiet, every door closed.

The boys crowded together, whispering as though in a library. Gav, the self-appointed leader, was at the front, though now he was here even he seemed unwilling to approach Stu's door.

'Go on,' he was urged, the inducement reinforced by a sharp shove in the back. Gav staggered forward, then regained his balance and rounded on his friends.

'All right,' he hissed, 'don't push. I'm going.'

As though treading barefoot on broken glass he walked to the door. He formed his hand into a fist which hovered for a moment beside the bare wood, then, suddenly decisive, he knocked. He sensed rather than saw his friends draw instinctively back, and heard their collective intake of breath. He felt twitchy, but resisted the urge to tap his foot. They all waited. Nothing happened.

'Knock again,' someone whispered at last. 'Maybe he's asleep or ... or something.'

Gav glanced at the group, then knocked. 'Stu?' he said, his voice wavering slightly. 'Stu, mate, are you in there? It's ... it's the lads.'

Still no response. Freddy, who was closest to the door that led to the stairs, said hoarsely, 'Have a look through the keyhole, Gav. See if you can see anything.'

Gav pulled a face. 'I dunno, guys, I – '

'Come on, Gav, it was you who wanted to come up here. Just have a look through the fucking keyhole.'

Grimacing, he stooped and put his eye to the keyhole. An age passed. The entire world held its breath. Then suddenly Gav's body went rigid and he shouted, 'I see him! I see him!'

That broke the spell. All the others except Freddy pressed forward to look. Those who couldn't get close to the keyhole were demanding, 'What did you see? What did he look like?'

'He was horrible,' said Gav, face pale, eyes wide. 'Fuck me, he was bloody horrible.'

'I see him too!' Moxy yelled, then straightened up and began to bang on the door. 'Hey, Stu, it's the lads. Come on out.'

Beastie and Glynn joined Moxy in his pounding and began to sing, 'Come on out, come on out, come on out.' The chant was taken up quickly and soon all nine of them, even Freddy, were thumping the door and shouting, their individual fear temporarily swamped by the aggression and bravado of the group.

70

The commotion outside his room made little sense to Stu. It might as well have been a swarm of bees or a violin concerto. His mind was not functioning as a human mind any more; like his body it had metamorphosed. He raised the vaguely featured tumour that had once been his head and mouthed toothlessly at the door like a crusty old turtle, then he turned slowly and dragged his bulk towards the window.

He extended a globular tripe-coloured appendage and nudged the curtains aside. His white slashed flesh trembled with anticipation as the night sky was revealed. The mad scramble of sensations that were his thoughts coalesced into a single shaft of purpose, straight and sure as an arrow released sweetly from the bow. Subliminally he sensed a mutual conviction and knew that the others were poised too. He raised and spread himself, opened the aperture that his mouth had become, and released a prolonged haunting note like the cry of a harpooned whale. Then, with surprising agility, he launched himself at the glass, which shattered like a brittle star, and plunged towards his Epiphany.

71

Curled up in Ian's arms, Annie was surprised to find she had fallen asleep quickly. When she awoke it was dark outside. Ian slept beside her, breathing through his open mouth, one hand resting limply on her hip.

She got up and stretched, shivered a little, then crossed to the sink and poured herself a glass of water. Her reflection in the window was wan, her eyes obscured beneath shadows.

Closing the curtains she walked across to the bed and sat beside Ian, looking down into his relaxed face. Already she could feel the pressure, the tension, building in her again, her stomach uncoiling like a drowsy snake. She had dreamt about sunshine and her brothers, and there'd been something about an aeroplane flight and a poodle called John which performed tricks. It had been a bright frothy dream, carefree and good-natured as an old comedy. For a brief precious moment upon waking, Annie had felt content, light-hearted, and then the weight of her burden had begun to weigh her down once more. She didn't want to disturb Ian, but she wanted company. She leaned forward and kissed him on the cheek.

Like an inverted scene from a fairy tale, the kiss from Annie awoke Ian. He lay and looked at her a moment, and then smiled.

'Hello,' he said.

'Hello yourself.'

'What time is it?'

'About twenty past seven. How do you feel?'

Ian sat up, patting his body as though checking for injuries. 'Okay,' he said. 'I had a funny dream. I was back at school and I was feeding dominoes to this blue rabbit which kept getting bigger and bigger.'

Annie laughed. It felt good to do so. 'I think you've got serious psychiatric problems,' she said.

'Probably,' said Ian. 'It's hardly surprising, is it?' He rubbed his hands across his face, then winced; he'd forgotten about his bruises.

They decided to complete what they'd been doing earlier that day — which was to fetch Annie's stuff from her room — and then to go to the bar for a drink. Ian argued that they'd earned one, and that if there were any new developments the bar would probably be as good a place as any to hear about them.

They descended the stairs, crossed the lobby and stepped out into the night. Clouds swarmed overhead, obliterating the stars. The air was cold and spiky and brittle, carrying the threat of frost.

The main University building was quieter than usual. Light streamed from the long second-floor windows of the library, but the place itself seemed unoccupied. Their feet clacked across the car park like wooden blocks on concrete. 'It's — ' Annie began, and then the sky shattered.

Or so it seemed initially. The cacophonous clash and tinkle of glass erupted around them. Both Ian and Annie ducked, hands flying to protect their heads. Annie saw an explosion of crystal shards to her left and swung in that direction.

At first it appeared that huge white sacks had been hurled simultaneously from windows dotted at random around the Halls of Residence. She saw maybe a dozen — a couple from nearby Lancelot Hall, three or four from Mordred, a few from Merlin, and had the confused impression of more white mounds plunging from the fizz of glass in more distant Halls.

'*Shitting hell!*' she heard Ian scream. The horror on his face and in his voice seemed to focus her eyes. With a shock like a jolt of electricity she realised that the white mounds were not sacks at all. They were living . . . things. Bloated, white, pulpy, naked, hairless, and yet still recognisable — though only barely — as human. They looked like people who'd padded themselves grotesquely with lard and tripe. Annie was rigid with shock and horror, so much so that she could not avert her eyes even when they started to land.

They made a sound like shells splitting when the concrete broke them. They burst apart, their remains flying in all directions, devastating as flies spattering against windscreens. But there was no blood; their bodies were like dry dough or papier mâché — their innards, twisted out of true, were compacted and dessicated, salmon-pink rather than blood-red. A white fist-sized chunk of this strange flesh scudded from the destruction of its parent body, some twenty-five yards from Ian and Annie, and bounced against Annie's ankle, airy as polystyrene. This contact roused them both from their stupor. Mindless and screeching, they hurtled for the bright lights of the main University building.

72

The din which reached Steph's ears was like the eruption of a glass volcano, and could mean one thing only: Judgement Day. It was here at last, as Dan had promised, the ultimate battle between mankind and the spirits.

Elation hovered within her. Its light shone from every gaping door, lifting her above herself, into the heady realms of Truth and Glory. Epiphany was so close; she could almost touch it. Only a few more steps and it would be hers. She would be Ultimate. Perfection would clutch her in its immaculate embrace. Tonight, Dan had said, their Mission would be complete and the last most vital door would be flung wide to admit the Light.

Nothing else mattered to Steph. She saw only the Mission and strived for its conclusion; this world, this physical body, were irrelevant, chains which bound her to a poisoned shore and which would soon be snapped and discarded. The final stages had already begun. It was time for her preparation, her Communion. Dimly, as though in a dream, she saw a number: 48; heard a beckoning voice: 'Come to me, Stephanie,' and entered a place where silence and shadows crushed blackly into the spaces between the holy flicker of candle-flame.

And there was Dan, sitting upright and regal, the Word made flesh. 'Come to me, Stephanie,' he said again softly, each syllable creating exquisite sensations within her, lapping at her most intimate places, soothing her, raising her up.

Seeming to float on rapture she approached him.

'Kneel before me,' he instructed.

She obeyed.

'Look at me,' he said. She looked. His teeth and eyes were glowing with an ethereal light. 'Do you know who I am?' he asked.

Mute with awe, she could only shake her head.

'I am the Abyss,' he told her. 'Watch.' And raising his left arm, he rolled up the sleeve of his glittering blue suit with his right hand, revealing flesh that was white as marble.

His right hand reached down to his exposed forearm. As though picking off a scab he dug in his fingernails and removed a coin-sized piece of flesh with a sound that was brittle as the breaking of a stale biscuit. 'Open your mouth,' he said. She obeyed. He placed the piece of flesh on her tongue. It was cold and seemed to writhe sluggishly. She swallowed it.

'I am the Abyss,' he repeated. He held up the wounded arm for her inspection. An eerie dark-light poured from the rent in his skin, purplish-black and yet somehow blazing. As she watched the wound re-sealed itself, white flesh knitting back together, stemming the flood of black-light. Dan's voice seemed to waver, indistinct as a whisper's echo.

'It is time,' he said.

73

Alerted by the sound of shattering glass and the screams of Ian and Annie, people were appearing from everywhere. As Ian dragged Annie into the entrance lobby through the glass doors a horde of students appeared around the corner, having presumably exited en masse from the bar, and came towards them.

'What's happening?' 'What's going on?' 'What's all that noise?' Ian hunched his shoulders against the barrage of questions bursting around him. He was neither in the mood for explanations nor physically capable (his chest felt bruised in its struggle for air), and so merely flapped a hand towards the car park, hoping it would deflect his interrogators.

It did. The glass doors hummed open and remained so as the crowd spilled through. Weight of numbers made them brave and reckless. After a short pause a smattering of screams and various other sounds of distress suggested that there were some who were quickly regretting their eagerness to investigate.

Annie was crying now, Ian gasping for air that wouldn't come. Head spinning, staggering on limbs that were beginning to feel detached, he maneouvred the two of them over to the hooded telephone and let Annie fall on to the orange leather seat that stood beside it. Fumbling his inhaler from his pocket he thrust it into his mouth and gulped eagerly at the Ventolin, closing his eyes in relief as he began to breathe again. His lungs eased, slowed; for a moment there he felt as if they were twitching and spasming their last. His chest hurt as if someone had been pounding it. He looked up to see the head porter, an old man with a rubbery face and a white moustache, scurrying towards him.

'Can I help you, son?' the porter said. He looked scared and confused, as if he felt he should be handling the situation but didn't know how.

Ian looked at Annie. She was bent double, face in hands, snivelling and shaking badly.

'Drink of water,' he gasped, 'please.'

'Of course,' said the porter. He scurried back to his office, grateful to be doing something but wishing it could be more.

Ian was half-aware of people still running backwards and forwards. Through the glass-fronted entranceway he saw lights flashing, the blue uniforms of police officers as they appeared from the direction of the Portakabin, people clinging to each other for comfort. There was a lot of noise, but it seemed somehow muted. The porter hurried back, water slopping from the mug he held, splashing over his hand.

'Thanks,' Ian said. He placed his hand on Annie's shoulder and squeezed. 'Here, Annie, drink this.'

She looked up slowly. Her face was red and damp, her eyes bloodshot as if she'd rubbed onions into them. She said nothing, but took the mug in both hands and dipped her head to it. The mug chattered against her teeth.

'Thanks,' Ian said again to the porter, who was still hovering, smiling uncertainly. 'Maybe you ought to tell one or two people about this? The ... the Chancellor or ... or someone.'

'You're sure you're all right?' the old man asked.

Ian nodded. 'We'll be okay.'

The porter glanced at Annie, smiled stiffly once more, then hurried away. Ian heard the ting of his phone, the whirr of the dial.

He picked up the dog-eared telephone directory from its shelf beneath the phone and riffled through it, trying to stop his hands from trembling. There was only one Carmichael, P. in the book. Ian rooted in his pocket for change, then dialled the number.

'Hello?' a voice said after three rings. The short greeting was not enough to determine whether this was their Carmichael or not.

'Mr Carmichael? This is Ian Raven. I'm ringing from the University. Something really ... really bad has happened.'

Breathlessly, stumbling and stammering, he told Carmichael what he and Annie had just seen. He heard his voice cracking as he said, 'They weren't human, Mr Carmichael, not properly anyway. I mean ... they *were* human, but something was ... was really wrong with them. They were like ... huge and white and ... it's not just murders and stuff that's happening here, sir, it's something else, something . . . unnatural . . .'

Ian didn't realise how hard he was pressing the telephone receiver to the side of his face until his ear began to hurt. He held it away a little, the plastic slimey with sweat in his grip.

'I'll be there in twenty minutes,' Carmichael said. 'I'd arranged to meet Inspector Kaye there anyway in an hour or so. He's decided to accompany me to Dan Latcher's meeting instead of Doctor Hunt.'

'No, sir, I . . . well, I didn't ring you to ask you to come here. I was hoping we could come to you. I want to get Annie away from this . . . this place. It's . . . it's bad here, sir. A bad place. Is . . . is it all right to bring Annie to your house?'

There was a brief hesitation. 'What about Kaye?' Carmichael said. 'I can't let him down.'

'*Please*, sir,' Ian said. 'There's nowhere else to go. I just . . . I just want to get Annie away from this . . . this whole place. It's not safe here . . . Please, Mr Carmichael? Even if it's only for a few hours.'

Another slight pause, then Carmichael said, 'Okay, come round. But I'll have to meet Kaye. I promised. He's anxious to talk to Latcher.'

'Yes, sir. I'll probably come back with you if that's okay, to try and find Steph. Just so long as I know Annie's out of harm's way.'

'I'd better give you directions then,' Carmichael said. 'Have you got a pen?'

There was a stub of pencil beside the phone. 'Yes, sir,' Ian said. He began to scribble.

74

Despite the assurances of Detective Inspector Jacks, Constable Daley was nervous as he approached the cell area. He was twenty-two years old, and reckoned that more had happened in the past day than in his previous three years as a policeman. He'd known death before, but never murder. The worst had been that old man they'd fished out of the reservoir last spring. That had been the only time that Daley had thrown up. He still had occasional nightmares about eels.

Judging by what people were saying in the station, though, he'd have thrown up again today had he seen the victims of this latest nutter. Why the fuck had the guy had to come to Maybury of all places? Why couldn't he have stayed in Newcastle? There was a bloody university up there too, wasn't there? Daley couldn't help feeling resentful towards the students; it was almost as if their presence had enticed the monster here. He'd always thought Maybury was too small a town to house a university anyway. If it wasn't for the students and their drunken behaviour, his and his colleague's workload would be at least halved.

This guy Neil Gardener, he was a student too, wasn't he? All day Kaye had been bragging that he was their man. But now a U-turn seemed to have been made. Jacks had told him that Gardener had not killed anyone; that he was perfectly harmless, if a little disturbed; that he was sure the boy would appreciate a ham sandwich and a cup of tea. Daley hoped that Jacks had not been lying simply to dispel his apprehension. His head told him that this was not the way things were done, but his heart said: Well, maybe it is. Maybe Jacks is being horribly careless. Maybe by sending him down here on his own the DI is making the biggest mistake of his career. Daley looked down at the metal tray he was clutching tight in his sweating hands. He wondered, if Gardener came for him, whether he would have time to throw the hot tea in his face.

Cell 4 was the only one of a dozen which was occupied. All the others had their doors lazily ajar. The cell area was set below ground, a white-painted corridor whose acoustics reduced any form of shouted disturbance to a chaos of echoes. The doors were thick steel, again painted white. A panel slid back at eye-level to reveal a square of unbreakable transparent plastic which gave a three-quarters view of the cell's interior. Balancing the tray in the crook of his left arm, Daley slid the panel back with his right hand and peered through.

It took him a moment to register what he was seeing. The prisoner was lying motionless on the floor, legs bare, blue denim bundled around his throat. His face was livid, a purpley-blue colour. Daley could see his protruding tongue, the glistening whites of his eyes.

He dropped the tray. The racket it made when it hit the concrete floor obscured a sound which the shock of what he was seeing had prevented him from registering immediately. Now he heard it, though only for a split-second before it was lost amid the crash of tin and pot. It was a sibilant hissing sound, like a gas leak or a snake.

'Help!' he yelled as he fumbled to get the door open. 'Someone, quick!' And then, in a quieter voice, 'Oh, Jesus.' The door swung open and he leaped inside. He'd always thought it impossible for someone to strangle themselves, but that, it seemed, was what Neil Gardener had done.

He threw himself on to his knees beside the still figure, urging himself to stay calm, stay calm. He was surprised at the steadiness of his fingers as he picked at the knot in the denim jeans which Neil Gardener had apparently tied around his own neck. The knot loosened suddenly and then came free. Acting with a cool efficiency that belied the turmoil in his mind, Daley checked that Gardener's air passages were clear and then began mouth to mouth resuscitation. He glimpsed movement from the corner of his eye and glanced up, thinking that aid must have arrived. He was mistaken, obviously imagining things. He couldn't really have seen a long white snake slip silently out of the cell.

377

75

At the same time that Constable Daley was urging himself to keep calm, Ian was doing likewise. He was rigid in his seat, hands clamped around the steering wheel, breathing hard and fast through his mouth as if he'd just run a race. Beside him Annie was huddled like an old lady, staring blankly through the windscreen with a doleful expression. Her features seemed pinched, her skin unhealthily white. Ian eased the pressure of his foot on the accelerator, aware that he was going too fast.

Darkness had swarmed across the last ragged streaks of twilight and drained the brightness from the earth. The trees at the side of the road were spiky eruptions of blackness; they seemed to swell, trunks bloated and gnarled, as the headlights swept over them. Behind Ian and Annie lay the University, full of light and noise though not of exuberance. Ahead lay Maybury, street lights like a jumble of giant glowing necklaces strewn on the ground, tainting the sky above the town a gritty orange-brown as if to defy the night.

'You okay?' Ian asked, glancing to his left. Annie didn't reply, didn't even give him any indication that she'd heard the question. 'We'll be at Mr Carmichael's soon, then we'll be safe,' he assured her. 'We can work out what we're going to do from there.'

If he had not seen Annie's hands tighten suddenly into fists, Ian might have killed someone. As it was the reflex made him glance up to see a crowd of figures, bleached by headlights, attempting to take evasive action. As Annie screamed he wrenched the steering wheel to the left with such force that hot pain tore jaggedly through his shoulder. The scattering figures veered from view to be replaced by a line of grey and very solid-looking trees.

They rushed at the car with such speed that Ian barely had time to shield his face. His foot was slamming down instinctively on the brake, which was lucky; it could just as easily have been the accelerator. Nevertheless the impact hurled him forward so violently that he thought the seat-belt would slice him in half. The windscreen jerked forward, then lurched away. Ian felt more pain spear through his neck as he was thrown backwards, though the head-rest did its job admirably, cushioning him against whiplash.

And then there was silence. The car was amongst the trees, one of which stooped, broken-backed, across the bonnet, pawing at the windscreen with a leafy limb. Ian groaned, feeling bruised and battered but not badly hurt. Pain crackled in his neck as he looked at Annie. She too seemed okay, if sobbing into her cupped hands could be labelled as such. For a moment he just sat, heart hammering so violently that it made his head throb. Each breath he took made him wince; it felt like a large heavy hand applying pressure to a bruise that spanned his entire chest.

The silence broke up, became shouts whose words he couldn't discern. Ian saw movement, jerking shadows around the car, then a shape loomed on his right and the door was wrestled open. Cold air rushed in, freezing him instantly. He began to shiver, his teeth to chatter uncontrollably. A head appeared, thin-faced, bespectacled.

'Hey, are you okay?' a voice asked.

Ian tried to speak, but his throat felt swollen, his tongue huge and sticky and dead. He compensated for his silence by raising a hand. Their would-be rescuer, who was about Ian's age, said, 'You must be pretty shook up. We'd better get you out of there. Can you stand?'

Ian got his inert tongue moving again, swallowed his shock and felt the saliva beginning to flow. 'Yeah,' he croaked, 'I think so.' With fingers that were numb and trembling he managed to release his seatbelt, which slid gently across his chest and over his shoulder like a snake. His legs felt like spars of wood. The one that had been stamping down on the brake hurt, but not too much. People came forward to help as he swung himself out of the car and tried to stand. He felt momentarily dizzy but the cold air quickly revived him. It hurt to move his shoulders and his neck around too much, and it still hurt to breathe, but he was okay.

On the other side of the car Annie was being helped out too. Her elbow was bleeding and she was holding her hip gingerly, but apart from that she also appeared to be fine. Ian went across to her and embraced her. She responded so fiercely that he had to bite back a cry as his bruised sternum flared with pain. He kissed her head and told her, 'It's okay, Annie. We're okay.'

'Car's a mess, I'm afraid,' said the bespectacled man, hands thrust into the side pockets of his leather jacket as he leaned over to inspect the damage. He straightened up and approached them. 'We're going to the University. Maybe you ought to come with us? You can ring from there — ambulance, AA, relatives, whatever.'

Ian felt Annie shrink back as if the man's suggestion could infect her. Uneasily he asked, 'Why are you all going there? You're not students, are you?'

The bespectacled man smiled. 'No,' he said, 'we're not. We're ...' He shrugged, looking around, obviously lost for words. 'We're

379

not really anything,' he finished lamely. 'At least,' he amended, 'we're no specific group, we have no name. We simply have a purpose, that's all. We know what we have to do. The University's our destination.'

Ian looked around at the milling crowd. There were dozens of young people, their ages ranging between late teens and early thirties. What had brought them all here? Surely not morbid curiosity. Dread scuttled inside him, a feeling almost of doom. He reached out and placed a hand on the man's shoulder.

'No,' he said, 'don't go up there. You're mistaken. Bad things are happening there. And there are ... there are police everywhere. They'd arrest you. Whoever or whatever made you come here, it was a mistake. Take my advice and turn back now.'

A few people had gathered to listen to Ian, but his hope that he could dissuade them from their purpose was soon dashed.

'Have you come from the University?' a girl with daisy-chains in her hair asked him.

'Yes, so I know what I'm talking about.'

'Is it happening yet?' someone else asked.

'Er ... yes, I think it is,' Ian said, a little thrown by the question.

Immediately he and Annie were alone, the crowd around them peeling away. A chain-reaction of shouts was transmitted to the far fringes of the group. 'It's happening! It's happening! Come on, it's already started!'

'No, wait!' Ian shouted, but the crowd surging past him paid no heed. He wondered what he should do − follow the crowd back to the University, go to the hospital, or follow the original plan and take Annie to Carmichael's house, out of harm's way. He looked down at her. She was still clutching him tightly, face unnaturally pale, eyes wide as those of a hunted animal. He would not take her back to the Uni and a trip to the hospital would be awkward and time-consuming. 'Come on,' he said, 'over here.' He indicated a bus shelter menaced by trees to which, limping, they made their way.

76

Kaye had made a cock-up, and he *knew* he had made a cock-up, which meant, naturally, that everyone else was getting it in the neck. In spite of his tough street-cop persona, this was the first time that Kaye had handled a crime of such magnitude. His normal enquiry load consisted of domestic disagreements, traffic violations, petty theft and the obligatory weekend punch-up between drunken students and drunken locals, which occasionally culminated in charges of assault, criminal damage or resisting arrest being brought. Kaye had handled the press before, but never had his word travelled so far or carried so much weight. The general consensus was that in trying to make himself look good, the Chief Inspector had been left with a whole carton of egg on his face.

Bragging to the press about the man who was helping them with their enquiries had now, with hindsight, been wildly premature. Because of his boast, and more specifically to prevent himself from looking a fool, Kaye had seen fit to keep a disturbed and obviously innocent teenager banged up in a cell. That had resulted in a suicide attempt which, Jacks had raged to his superior during a slanging match which had the entire station cowering, was entirely preventable. Kaye had passed the buck firmly back to Jacks, claiming that the boy had been improperly supervised, an arrangement which Jacks should have seen to.

The place was simmering now like a dormant volcano. Footfalls were light, voices subdued; no one wanted to precipitate an eruption. The fact was, Neil Gardener, prime suspect in this case, was now comatose on a life support machine in Maybury District Infirmary. It was only a matter of time before Withers and his cronies gleefully pounced on this latest development and began talking of police brutality and summary justice. Kaye sat like a statue at his desk, mouth set in a terse line, hands steady on the table-top before him, as though already practising the dignified manner he would adopt when the accusations started to fly.

The phone rang. He picked it up and barked, 'Chief Inspector Kaye,' to show how unmoved he was. The caller was Sergeant Craig, senior officer at the University site. Kaye listened to what Craig was saying – that a large crowd of youths, probably the hippies who had arrived that morning, could be seen further down the road that wound past the University, heading towards the campus.

381

Kaye's face darkened like an eclipse. 'Hold the bastards off as best you can,' he snapped, 'and don't let anyone go near those corpses. Use whatever force you deem necessary. I'll be there as soon as I can with back-up.'

He slammed the phone down before Craig could reply, and snatched it up almost immediately, fingers jabbing out a three-digit extension. On the second ring the phone was picked up.

'Hel –'

'Jacks, this is Kaye. I want you in my office *now*.'

77

'I thought you were never coming,' Carmichael said, and then taking stock of Ian and Annie's dishevelled appearance, 'What happened?'

'We crashed the car,' Ian replied briefly. 'We had to catch the bus in the end.'

'Crashed the car? How did you manage that?'

'I swerved to avoid someone. I wasn't concentrating properly,' Ian said, not wishing to launch into long explanations.

Carmichael stepped back to allow them in, expressing concern over Annie's bleeding elbow, asking if they had any other injuries.

'No, we're okay,' Ian said, though his chest still hurt when he breathed and his neck and shoulders felt clamped with pain.

'Sit down, sit down,' Carmichael said when he had ushered them along the corridor to the lounge. His bungalow was small but immaculately tidy. Plants trailed down over bookcases stocked largely with the orange spines of Penguin classics. The subdued light from well-shaded wall lamps, the russet carpet and oatmeal rugs gave the place an autumnal feel. The furniture was modern, designer-skeletal, but surprisingly comfortable. The pictures were mainly abstracts in subtle shades, though above the fireplace was a framed batik depicting semi-naked Asian figures apparently engaged in some vaguely erotic act.

Annie sank back with a sigh, half closing her eyes, as if exhausted from all the shocking events that had been heaped upon her. Ian perched on the edge of the settee, leaning forward, elbows on knees, as if to admire his bruises in the glass-topped coffee table.

'You look as if you need a drink,' Carmichael said. 'Tea? Coffee? Something stronger?'

'Well actually, sir,' Ian ventured, 'I was wondering if I could ask you a big favour?'

'Another one?' Carmichael replied, then smiled to show he was joking. He waved a hand. 'Go ahead.'

'I was wondering ... could I borrow your car? I think something's going to happen at the University. I have to get back there straight away.'

Carmichael was silent for a few moments. He looked surprised by the request. He strolled across to the mantelpiece and leaned against it. Finally he said, 'What do you mean — something's going to happen? Can you be more specific?'

Ian sighed and lowered his head, making his neck crackle with pain. He should have known he couldn't get away without offering explanations. As briefly as he could he told Carmichael about the crowd of young people who had been making their way, as if summoned, to the University.

Carmichael glanced at his watch. 'Look,' he said, 'it's eight-fifteen now. I'm due at the University in forty minutes myself to meet Chief Inspector Kaye. We may as well all go back there together. If something dangerous is about to happen we can't have you heading off on your own.'

'No!' said Ian forcefully. 'I brought Annie here to get her away from the place. There's no point just going straight back there.'

'But ... but ...' Carmichael looked ruffled. 'I *have* to meet the Chief Inspector. And Annie can't stay here, can she?'

Ian looked at her. Her eyes were still closed. She was breathing deeply. He could almost *see* the tension ebbing from her body.

'Why not?' he said. 'She'll be safe here, out of harm's way. She can lock all the doors behind us. She's got the telephone, neighbours on either side. It's the best place for her.'

But Carmichael looked dubious. 'I don't know,' he said. 'She's obviously upset. I don't like the thought of leaving her alone.' He frowned, thinking hard. 'How about if you and I drove back to the University and dropped Annie off at the police station on the way?'

Ian considered this, but before he could reply her voice broke in: 'No. I don't want to go there.'

The two of them turned, surprised. This was the first time she had

383

spoken since the mass suicide at the University. Ian was delighted that she was back with them, but also dismayed to see tension tightening her body once again.

'Well ... why not?' said Carmichael, spreading his hands.

'I don't, that's all. I don't like it. I want to stay here.' She drew in her legs and pulled one of Carmichael's fat pancake cushions into her stomach like a sulky child with a favourite teddy bear.

'But you'll be safe there,' Carmichael protested.

Annie glared at him. 'Don't want to.'

Carmichael looked exasperated. Ian placed a hand on his arm.

'Maybe it would be better to leave her here,' he said. 'She needs somewhere quiet where she can relax, and Maybury police station hardly qualifies as that, does it? If we took her there they'd only ask her loads of questions − or at best dump her on a hard bench with a cup of tea. I couldn't bear the thought of Kaye finding out she was there and picking on her again.'

'But hasn't she got other friends she can go to? I mean ... I don't want to leave her here on her own. I ... I don't want the responsibility.'

Ian was silent, thinking hard for a moment. 'How about,' he said, 'if I go back to the Uni in your car and meet Kaye in your place? I mean, this isn't really your battle anyway − Annie and I dragged you into it. And, besides, I want to try and find Steph and get her away from the place, and you don't even know what she looks like. I reckon you'd be better staying here and looking after Annie for me. As long as Kaye's there with his riot squad it won't matter whether there's one of us or two, will it?'

Carmichael looked doubtful, but it was obvious he could see that Ian was talking sense. 'I don't know,' he said. 'It's the thought of sending you back there while I stay here ... babysitting.' He flapped a frustrated hand towards Annie, who had closed her eyes once more and this time seemed to be genuinely asleep. 'It's my University, after all. I feel as if I should be doing something more positive.'

'But you will be. As far as I'm concerned, looking after Annie is just as important − more so, in fact. As long as she stays here she's safe, and if I know there's someone looking after her I won't have to worry. I can concentrate on getting Steph out.'

Carmichael sighed. He had the expression of a man who'd been edged into a corner. He looked at Annie sprawled on the settee, and then back to Ian. Sighing again he reached into his pocket, his hand emerging with a set of car keys which he reluctantly held out.

'Okay,' he said, 'you win. Third gear's a bit stiff. I'm supposed to be meeting Kaye in the main entrance lobby at eight fifty-five. If you can, Ian, give us a ring, let us know what's going on.'

'I will,' said Ian, taking the keys. 'I'll see you later.'

Carmichael nodded. 'Take care of yourself,' he said.

78

Pale and hollow-eyed, the procession descended slowly from the topmost floor of Guinevere Hall. Dan Latcher, by contrast, capered at its head like a demoniac Pied Piper, face stretched to its limits by a ferocious grin. From his spiky cropped hair to his white winkle-pickers he exuded an energy which sizzled and hissed like an angry cat. His silver-blue suit gleamed, a cold fireball throwing out sparks. His long fingers writhed and snapped, his eyes flashed like slivers of topaz.

This in itself would have been an unsettling sight, but what made it even more so was the eerie black-light which slithered and curled around the group, linking one to the next like a black umbilicus. Roped thus the pitiful procession was plucked down the stairs, a straggling line of glazed eyes, slack mouths, grubby clothes and tousled hair. No one saw them, no one heard them; all eyes and ears were turned to the pandemonium below. In moments, however, The Crack would enter that pandemonium and change its focus irrevocably. The time had come for Dan Latcher and his shuffling, crackling army of darkness to enter the fray.

When Warren Royle and the rest of the group stepped through the gates of Maybury University they found chaos and hostility waiting for them. The long drive which widened into the car park in front of the main building was like a battleground. Students were huddled in groups or milling about; there was sobbing and shouting, upset, frayed tempers, shock and confusion. Shapeless mounds were concealed beneath white sheets; fragments of glass glittered like diamonds on the tarmac and were crunched underfoot by the booted feet of uniformed constables. A sergeant in a peaked cap straightened as he saw them enter, as though bracing himself, hand tightening on a loud hailer. He barked an order and the constables, perhaps a dozen or so, formed a pitiful line of defence in front of him, obviously primed in advance. Warren saw nervous fingers caress the handles of truncheons. The sergeant jerked the loud hailer to his lips.

'*Halt!*' Though only one-syllabled and distorted, Warren thought he could detect alarm in the order. There was a short pause as though the sergeant had no idea what he should do next. Then he demanded, 'Please vacate this area. This situation is under control. I repeat: please disperse quietly. This is a police order.'

Warren had responded to the sergeant's request to halt instinctively, as had around half the others, but the rest were still moving forward. Seeing this the sergeant raised the loud hailer again.

'I appeal to you, please do not come any further. We have an emotive and delicate situation here. Your presence will only confuse matters. Please disperse quietly.'

A few of Warren's group began to shout explanations, to attempt to justify their need to be here, but to the waiting students and the scattering of policemen the sound must merely have been perceived as a mob-rumble. After a few moments hesitation, Warren began moving forward again with the others. This time the amplified voice contained more than a hint of panic.

'This is a police order. Please turn back. Your presence here will only worsen this situation. If you do not comply immediately my men will be forced to take evasive action. We do not want to use force and we do not want to start arresting people, but if you compel us to we will.'

His words had no effect. Warren sympathised with his situation, but he and his companions were motivated by a far greater need.

The pleas of one policeman were as chaff to the wind compared to their mission, to the realisation of their intertwined destinies. He saw uniformed policemen stiffen in readiness, saw truncheons drawn, light sliding on their polished surfaces. So be it, he thought. Whatever happened they could not turn back now.

The scream of sirens must have been the sweetest sound on earth to the police and students who were gathering to meet these strange invaders. Royle turned. The sirens were coming from behind him. He saw four black Marias and half a dozen police cars, each topped with a flashing blue light, tearing up the road towards the University. There was also an ambulance; no, two ambulances; no, three. Shouts rang from the throng around Royle. They were not exhortations of violence; there was no anger, no hate. They were calls prompted simply by desperation and urgency. Despite their faith that whatever happened now was *meant* to happen, surely that did not preclude their taking some initiative? They were too close for their own passivity to thwart them now.

And so they charged. Not to engage in conflict but to avoid it, to run through it and away from it, to lose themselves in the University grounds where they would play cat and mouse with the authorities until 'it' began to happen. There were casualties, of course: those who lost their footing in the stampede, those whose last movement before unconsciousness was an attempt to dodge a descending truncheon. Dimly, in the confusion, Royle was aware of cars screeching to a halt, of furiously shouted orders, saw blue uniforms flashing by, fists pummelling, blurs of faces creased in pain or hate, some masked in blood. Something crashed into his ear, but he kept running, hoping that he had not been singled out and was not now being pursued. Apparently not, for there was no further violence, though a hand reached for him, perhaps in supplication. He veered away from it and looked around frantically for a door, a wall, a dark corner, anything that hinted at sanctuary.

And then ... something happened in the crowd, an imperceptible shift of mood that had him slowing down, ranging about wildly for its source. All about him running bodies were coming to a halt, shouts and screams were decreasing in volume, heads were turning, struggling figures were loosening their grip.

Following the trend, Royle twisted to his right. At the entrance to one of the boxy Halls of Residence he saw a semi-circle of figures backing away from what appeared to be a shimmering blue shape. The shape strode forward, and now he saw it was a man: tall, gangly, with burning eyes and a death's-head grin, wearing a suit that was like an electrocution in a cartoon. Behind the man were a line of shuffling

387

figures, bedraggled as refugees. What fascinated Royle about the group, and what was creating the atmosphere of awe among the erstwhile combatants, was the sinuous thread of eerie black-light which linked one figure to the next like a climber's rope.

Royle stared at the shining, wolfish apparition as it slowly advanced, and felt something lurch inside him, as though the scab of his soul had been peeled away to release a flood of instinctive and overwhelming emotions. He felt a raging love for this man, both familial and sexual, he felt allegiance, trust, a sense of wondrous well-being. He wanted to reach out, close his eyes and be engulfed, wanted to prostrate himself, smother the ground with worshipful kisses in the wake of the man's passing. This is it, part of him was squealing excitedly, this is it, this is it. But he didn't fully understand until he heard someone whisper, 'Dan Latcher.'

Dan Latcher. Of course. He felt his mouth turn to sand, his heart to a beating ice-hammer, felt his stomach shrivel to an aperture the size of a walnut. *Dan Latcher*, Creator. *Dan Latcher*, Opener of Doors. Here he was in all his glory, come to lead his people from the wilderness.

Only yesterday such fervour would have seemed risible to Royle, but now it seemed the right way, the only way, to think. As students and policemen backed off fearfully, his companions moved forward; it was like cream rising. Hands reached out, aching to be grasped. Dan Latcher spread his arms and said, 'My children. Join me.'

Royle sobbed at the words and shuffled forward on his knees. He saw a tendril of black-light snaking towards him, felt its heat spreading over him, embracing him, drawing him in. He was plucked to his feet, in thrall now to Latcher, but overwhelmingly grateful to be so. He was sucked into the throng behind the capering Messiah, saw the bliss on the faces of his companions as they too were anointed with black-light, invited to swell the ranks of Latcher's followers.

'Dan Latcher?'

Royle heard the name spoken again, but this time harshly, accusingly. He looked up. A man had planted himself in front of Latcher, barring his way. He was brutish, broad-shouldered, his right hand clenching and unclenching as if he itched to throw a punch.

'Yes,' Latcher said softly, and Royle felt a delicious ripple run through him as if the word were an erogenous charge.

'I'm Chief Inspector Kaye. I'd like to talk to you, please.'

'Yes?' Latcher said again — and again, for Royle, ecstasy.

The policeman's scowl deepened. 'Not here. In private. We'll use the Portakabin around the corner.'

Latcher gazed at Kaye with his ochre eyes, but to his credit the policeman didn't flinch. At last Latcher said, 'No, I don't think so. I have more important matters to attend to.'

He made to step around Kaye, but the policeman veered, planting himself firmly in Latcher's path once more. 'I don't think you understand,' Kaye said. 'I'd like to speak to you now. This may seem a polite request, but you don't really have a choice.'

Latcher laughed and Royle writhed, believing he would die with delight. 'On the contrary,' Latcher said, 'I have every choice. I have a world of choices. I can do exactly as I please.'

'You little shit,' Kaye snarled and reached out to grab Latcher's arm. There was a sizzling crack, a surge of black-light, and the next moment Kaye was lying on his back ten feet away, face creased in fury and pain as he clasped his singed and smoking hand.

'*Arrest them!*' he bellowed to his gaping subordinates. 'And don't bother being gentle about it.'

Truncheons drawn, blue-uniformed figures converged unhappily on the shimmering, dark-wreathed crocodile. Like Kaye they were hurled back as though by sizzling bolts of electricity. Untouched and untouchable, Dan Latcher led his minions towards the glass doors of the main building.

389

80

'Swine,' Ian muttered, struggling to get the car into third gear. He took a deep breath, then slammed it into position, biting his lip at the crunching pain in his shoulder. He passed the wreck of his own car, fallen tree still draped across its bonnet like bad camouflage. Any other time and he was sure that within minutes half of Maybury's police force would have been sniffing round the accident scene, thankful for something to do.

It just shows how bad things are getting, he thought, as the University came into view, an island of light in a sea of black fields, black hedges, black hills. He pulled in through the entrance gates and immediately slowed the car. Up ahead, in front of the main building, the car park was scattered with the debris of what appeared to have been a pitched battle.

Odd shoes, caps, a denim jacket; hunks of wood, perhaps used as weapons; broken glass, buttons, coins, a crushed policeman's helmet: these were all items which spoke of aftermath, of violence now quelled.

And people. Bodies. The most chilling and irrefutable evidence of all. Ian noted that the doughy, smashed corpses of the suicides had been cleared away, their pieces presumably swept up and dumped in one of the ambulances which were parked with their back doors open, lights still flashing unnecessarily. There were police vehicles here too, though they were silent and still, the majority of their occupants obviously employed elsewhere. Perhaps half a dozen policemen had been left to tend to the injured, take statements or generally just stand around and try to look authoritative. All in all Ian counted approximately thirty people in the area, some of whom were sitting down, bandaged and bloody, a few of whom were motionless as though asleep, heads cushioned by white pillows, a grotesque and incongruous detail. As he watched from the entrance gates, engine idling, he saw two ambulancemen emerge from the back of a vehicle carrying a stretcher, and hurry towards one of the motionless figures.

So far Ian had not been spotted and he didn't intend to be. Urging the car to be quiet, he took the narrow road to the left which led to the back car park by the kitchens where the police Portakabin had been situated. He eased into a parking space, as far from the temporary incident room as he could get. He hoped no one was looking out of the Portakabin windows at that moment, and if they were he hoped they were too busy to question his presence.

He got out of the car gingerly, stiffened joints complaining, and locked the door. For a moment he stood and breathed the night air, and wondered what he should do. He could think of nothing more purposeful than entering the University via a side or back entrance and simply wandering around until he found out what was going on. If, in twenty minutes time, he hadn't achieved that, then he might as well go and meet Kaye as Carmichael had intended.

He began to walk away from the car, and had taken around a dozen steps when it occurred to him that a weapon of some sort would not go amiss. The whole situation reeked of potential violence; he might have to defend himself. He looked around for something suitable but without any luck. Sighing, he made his way round to the back of Carmichael's car and opened the boot.

It did not look promising. There was a plastic container for petrol, a cardboard box of bits and pieces, a portion of an old sheet stained with oil and dirt. Ian tutted and leaned further over, wrinkling his nose at the pungent smell of Dettol. Light caught the edge of something which was just peeking from the crack where the lid of the spare-tyre compartment met the back wall of the boot. It looked like metal; some sort of blade perhaps? Ian pincered the sliver of brightness between the index and third finger of his right hand and drew it out carefully.

It was not metal, it was plastic. Ian saw with disappointment that it was only the size of a credit card. He flipped it over, saw 'NUS' in white letters on a green background, above a photograph that was all but obscured by a reddish-brown smear. He wiped it away with his finger, presuming it was rust. He'd seen the face beneath the smear before. It was John Pedder.

He stared for a long moment at the image of the dead student, not understanding. What was this doing in Carmichael's car? The tutor couldn't have known it was here; Ian had only noticed it himself because light had flashed on the plastic. He was bewildered for a moment, then suddenly, shockingly, his mind clicked into gear. 'Oh God,' he breathed, and stumbled on rubbery legs to the driver's door, stomach flipping like a beached fish. *Now* he understood why Carmichael had been reluctant to give Annie the run of his house – obviously there was damning evidence there. 'Oh God,' he repeated. 'God!' Fumbling the car keys from his pocket he tried to pierce the lock with hands that shook like palsy.

81

It had been awful, shock upon crushing shock, stifling as suffocation, but now at last Annie felt as if she were pushing the debris aside and rising into the fresh air again. The house was quiet, the room warm, the settee comfortable. She looked up and smiled as Carmichael appeared with two mugs of coffee, one of which he handed to her.

'Hope it's not too strong,' he said. 'I like it strong. I didn't really think.'

Annie took a sip. It *was* strong, but it was good. 'No,' she said, 'it's fine.'

Carmichael looked relieved. He sat on the chair facing her, the coffee table separating them. Away from the University he seemed different: younger perhaps, less confident. Holding the mug with his right hand he fingered it nervously with his left, like a blind man reading braille.

'Have you – ' Annie said.

'It's not – ' Carmichael began simultaneously.

They both stopped talking, each waiting for the other. Then Carmichael laughed a little forcedly. 'After you,' he said.

Annie shrugged. 'I was just going to ask, have you lived here for very long?'

Carmichael looked around as if for some clue. 'Five or six years,' he replied.

Annie nodded. 'Oh.' Silence followed the word, sealing that particular line of conversation quickly into a dead end. They each gulped their coffee. At last Annie asked, 'What were *you* going to say?'

Carmichael wrinkled his nose and wafted a hand. 'Oh, nothing much. Just that this hasn't exactly been the ideal start to University life for you, has it?'

Annie wanted to laugh but couldn't. There was too much fear and pain for her to find any humour in his understatement. Even her smile emerged as a grimace. 'No,' she agreed, 'it hasn't. And the way I feel now, kind of detached and strange ...' She frowned as though unsure what she was trying to say. 'Well, it's almost as if I could click my heels together like Dorothy and say, "There's no place like home", and ...' She broke off again. 'Oh, I don't know. I just keep thinking that this can't be happening, that it's a dream, a nightmare, and soon I'm going to wake up.' Now she did laugh but it was humourless, self-conscious. 'That's such a cliché, isn't it?'

Carmichael shrugged. 'Is it? I suppose so, but clichés are sometimes very valid, I think. When faced with extreme situations, disasters and so on, people always say the same things: it was like a nightmare, I couldn't believe it was happening, it was like being in Hell.' He sat back. 'We're not used to the realities. We're cushioned against them, they're distanced from us and made into fiction, into images we can cope with. But the irony is, they're not fiction. They're the realest things of all. The very essences of life, the basics, the purest things, are the nightmares come true.'

He seemed more relaxed now. He smiled at Annie's frown. 'Do you understand what I'm talking about?'

'Not really,' she said. 'Do you mean ... supernatural stuff?'

'No, no, that's only a symbol of our real fears. We all of us live in fear, all of our lives, even if we don't realise it. We're scared of death, which is the ultimate, inescapable end for all of us. Violent death is a terrifying prospect, but it's not real, is it? It's something that happens to someone else or to made-up characters in books and films. We can't really imagine that moment when a pain big enough to stop our lives will come. But it will. Someday. And it's going to be all the harder and more shocking to face because we've been denying it for so long. It's like ... I don't know ... it could be something simple. A few stomach pains, a feeling of listlessness, a visit to the doctor's, tests, and then suddenly a thunderbolt: I'm sorry but you're riddled with cancer. We can't do anything for you. In three months you'll be dead. Bang. Reality. Nightmare come true. As simple as that. *Now* do you understand?'

Squirming, Annie gave a short nod. She felt uncomfortable hearing Carmichael talk like this. It was not something she wanted to hear, and his quiet intensity, too, was unsettling. To change the subject she said, 'I hope Ian's all right. I wish he'd ring.'

Carmichael smiled and finished his coffee. 'You don't really understand, do you?' he said. 'You won't allow yourself to think about it.'

The condescension in his voice, the release of the pent-up tension which he'd created, made her snap, 'Yes, I *do* understand, but I don't see the point in thinking about it.'

'There's every point.'

'No, there isn't! Life's to be enjoyed. You can't make yourself

393

miserable by brooding on all the awful things that *might* happen to you.'

'That *will* happen,' Carmichael corrected quietly. 'There's no might about it.'

Despite herself Annie argued, 'Of course there's a might. What about people who die quietly in their sleep of old age? What if they find a cure for mortality tomorrow, a big breakthrough? What if ...' She felt the pressure beginning to crush down on her again and shook her head. 'Oh, look, let's not talk about this, please. I don't know how it came about in the first place. Let's talk about something else.'

Carmichael shrugged, seemingly compliant. 'Okay,' he said. 'What do *you* want to talk about?'

'Anything,' said Annie. 'The course. Anything. I don't know.' Carmichael was smiling at her — indulgently, she thought with irritation. 'How about some music?' she suggested.

'Sure.' Carmichael stood up and crossed to the music centre. 'What do you like?'

'What have you got?'

'Lots of stuff. How about some jazz?'

'Yeah, okay.'

Carmichael selected a CD and put it on. The jazz was sleazy and languid, the volume soft. Annie quite liked the sounds that were being made, but as always she wondered whether the musicians were making up the tune as they went along.

Carmichael sat down again and crossed his arms. 'So what shall we talk about?' he said, smiling.

Annie sighed inwardly. She wondered whether it was her mood that made Carmichael seem tiresome. Certainly she'd always considered him relaxed, solid, sensible, but now she felt edgy. 'Do we have to talk?' she said. 'Couldn't we just listen to the music?'

'Conversation will pass the time more quickly.' Carmichael presented the statement not in the manner of an argument, but rather as a helpful suggestion. Before Annie could respond he said, 'Whereabouts do you come from?'

Annie wondered whether he'd meant the question as a sarcastic banality but he seemed genuine enough. 'Preston,' she said.

'And have you always lived there?'

''fraid so.'

'You don't like it?'

'No, no, it's okay. It's just not very interesting, is it? But I have been abroad quite a lot.'

'Where abroad?'

'America to visit my penpal. She lives in New Jersey, not far from New York. Um ... quite a few places in Europe: Holland, France, Germany, Austria, Italy. I think that's about it. I'd really like to go to Egypt to see the pyramids, but I don't think I'll be able to afford that while I'm still a student.'

'I'll bet you've got brothers and sisters, haven't you?' Carmichael's voice was light, but there was a hint almost of accusation in the question.

'Brothers, yes. Two. Ed and Matthew. I'm the —'

'I haven't. I was an only child,' Carmichael interrupted smoothly.

He was still smiling, but now there was something beneath his easy-going surface, a sense of containment, of something coiled, restless to spring. Annie should have felt annoyed at his casual rudeness, but instead felt uneasy.

'Oh,' she said, and was unable to think of anything to add.

However Carmichael needed no further prompting. 'I'm originally from Newcastle,' he said, 'a place called Kingston Park. My dad was a sheet metal worker, my mum worked on and off when things got tight at home. My dad didn't really like her working. He was one of these "a woman's place is in the home" sort of people. He smoked himself to death in the end. My mum's still alive though, lovely as ever. A very gentle woman. Very delicate.'

His voice had dropped to a murmur as though he were talking to himself. Now he looked up and smiled at Annie. 'What are your parents like?' he asked. 'Do you have a happy home life?'

Annie nodded, trying to convince herself that there was nothing really wrong with Carmichael's manner, that she was only imagining it. 'Yes,' she said, 'I do. My dad sounds like your mum. He's very quiet and gentle. My mum's noisier. Dad calls her Roseanne, after that character on the telly, though she's not really as loud as that. Ed, my eldest brother, takes after her. I'm more like my dad, and so's Matthew.'

Carmichael was still smiling. Surely there was no trace of a sneer in his voice as he said, 'It sounds idyllic.'

Annie laughed nervously. 'Oh, I don't know about that. We have our ups and downs like most families, I suppose.'

'My dad was an evil fucking bastard,' Carmichael confided, leaning forward in his chair.

The words were shocking and ugly coming from the lips of the tutor, and the cold venom of his tone both embarrassed and disturbed Annie.

'Oh,' she said in a small voice. 'Was he?'

'Yes. I never actually saw him hit my mother, but I'm sure he did;

he hit *me* plenty. He was a bully and I wasn't sorry when he died. He never even gave me any sympathy after ... after my accident. In fact, he was worse then ever. Once he told me that I ought to be put away.'

Annie remained silent. Despite Carmichael's apparent nonchalance she could see that his hands were trembling. She wondered whether this was from rage or the memory of some long-past trauma. She didn't want to hear what he was telling her, but it seemed unavoidable, as if events earlier that evening had set a trend from which it was impossible to break away. However hard she tried, it seemed she could not halt the descent into darkness. She tried to tell him to stop, to change the subject again, but the words would not come; her throat felt clogged and thick.

'Aren't you going to ask me about my accident?' Carmichael said. 'Isn't that what comes next?' He was joking, but his words were somehow inevitable, like a further step into the blackness. They were enough to spur Annie to her feet, quarter-full mug of cold coffee still clamped between her hands.

'Where's the bathroom?' she said. Her voice sounded strangled, panic-laden, but apparently only to her; Carmichael seemed to notice nothing unusual in it.

'The bathroom? Why?' he said defensively.

'The toilet, I mean. I need to go to the toilet.'

'Oh, it's ... er ... out of here and third on the right.'

'Thanks,' said Annie. The cup clattered as she put it down on the glass-topped table. Her legs felt hollow as they propelled her from the room.

Out in the corridor she paused and caught her breath and told herself: This is ridiculous. Perhaps her careering emotions and her temporary withdrawal from them had left her hyper-sensitive, reading meanings, nuances, veiled intentions into a conversation that was in truth perfectly harmless. She tried to analyse his words objectively but found it impossible; her thoughts were too much of a jumble. Okay, she thought, just take five, calm down, then go back in there and talk about the most banal subject you can think of.

From the sitting room, the door of which was slightly ajar, she could hear the muffled strains of a trumpet solo. She faced the corridor which terminated in the front door. Seven further doors hid their interiors from her, three to the left, four to the right. Now which of these had Carmichael said was the bathroom? She couldn't quite remember − second or third on the right, wasn't it? Dismissing the first door she tried the second. The room beyond was dark. She walked into it.

396

She decided that this wasn't the bathroom at the same instant that her thigh bumped the corner of some small item of furniture. The arrangement of shadow-tones, which her eyes were quickly adjusting to, informed her that it was in fact the bedroom, and that she had collided with a small bedside cabinet, which was now tipping, but which would simply rock backwards and forwards a couple of times, too squat to fall over. However the two objects on top of the cabinet, a clock and what appeared to be a large glass jar, slid on to the floor with a double thump. The impact caused the lid of the jar to fly off. Some dark liquid, darker than the shadows and foul-smelling, spilled from the jar and spanned out over the carpet.

'Hell,' said Annie. She moved slowly across to the light switch and pressed it down, wondering what the liquid was, hoping it wouldn't stain, wondering whether she would be able to clean it up before Carmichael came to see what was taking her so long. When the light came on she turned back to assess the damage — and stood there in appalled disbelief, staring, staring, as if the intensity of her gaze could make the obscenity disappear.

There was blood, dark and glutinous, full of blackish lumps. There were organs and skin and hair: at least two eyeballs, one of which was punctured, and some things her mind would not permit her to identify. Annie felt something rise in her, a scream perhaps that seemed as if it was being torn from her womb like an under-developed foetus. She felt pain and wanted to double over, but paralysis held her.

It broke when a tiny sound behind her made her whirl.

Carmichael was standing perhaps five yards away, looking down at the results of her clumsiness with glazed eyes. His hands were hanging loosely by his sides. His features were fixed in a faint smile. His eyes flickered from the pool of offal to her face, and his smile became stronger, both winsome and regretful.

'So now you know,' he said. 'I'm sorry.'

He reached out as if to stroke her face.

82

Seen from above, the procession of people which made its way to the Auditorium would have resembled a giant snake.

Its head was perhaps its most stunning feature. Like a blue-white diamond it flashed and shimmered, encapsulating light. The main section of the body by contrast was drab, though the ever-twisting rope of black-light which entwined it was a curiosity, resembling a smaller snake coiling about its parent, or a rebellious shadow, or a burnt length of rag, still glowing with dark heat. The tail of the snake was deep blue, and seemed slightly detached from the rest of the body. Once inside the Auditorium, however, the snake abandoned its shape, became a diffusion of separate shards, though the second serpent, the black-light one, continued to unite the giant snake's body whilst simultaneously repelling its tail.

One portion of that tail, Chief Inspector Kaye, stood and surveyed the scene with fury biting at his temples. The seats of the Auditorium were filling up as though for a lecture. Dan Latcher was standing at the lectern facing his adoring audience, Cheshire-cat grin fixed as rigor mortis. How Kaye would have liked to have pummelled that grin, shattering the teeth, drawing a veil of blood and pain across the little shit's arrogance. But he couldn't. Something like a force-field protected both Latcher and his followers. Kaye nursed his badly singed hand and plotted dire revenge.

He hurt. Both his body and his pride yelled out in pain. And when Kaye hurt, the only way he could assuage it was to ensure that those around him hurt twice as much. Apart from his hand, and the migraine which would split his skull if he allowed it purchase, his stomach felt like a bubbling well of acid. For a while he'd suspected that his belly was nurturing an ulcer, and now with anger filling him that self-diagnosis seemed confirmed. And it's all that little twat's fault, Kaye thought savagely, eyes trained like shotgun sights on Latcher's resplendent form. If looks could kill they would have been measuring the turd for a coffin now.

Impotence. There was nothing so infuriating. Tearing his attention a moment from his bête noire, Kaye allowed his gaze to sweep about the room, scrutinising the stance of his own men. They filled the narrow aisles around the central seating area like a blue border, truncheons drawn ineffectually. The majority of them looked nervous, some downright terrified — those that didn't seemed entranced by the sinuous gyrations of the black-light serpent as it swirled and crackled like a hazy marbled mist above the heads of Latcher's followers.

Wimps, thought Kaye. Mummy's boys. There'd be some bollockings to mete out once this farce was over. Admittedly he too had wondered how Latcher was creating the force-field effect but had quickly dismissed the conjecture. Their main concern was the simple fact of its existence, and consequently the charges which could be brought against Latcher once they worked out a way to neutralise the bloody thing and nab him. Already Kaye was thinking along the lines of resisting arrest, inciting a riot, assaulting a police officer, perhaps even kidnap if one or two of these hippy bastards could be persuaded to state that they were being held against their will.

'We'll fucking get you, Sonny Jim,' he said quietly, gaze turning once more to the group's figurehead. 'We'll have a nice chat, just you and I, somewhere very, very quiet. I'll soon wipe that smile off your face, don't you worry.' He winced as a tendril of pain shot through his head and then withdrew, like a bow being scraped across the strings of his nerves.

There was an excitable hum of conversation among The Crack and its new affiliates. The original members had become animated the moment they'd entered the Auditorium, eyes bright, faces eager, like Pavlov's hounds salivating at the bell. Now, however, they all fell silent as Latcher raised his hands. His gaze swept the hall like searchlamps. 'Children,' he said, 'welcome to my final and most momentous performance.'

A sigh almost of ecstasy rippled through the crowd. Kaye looked around with disgust, wondering at the feeble-mindedness of those who could find a Messiah in a grinning clown.

'Tonight, my children,' Latcher was saying, 'you will bathe in the blood of the prophet. The Promised Land will be yours forever. I will perform the ultimate sacrifice so that you may feast on Epiphany.'

Just what kind of bollocks was this? Kaye wanted to ridicule and heckle, but he supposed procedure must be adhered to; with all these young namby-pambies under his jurisdiction he had to set an example. Cupping his hands around his mouth he readied himself to make a new appeal to Latcher to halt this nonsense now. 'La ...' was all that left his mouth, however; the second syllable was stillborn. He blinked rapidly, several times, unable to believe the evidence of his own eyes. Apart from the faint crackle of the ever-swirling black-light, the room was suddenly graveyard still.

As though his skin had been merely bandages, Latcher was beginning to unravel. It started innocuously, with a fraying at the

399

fingertips. Then the shedding became more pronounced, pink-white flesh uncoiling from the hands and the bony wrists, and hanging down in loops like bleached orange peel. From beneath the self-flayed flesh an eerie black-light was flickering, nudging itself forward into the world. Kaye saw Latcher's face coming apart too, the skin sloughing away, the eyes sinking like accelerated putrefaction. Latcher opened his mouth and a column of black-light spewed forth, creating a haze around his decomposing form, causing Kaye to shield his eyes. When Latcher tore open his jacket and ripped his shirt away, he was engulfed by a sizzling torrent of black-light, which quickly established itself as a wall, an impossible upstanding chasm ...

A gateway, thought Kaye with sudden and terrible clarity. He could only stand immobile and stare into the shifting, ethereal patch of luminescent blackness which had replaced Dan Latcher. It was not solid; it was more like a blemish on the eye, and it created a floating, almost hypnotic effect, like perception veiled by drugs. Kaye's limbs felt heavy, his thoughts slow and treacly. Even when a shape began to form in the black-light he could feel only vague alarm.

The shape was vast and white and bloated as a whale. It formed slowly, glutinously, spinning and curling like a snake attempting to swallow itself. At last it became recognisable, more solid, and then it stepped from the black-light into the room. Light streamed from it like fluid, evaporating into sparks. It looked around, blinking and smiling, like a man released into daylight after years underground.

It was Stitch. But a Stitch more dynamic and more repulsive than the rotund figure in the shabby suit. This Stitch was at least ten feet tall, naked and hideously obese, almost dinosaur-like in his movements. To his flabby right breast, like a pendulous sac of flesh, clung a scrawny creature which various others had known as Spider. The creature, hairless now, was suckling noisily, eyes squeezed closed as a new-born pup's. Kaye wondered dreamily what he'd been eating to create an illusion like this.

But there was more to come. The show was not over yet. Like Latcher before him, Stitch immediately began to shed his skin, stubby hands reaching up to strip away the mask and reveal his true face. At first it seemed he was composed of maggots, of insects, of writhing things. Little by little realisation seeped into Kaye's brain. The truth, when it came, was devastating.

They were not maggots but *people*. Tiny, naked, twisted out of true, black dots of mouths screaming their agony. Torsos compacted to form solid flesh. Limbs and spines were bent, intertwined to form lips, eye sockets, ears, nostrils. Stitch was a man of souls, every one

400

of which was alive and endlessly suffering. Not just his head but his whole obscene body was constructed thus. And as Stitch tore away his skin like a body stocking, the screams of the tormented rose and rose and rose ...

83

The car mounted the pavement in front of Carmichael's bungalow and came jerkily to rest. It would have been an understatement to say that Ian had driven recklessly. His body felt charged with adrenaline − overcharged, in fact; he was shaking as if he'd taken too much Ventolin into his system. His neck and shoulders hurt, his bruised face hurt, his chest felt like a vice that was tightening slowly, compressing his lungs. But all this was as nothing in comparison to the succession of hideous scenarios playing in his mind. An endless silent litany had been running through his head, *AnnieAnnieAnnieAnnie*, as though repetition of her name could somehow prevent the realisation of his worst fears.

He ran to the front door of Carmichael's bungalow, leaving the tutor's car wide open, keys in the ignition, a gift for potential joy riders. At the front door he had to stop and suck on his inhaler because black sparks were dancing before his eyes and his thoughts were threatening to float into incoherence. He could hear nothing from inside the house − no screams, no clattering of furniture; he was not sure whether this was a good thing or a bad one. When his lungs were working again he tried the front door. It was locked.

'Annie!' he yelled, banging furiously. 'Annie, it's Ian. Are you okay?'

No answer. Abandoning social niceties, he stepped back from the door, lifted his right leg and slammed the sole of his foot into the wood beside the door handle.

It didn't budge. He tried again. It didn't budge. Again. Again. Eventually the wood around the door began to splinter and crack, the door itself to buckle inwards. Despite the row, not one of the neighbours came to see what was going on. Typical, he thought.

Probably all cowering behind their lace curtains, hoping the noise would stop soon, and convincing themselves it was best not to become involved.

All at once, with a screech that sounded like pain and protest, the door twisted inwards and collapsed. Ian glanced around before jumping inside. Not a curtain flickered. He was panting so hard he felt he was leaving his breath behind. Sweat poured from him, both from exertion and dread. He ran blindly down the hall to the room where he'd last seen Annie and Carmichael. The door was slightly ajar.

He shoved it fully open with the flat of his hand, pain harpooning his shoulder. Tears sprang involuntarily to his eyes so that his first sight of the room was a blur of autumnal colours. He blinked the tears away, feeling momentarily horribly vulnerable. The room was quiet, empty, undisturbed. Two coffee mugs reflected themselves on the glass-topped table.

Ian spun back to the hall. 'Annie!' he shouted, and then in a quieter, more fractured voice, 'Oh God, please answer.' But the house remained ominously silent. Ian pictured Carmichael waiting for him behind one of these doors, weapon poised; he didn't dare think why Annie was not responding. Night air swirled into the hallway and caused one of the doors to creak ever so gently. *There.* Could that be where ...? He didn't stop to think. He floundered down the hallway, heart booming in his chest like the footsteps of an approaching giant.

The door, second on the right from the sitting room, was the only one that was not closed. It was open perhaps half an inch, yellow light spilling from the crack. Now, more then ever, Ian could have done with a weapon. The irony of his plight did not escape him. As though gingerly testing water temperature he extended his leg and nudged the door further open with his toes, retreating immediately in case Carmichael should rush at him.

But he did not. Nothing happened. There was no sound, no indication of movement whatsoever. And yet as the door swung back a spasm of cold horror, sheer despair, flooded through Ian. 'Oh God, Annie,' he moaned. 'Please, Annie, no.' He stumbled forward, heedless now of his own safety. He could see Annie's legs, flecked with blood, and knew that she was lying motionless on the carpet and that he had come far too late to save her ...

84

As Carmichael stretched out an arm towards her, Annie took a step back, out of his reach.

'Don't be afraid,' he said, 'I won't hurt you.'

She didn't reply. She couldn't. A pain had started in her stomach, in her womb, which was now expanding and intensifying. It was not the prelude to a scream as she'd thought, nor was it simple terror. It was something allied to both of these things, and yet it was far more a physical reaction than an emotional one. She felt as if there was an altering of her blood and her meat somewhere inside, as if she was about to experience the worst period pains ever. The only other time she'd felt like this was in the presence of Dan Latcher when, she believed, the fact that she was menstruating had somehow shielded her from his influence. But if the pain was some form of primitive inner defence, as she'd surmised, this time it could surely only work to her disadvantage, incapacitating her. The threat from Carmichael was far more immediate than Latcher's had been. As he moved forward into the room she stumbled another step back. Her foot caught the storage jar which clunked and rolled. Her heel came down in the pool of gore and was immediately coated in it.

Annie's body was beginning to feel cumbersome as a clay statue which her soul had been condemned to drag around. Pain and fear caused her mind to flirt with unconsciousness; she fought desperately against its promise of oblivion, alluring though it seemed. And yet strangely, through the pain, she felt somehow ... divine, as though for that instant her state embodied the nature of all women. She felt an ancient mystique enshrouding her, ensuring protection. But what protection could be potent enough to defeat the reality of a man with murder in his eyes?

'I won't hurt you, Annie,' Carmichael said again, and maybe he meant it, but only in that he would grant her a painless death. He came to the head of the bed, reached down and grabbed the corner of the bedspread. Like a magician he whipped the coverlet away, so violently that it cracked before billowing to the floor in a heap. Annie gave a small whimper at what was revealed. A crescent of metal blades, a huge savage grin, gleaming knives meshing together like the tapered teeth of a vicious carnivore.

Smiling, Carmichael selected a large carving knife and picked it up. He held it loosely, casually, by his side like a shopping bag. He took two more steps towards Annie, his face a mask of serenity. 'There are some things that have to be done,' he told her in a reasonable tone. 'And there are many kinds of love, the deepest of which disguise themselves and don't always seem quite fair. But it's the other way round really, isn't it? What's supposed to be love is just cruelty. Even if the body doesn't suffer it's still torture, it still causes pain to the mind. But what I'm trying to do is love people and help myself at the same time. I show people what's real and I change them. It's true Art. It's the symbol of our lives. I'm special, you see. I'm the Unmaker and the Artist. My masterpieces are helping me to transcend, to have real control, and I'm helping *them* by changing them so that they'll be loved.' Carmichael smiled again as though content with his destructive, ever-changing, self-devouring logic. He thought only of love as his grip tightened on the chunky wooden handle of the carving knife; he thought only of gentleness. Now, at these moments, he knew that he was right, that the confusion he sometimes felt was nothing but a momentary lapse, a temorary frailty, proof of his compassionate humanity. 'If you close your eyes,' he told Annie, 'I promise to be quick and kind.' He hoped Corcoran and Simmsy were watching this and taking note of how gracious he could be.

Pain boiled in Annie. She heard Carmichael's words but she made no sense of them; searing waves of agony were sluicing through her system like the most powerful toxins. She felt on the verge of erupting, or of burning up, lit from within by the most blistering heat. Its core, like a tinder box, was her womb, throwing out spark after spark which blossomed and ignited like fiery conception. She almost swooned, and put a hand to her head as though to re-locate her brain. She felt sick but brimming with positive, powerful energies, as though illness was creating a euphoric delirium inside her.

Carmichael came closer. Snatching details through the blur of her debility, Annie saw his grip tighten convulsively on the knife handle, saw the tip of his tongue peek out from beneath his moustache before slipping back between his lips. She was not aware of moving backwards but suddenly the room had slid past her and the cold wall was at her back. She writhed against it, open palms roaming across its surface as though searching for some hidden spring that would unlock a secret door. Carmichael came closer, eyes full of love. As though offering her flowers, he raised the knife. She screamed.

And that was enough. That was what the boiling pain inside her had been waiting for. Her mouth was like a door opened just a crack to admit a kitten and then hurled back against the wall by the dozen snarling tigers behind it. The pain, the sickness, the delusions, all rose in her like the pressure that propels the upsurge of water in a geyser. Annie felt sheer, unadulterated *power* whooshing up to follow her scream and then erupting from her mouth in its wake.

She could not see the power but she was vitally aware of it. It engulfed Carmichael, swooped on him like something alive, twined invisible threads around and around and around him and held him motionless. Annie wondered briefly whether she was merely a channel for this force, whether its source lay elsewhere, but she quickly dismissed the conjecture. No, the power was hers – wholly and undoubtedly. It was the most intimate, instrinsic part of her. It was the raging of her soul, ancient and awesome, roused by Latcher and what lay behind him, and now brought to the fore, unleashed by the extremities of her emotions. Annie was both exhilarated and terrified, and as the power fled from her she felt herself strengthening, her mind turning razor-sharp, as if all impurities were being stripped from her system.

Carmichael remained poised, brandishing his knife, a joyous smile widening on his face as if a feeling of intense well-being had suddenly swept over him. He was breathing deeply, rapidly blinking his eyelids; he gave the impression that he had paused through choice and not through coercion. 'Yes,' he whispered at last. 'Yes, come to me. Come to me. Fill me with your glory.' He lowered the knife to his neck, turned it so that the blade rested against his flesh. 'Transcendence,' he murmured rapturously, and in a single swift motion drew the blade across his throat. Blood came quickly, some of it spattering Annie's legs. Carmichael dropped the knife. When his body crumpled he was still smiling. Not realising she was about to do so, Annie passed out. Ten minutes later, when the front door crashed open, she didn't even stir.

85

When Ian stumbled into the room his first confused impression was of sprawled bodies and spilled blood. For half a dozen long, dreadful seconds he thought that Annie was dead. His mind, cramped with panic, absorbed the truth only slowly. And then a racking sob of both relief and horror lurched from his throat and he fell to his knees beside her still form.

She was not dead. He could see her breathing. Indeed she seemed not even to be injured; the blood on her clothes and her skin was not her own but Carmichael's, who had died a messy death, apparently by his own hand. The English tutor had fallen sideways and was lying on the floor at the foot of the bed. Perhaps he had even hit the bed and bounced off. There was a streak of blood, like jagged red lightning, across the white sheet, as though to underline the chilling significance of the knives and axes and razors which had been lovingly arranged into a crescent shape.

Carmichael was on his back, eyes and mouth open, right hand outstretched as though reaching despairingly for the blood-streaked carving knife which lay a few inches away. His throat was a gleaming collar of red. Gouts of blood stained the walls, the carpet, even the ceiling. More blood, much of it congealed, had spilled from a jar which was lying sideways on the floor, together with fleshy lumps which Ian realised with horror were human organs. Trying not to inhale the sickening smell, swallowing his nausea, he took Annie's hand. 'Annie,' he murmured, 'Annie ... it's me.' He leaned over and kissed her flushed face. Like the Sleeping Beauty she awoke immediately and regarded Ian with wide eyes.

'He's dead, isn't he?' she said at once. Her voice was flat.

Ian glanced at the tutor's sprawled corpse as if to make doubly sure. 'Yes,' he said, 'he's dead.' And then, after a pause, 'What ... what happened?'

Annie sat up and looked at Carmichael. She betrayed little emotion at the gory outcome of the tutor's self-immolation − evidence, Ian concluded, of her deep shock.

'He cut his own throat,' she said.

'But ... but why?'

'I made him.'

'*You made him*? Annie ... what do you mean? I don't understand.'

She got to her feet, walked over to Carmichael and stared down at him. She seemed calm enough, but Ian hovered at her shoulder, wondering whether he should steer her from the scene. He was grateful when she turned back to him, took his hand and squeezed it.

'He was going to kill me,' she said. 'I protected myself. My energy, my white magic as you call it, just kind of flowed out of me and encircled him and made him think it was his own. He talked about transcendence. I think he'd been waiting for his own power, and when he felt mine ... I *tricked* him into ending his own life.' She looked Ian directly in the eyes. 'But it had to be done, Ian. I'm sure I should feel guilty for killing him, but I don't.'

Ian said nothing. He didn't know how to react. He was glad Carmichael had died and not Annie, but all the same the knowledge that this power of hers could kill shocked and scared him. Annie released his hand, walked to the window and looked out. 'What time is it?' she asked.

Ian looked at his watch. 'Nine.'

'Then we might still have time.'

'What do you mean? Time for what?'

She turned from the window and Ian saw the frown on her face as she struggled to express herself.

'I ... saw things,' she said. 'My white magic enabled me to glimpse a little of the truth of Carmichael and Dan Latcher. They're part of the same influence, Ian. It's like a great web encompassing all the darkness.' Her frown deepened. 'I'm not sure but I think I've got more control now. I think I might know a way that we can fight them. Things are changing inside me; I'm learning all the time, being shown things. We'll have to go back to the University, Ian, or at least I will. If you don't want to come you don't have to.'

'Of course I'll come,' he said indignantly. 'You know I will. We'll do whatever we have to do together. I love you, Annie.'

She smiled softly. 'I love you too,' she said, and then she appeared to brace herself as if for some unpleasant task. 'I have to do something in here now,' she said, 'something you may not want to see. Maybe it'd be better if you waited for me in the car.'

Ian's mouth was dry but he shook his head. 'I'm staying with you,' he told her.

Annie was silent for a long moment and then said, 'All right. But stand over there and keep quiet. Promise you won't say anything.'

Ian's immediate reaction was to protest, to demand answers, but

407

he simply muttered, 'Okay, I promise.' and went to stand where she had indicated. He watched her to see what she would do, his hand instinctively creeping to his jacket pocket to trace the familiar outline of his inhaler.

For a couple of achingly prolonged minutes she seemed to do nothing, simply stood in the middle of the floor, apparently urging her body to become limper, more relaxed. She closed her eyes. Her breathing became deeper, steadier, as if she were falling asleep on her feet. The air thickened, seemed to bristle, as if charged. Ian's bruised body throbbed. At last Annie opened her mouth, presumably to speak, thought Ian.

But she said nothing. Her back arched, her lips spread wide. It was as if she was emitting a note so piercing that it was inaudible to the human ear. Ian sensed rather than saw something emerging from her mouth. A faint shimmering, an oily swirling of air through which the room flickered and wavered slightly, like a distant horizon on a baking summer's day.

He gasped and took a step back, bumping into the edge of the wardrobe. He watched the corrugating progress of the cloud as it drifted down towards Carmichael's corpse, stretched itself like a sheet and settled silently over him. It was like watching the tutor's body rise up through a few feet of ice-clear water. The cloud appeared to enter his dead skin through his pores, through his nostrils and mouth, through the rent in his throat. Finally its swirling motions on his dead flesh ceased and all was as before.

Though not for long. Ian gasped again as a hand jerked − but it was not Annie's hand, it was Carmichael's. His immediate thought was that he'd been mistaken. But then the dead tutor shifted his foot, his heel scraping across the carpet. The hand that had jerked began opening and closing its fingers. The head turned a little on its slashed neck, the movement inducing a fresh flow of blood. Ian tore his eyes from the ghastly resurrection and looked at Annie. There was an expression of horrified rapture on her face. He shuddered. She was like Frankenstein engrossed in the birth of his monster.

Carmichael, modern day Lazarus, sat up slowly. Ian shrank back against the wall, breath turning asthmatic again. His hands were shaking so much that he could barely work his inhaler. At last, however, he got it into his mouth and sucked on the plastic tube like an alcoholic who drinks to forget.

The English tutor stood up, the manoeuvre prompting a further rush of blood from his gaping throat. The worst thing about this miracle was Carmichael's face; despite overwhelming evidence to the contrary his expression remained that of a dead man. Glassy eyes, slack open mouth, the cheeks somehow shrunken as though deserted by the afflatus of life. Carmichael is a zombie, Ian thought, and felt a sudden urge to shriek with laughter, which thankfully he stifled.

As though responding to remote control, Carmichael walked stiffly to the bed, reached down and began to gather up his weapons. Machetes, skewers, cleavers and hatchets disappeared into his pockets or were stuffed into his belt, pirate-fashion.

Ian found his voice, though barely. 'What have you done?' he managed to croak.

Annie turned to him with shining eyes. 'He'll fight for us,' she whispered.

Ian shook his head. 'It's obscene.'

Her face fell. 'Why obscene? Carmichael's only a shell now. It's Latcher and what's behind him that's obscene. Please support me, Ian. This is the only way I know how to fight him.'

Ian glanced at Carmichael − at the *corpse* of Carmichael. The dead thing was still gathering its armoury together, movements jerky as a puppet's.

'Annie . . .' He struggled for words that could keep the revulsion from his voice. Finally he shook his head. 'It doesn't matter.'

She walked across and kissed him. He tried not to flinch. 'I'm doing this because I can,' she said, 'and because I have to.' She turned abruptly. 'Come on, we'd better go.'

Ian stayed where he was, reluctant to approach Carmichael, who was now standing motionless by the door, glazed eyes staring at nothing. Already knowing the answer he said, 'He's not coming, is he?'

'Of course he's coming,' said Annie. 'Are you?'

'But his face . . .' said Ian. He waved a hand, unable to express in words the horror he was feeling.

Annie looked at Ian, then at Carmichael. She crossed to the bed, stripped off a white pillowcase and pulled it down over the corpse's head like the hood of a condemned man.

'Better?' she said.

'Yes,' said Ian, but he was lying.

'Then let's go,' said Annie firmly.

She walked from the room, Carmichael's corpse clanking jerkily after. Ian brought up the rear, feeling more sickened, more despairing, than he'd ever thought possible.

86

There had never been a sensation like it. This time for sure it was Epiphany. Steph writhed and moaned as she was probed and infiltrated, as the black-light filled her, body and soul, blazing an exquisite trail through the empty corridors of her being. Dan's ministrations, his opening of doors within her, had been as nothing compared to this. His task, she realised now, had simply been to lay the foundations, to clear the way, like a minor official unrolling the red carpet for his king. And here the king came, and his name was Truth and Love and Glory. Steph felt she would be pulled apart by the sheer rapture his passage generated, felt she would surely die from the sweet excesses of his Love.

She peaked. And peaked. And peaked. Pleasure was too feeble a word for such elevation. Indeed there was nothing in the pitiful boundaries of human experience which could ever have conceived of such splendours. Even the words Latcher had used – Epiphany included – seemed woefully inadequate now. Steph merely *experienced* while vague notions of Heaven, of Paradise, flitted within her. Memories of her past life, of thoughts and ideas and values she had once held, seemed as ungraspable and as alien as the echoes of an insect's dream.

And then, like the swift shocking insertion of a needle into unsuspecting flesh, came the first pain. It yanked her back from rapture's brink. Numbing solid reality was revealed, made filthy in light of what she had just experienced. The room she was in seemed dark, full of dirt and dust, the people around her a repulsive mass of sweating lice-ridden flesh. A creature cavorted on the stage, vast and made of pain. At once Steph realised the creature was scattering that pain, sowing it like handfuls of hooks into the pool of black-light. The hooks were sharp and cruel, and they were snagging the exposed, vulnerable souls of The Crack, finding purchase in the soft meat of their beliefs. And only now, when it was far too late, did Steph realise that she had been tricked, that she and all the other members of The Crack had been gorged and nurtured for the sole reason that their slaughtered flesh would be all the sweeter.

She struggled, knowing it was no use. She screamed and sobbed as pain pierced her. She could feel her soul, her spirit, being roughly torn away. It was a hideous sensation, like being skinned from the inside. Around her the screams of her companions rose, increasing

410

in agony and volume as the hooks caught and tore. The revelations of the past few days taunted her, flew and crumbled like ashes before the truth of her spiritual insemination by Latcher. She saw now that he had been no Messiah, but a straw-man with a smiling paper mask, handing out trinkets and calling them miracles. And his philosophies, which had seemed so profound, so full of light and revelation, she now realised were shallow and meaningless, a nonsensical jumble of sound which she had interpreted as truth. She would have felt embarrassed if the pain was not so great and the consequences not so tragic. She might even have laughed. But around her people were dying as their essences, their lifeforce, their souls, succumbed to the cruel hunger of the waddling monstrosity on the stage. By her side the choking pleas of a young man ceased as he slumped against her, his eyes rolling up into his head, frothy spittle dribbling from his mouth, hands clawing in a final spasm before relaxing in death.

And then inevitably, hideously, it was her turn.

With a final wrench which brought unbelievable, all-consuming pain, Steph felt herself leaving her body. It was like an abortion, like being torn from the womb of her life. She felt herself hoisted aloft as though on the tips of spears while below her the glove of flesh which she had inhabited for eighteen years collapsed, lifeless as a marionette. She felt like sobbing, but could not. Inexorably she was turned around, spun and manipulated by the black-light, and then, with increasing speed, was borne toward the leering collossus on the stage. Helpless now, she had no choice but to endure as she was swallowed, absorbed into the endless morass of pain of which this ogre was a manifestation. And as the blackness took her she wished she would die. But she suspected that only God would be so merciful.

87

To avoid the crowds Ian, Annie and Carmichael's corpse entered the University through a side door. Annie led the way, the hooded, heavily-armed zombie trailing close behind like an obedient pet, and Ian brought up the rear, an unwilling conscript in a war he did not understand and had no stomach for.

As soon as they entered the building they heard screams drifting from the Auditorium, the sound acting as a tourniquet to Ian's nerves. Setting her face to hide her fear, Annie headed towards the sound. She walked stiffly, though Ian saw her flinch at the cries, which were full of ragged exhaustion, of terror and agony. He clenched his teeth and huddled within himself, feeling his own fear and panic building inside him. There was a bass rumble beneath the screams – shouts and barked orders, adding to the cacophony. When Annie pushed open an unmanned, little-used side entrance into the Auditorium, the din swept over them like a wave.

And the scene revealed was every bit as terrible as the noise had promised. It was like the vision by Bosch made flesh, a Medieval image of Hell, complete with devil and wailing, tormented souls.

This 'devil', however, was not the horned, cloven-hoofed creature of legend. He – it? – was a tottering giant, so obese he seemed almost formless. Black mouths were opened everywhere in his skin, as though he were covered in moles, and each of the mouths, and thus his body, was screaming. It took Ian almost a minute of staring before he realised that the mouths belonged to heads which in turn belonged to bodies, and that the bodies were twisted and twined together, a complex melding of flesh and bone of which this wallowing behemoth was the ghastly end result.

And though the bodies which made up the collossus seemed doll-like, absurdly tiny, Ian had no doubt that they were genuine and that their agony was real and excruciating. The Pain-Man had a nightmarish, ethereal quality to him. Looking at him was like gazing down the wrong end of a telescope whilst drunk, seeing other shapes hovering just out of sight behind the central image.

Tearing his gaze from the demon, Ian absorbed further details, equally as appalling. A black-light, like dark electric fog, flickered over everything, and this, coupled with the screams of the suffering, reduced the scene to a fugue-like unreality that was nevertheless shatteringly intense. Cramming the tiered seats of the Auditorium, enclosed within a dome of black-light, roped together with tendrils of the stuff like rotting ectoplasm, were The Crack and the dozens of young people whom Ian and Annie had encountered on the road. Some were thrashing about in their seats, screaming, begging for help. Others were slumped, unconscious, or perhaps even dead. Desperately Ian's gaze slithered from one agonised face to the next, searching for Steph. But he couldn't find her. He wasn't sure whether to feel relieved or alarmed.

Most of the shouting he had heard, snatches of words virtually lost amid the general cacophony, came from Chief Inspector Kaye. The policeman was standing about half-way up the steps that formed the left-hand aisle. He was waving his arms, raging apoplectically. But however furious he became it was clear his orders would have no effect. Whenever one of his officers ventured too close to the encompassing dome of black-light, a tendril of sizzling energy lashed out like an electric whip and slammed the unfortunate victim back against the steps or, in one or two cases, poleaxed him completely. Despite this, Kaye waved his men forward with ever-increasing fervour. His actions seemed based on the ruthless, even insane, logic that the enemy would eventually run out of ammunition if enough cannon fodder was provided to soak up the onslaught. Ian found himself both appalled by, and oddly sympathetic to, Kaye's tactics. The policeman had a strong sense of duty and responsibility, however implacable he might be. Simply to have stood back and watched what was happening was not his style at all. Ian did not think that letting Kaye know he was here would be a good idea just now.

He looked at Annie, wondering how she was taking all this. She was standing perhaps ten feet in front of him; if she had reached out she could have touched the lip of the stage on which the Pain-Man was standing. Black-light crackled around her like a pack of unearthly guard dogs but seemed unable to penetrate the invisible nimbus which sheathed her body. Her expression was now fixed, trance-like, her face the colour of baked cement.

Carmichael, still hooded, hovered as ever by her shoulder. But now, as though at some unspoken command, he began to edge closer to the stage, drawing a meat cleaver from his belt with his left hand, a dagger with his right. Black-light spat and hissed around him, but like Annie he seemed insulated against it. Moving slowly but remorselessly he reached the edge of the stage, climbed clumsily onto it, and began to make his way towards the Pain-Man.

'Hey! You!' Ian heard, and turned to see Kaye waving an arm at Carmichael's shuffling figure. Not surprisingly the corpse did

413

not respond. Kaye shouted something more complex, the words of which eluded Ian but the gist was clear: Get the fuck away from there! Infuriated by the disregard being shown him, Kaye began to stamp down the steps, presumably with the intention of hauling Carmichael physically from the stage. He was almost at the bottom when he saw Ian. He did not exactly grant him a warm reception.

'What the bloody hell are you doing here?' Kaye demanded. His expression was so discouraging that Ian felt an urge to cover his face with his hands so that his bruises would not be added to. 'What do you know about all this?'

'Not much,' said Ian defensively. 'I came with them.' He pointed to the motionless Annie and the knife-wielding Carmichael.

Kaye reached him. His eyes were wilder than they ought to have been. 'You never listen, do you?' he said. 'What the fuck is it with you?'

Taken aback, Ian muttered, 'I don't — '

'I made it crystal-clear outside, didn't I? This is a *police* matter. Any student found inside the Auditorium will be arrested and charged with obstructing this inquiry.'

Without warning he grabbed the back of Ian's collar and hauled him up on to his tip-toes. Ian squawked. Kaye pulled him close as if to kiss him. A dangerous light flickered in the policeman's eyes; froth collected at the corners of his mouth.

'I thought we had an understanding,' he said. 'I thought you were finally beginning to realise how we do things. I've been fair with you, Raven. Fairer than fair, in fact. Downright generous, I'd say. So why haven't you been fair with me, hmm?'

He shook Ian as if he were a can, his answer a coin that was rattling inside. Feeling strangled, Ian said, 'I don't know what you mean. I wasn't around earlier so I didn't know we weren't supposed to come in here. I've been at ... at Carmichael's. I've only just got back.'

Kaye stared at Ian as if his lies might be visible on his face. In a voice no less dangerous he said, 'Okay, we'll pass on that one, I'll give you the benefit of the doubt. But you're not going to tell me you've been giving me the whole story, are you?'

'What do you mean?' said Ian again, and then choked off as Kaye gave his collar another twist.

'You know exactly what I mean!' the policeman bawled. 'You've been withholding information, haven't you? You haven't been one hundred per cent truthful.'

'Please,' Ian croaked, placing his hand over Kaye's much heftier one. 'Please ... let me breathe ... I'm an asthmatic.'

Grudgingly Kaye loosened his throttling grip a millimetre. 'You haven't, have you?' he demanded.

Ian hadn't felt like this since he was bullied on his first day at secondary school. 'No,' he said in a small voice.

Kaye almost snarled. His teeth clamped together, making his jawbone jut. 'Why not?' he said.

'Because ... because half the time I didn't know what was going on, and the other half I didn't believe it.'

Kaye gestured at the pendemonium. 'But you believe it now?'

'Yes.'

'So fill me in. I want to know.'

Ian's mind reeled. Where to start? Even now his knowledge was a warren, full of holes.

He pointed at the hooded figure on the stage.

'Well, that's Mr Carmichael. He was the killer all along, not Neil, not even Latcher. I don't quite understand why, but somehow, because of Latcher, Annie got this ... this power; white magic I call it. She was at Carmichael's house and he was going to kill her, so she somehow used this magic and made him kill himself. And then she brought him back to life and we all came here.'

He shook his head at his own ridiculous explanation. Whatever was happening — and even now he wasn't sure — he felt it gnawing away at his reason and emotions, tipping his world on its head. He felt an urge either to shriek with laughter or cry like a baby, felt a need to release an awful pressure from his system, and yet was too stunned to do so. He looked at Kaye, who had closed his eyes and adopted an exasperated expression, like a schoolmaster trying in vain to introduce some simple theorem into the mind of a dim pupil. 'I'm sorry,' said Ian.

Kaye opened his eyes. Now he looked surprised. 'What for?' he said.

'For ... for ... I don't know. For making things more complicated, I suppose.'

Kaye sighed and released Ian. Suddenly he looked weary, haggard, thoroughly sick of the world and everything in it. There was a sound from the stage, a flicker of movement, of energy, something that made them both turn.

The Titans had clashed.

Carmichael was little more than a shimmering, hissing, crackling ball of black-light in vaguely human form. The Pain-Man's energy enclosed him like a shoal of piranha, trying to bite, trying to kill, but unable to penetrate whatever defences Annie had woven around his cold flesh. Within the black-light steel flashed and a stripe of raw

415

meat was carved into the Pain-Man's tortured anatomy. A welter of screaming mouths were instantly silenced.

Released, Ian thought instinctively, and was astonished at how suddenly buoyant he felt.

The blades cut again, sweeping down like the Reaper's scythe to free further souls. More black-light poured from the rents in the Pain-Man's body, but this black-light was listless, sluggish, mindless and wriggling as maggots spilling from a paper bag. The spindly creature clinging to the Pain-Man's breast was despatched in a numinous flash of sizzling metal. It dropped to the floor and lay still, sickly light oozing from the wounds in its etiolated body. The Pain-Man was withering, collapsing; it seemed only a matter of minutes before he too would fall.

But then, gradually, the Pain-Man began to fight back. It was like watching a dream, this battle: slow, liquid, almost leisurely, and yet at the same time intense and devastating. Like a wounded general calling on his troops to protect him, the Pain-Man opened his vast mouth and began to gulp in the black-light, to reel it like twine into his stricken form, to re-knit and indeed strengthen himself. The dome above his captive audience unravelled, disintegrated. Defences down, the police rushed in among the dead and the damned, to offer help where they could, much of it worthless as crumbs to the starving.

The Pain-Man rallied. Like a thirsty alcoholic he drank energy and was in turn consumed and invigorated by it. His wounds stitched themselves together, using black-light as thread, though the screaming mouths silenced by Carmichael did not re-open: those souls, at least, had been freed. Carmichael raised his cleaver to strike again — and the Pain-Man stopped it with a breath of black-light like dragon's fire. The cleaver hovered, raised; Carmichael, hooded, was like a life-sized statue of some movie maniac. Another gout of black-light from the Pain-Man's roaring mouth, and the cleaver spun away, flashing through the air before embedding itself in a wooden door frame.

The Pain-Man seemed to take an enormous breath, inflating himself, and then vomited the most virulent and comprehensive stream of black-light yet. It struck Carmichael like a charging bull and sent him reeling backwards; simultaneously Annie staggered too, as though she and her grisly creation were performing complex synchronised dance-steps.

'Annie!' Ian yelled, and rushed to her side as she swayed and stumbled, threatening to fall. He put out his hand to steady her, but the shimmering field of black-light which covered her body lashed out at him and he felt sizzling pain enclose his hand, a jolt of force which shoved him sprawling backwards.

416

'Not a wise move,' Kaye said from behind him. 'I tried it with Dan Latcher. I'm only just starting to get the feeling back.'

'*Latcher*?' Ian exclaimed. With everything else he had forgotten about The Crack's leader. 'Where's he? I haven't seen him anywhere.'

He looked at Kaye, who for the first time since Ian had known him had a weary kind of conciliation in his expression. Nodding at the stage the policeman said, 'Believe it or not, that's him. Or at least it was. One minute Latcher was there and the next ...' he snorted '... that thing.'

Tucking his throbbing hand beneath his armpit – just one more pain to add to his myriad others – Ian said, 'We've got to help Annie.'

Kaye shrugged. His fury, the anger which drove him onwards, seemed to be leaking away to be replaced by a kind of blasé defeatism. 'How?' he enquired.

How indeed? This time Annie was not immured behind anything so simple as a locked door. Venturing as close as he dared to her, desperation gnawing at him, Ian shouted again, 'Annie!'

Like an old frail woman she turned towards him. Her face had lost its waxen impassivity; now it was twisted with unbearable strain. Speaking haltingly, lips curled back over clenched teeth, she said, 'I can't ... beat ... it. I'm not strong ... enough.'

Ian saw her gasp and twist, squeeze her eyes shut and clutch her stomach as though poison was working in there. 'What can I do?' he wailed, feeling helpless. 'Annie, tell me, what can I do?'

'Nothing,' said a voice behind him. He whirled, causing a spike of pain to twist in his shoulders and neck. He recognised the girl standing there, though not immediately. She looked Scandinavian – clear-complexioned, her head a mass of straw-blonde corkscrew curls.

'Oh, for God's sake,' said Kaye with a flash of his old hostility, 'this isn't a party, you know. Please go away.'

'I'm here to help Annie,' said the girl. 'I heard her calling. I had to come.'

'Heather,' said Ian.

The girl turned her blue eyes on him. 'Yes.'

She moved towards Annie, effectively dismissing Ian and Kaye. Annie saw her and stretched out a hand imploringly. Heather reciprocated.

'Don't!' Ian warned, thinking of his own encounter with the black-light. But he needn't have worried.

The black-light did not repel Heather as it had done Ian. Instead it swarmed over her, seemingly unable to penetrate whatever defences she had secured around her body. Heather reached into Annie's envelope of black-light and grasped her hand. Ian thought of a rescuer hauling a stricken mountaineer from the brink of disaster, extending a lifeline to be clutched for.

Certainly, with Heather's support, Annie seemed to revive. She straightened gingerly; little by little the agony left her face. Up on stage Carmichael was on his knees, head bowed, like a chained and beaten prisoner. But as Annie recuperated so did he. He raised his head slowly, slowly. Fighting against the black-light which was lashing him like handfuls of whips he struggled, tottering, to his feet. The black-light increased, whirling and gnashing, trying to bear him down again, but he remained standing, albeit unsteadily.

Heather embraced Annie, then kissed her on the lips, tender as a lover. Ian found their intimacy unsettling but said nothing; he understood little of what was going on and felt unqualified to protest. The two women broke apart though still held hands. In unison they turned towards the stage, their faces set in concentration, eyes glassy. For a few moments deadlock reigned; the Pain-Man was using the energy of the black-light to keep Carmichael at bay. By the same token Annie and Heather combined seemed a match for his power. Ian watched, mesmerised, to see who would break ...

Then Carmichael took a step forward.

There was a subtle shift in the black-light around the corpse's and the women's bodies; it seemed to become more agitated, buzzing like an angry cloud of wasps. Ian realised that the Pain-Man, his grotesque features writhing with effort, was throwing everything he had at Annie and Heather, risking his all in a final desperate bid to overpower them. Carmichael staggered and the women gasped as though punched. Ian's stomach crawled like a crate of lizards.

With slow deliberation Carmichael straightened once more and took another step forward. Ian's attention was now focussed solely on the dead man's shoes. He saw the left one lift, painstakingly slowly, jerk forward in tiny spasms as though pushing through setting concrete. It came to rest. Another step. The process was repeated with the right foot. The whining, crackling shriek of the black-light became higher and yet higher pitched. With great deliberation Carmichael reached into his belt and dragged out what appeared to be a curved Samurai sword. He took another step forward. Another. Another. The Pain-Man's face was contorting, blurring. Ian was certain he saw fear in it.

The wailing of the black-light reached a crescendo. Annie and Heather seemed consumed in a ball of negative lightning whose ferocity allowed only brief glimpses of their clothes, their clasped hands, their fixed intent expressions. Carmichael was similarly enclosed, though the web that the Pain-Man was attempting to weave around him kept collapsing and then shakily renewing itself, as if most energy was being directed at the girls, the source of Carmichael's grisly animation. Subliminally Ian was aware of the activity behind him, of bodies being carried from the Auditorium, of police officers comforting survivors, coaxing them from the scene of the Pain-Man's carnage. Soon the place would be empty of peripherals, leaving only these final battlers and he and Kaye as witnesses.

Carmichael took another step. Another. He was only a few feet now from the Pain-Man's collossal bulk. Ian clapped his hands over his ears, unable to bear the piercing scream of the black-light. As though relishing the moment, Carmichael threw aside the dagger he held in his right hand and gripped the sword handle in both. He extended the sword as though about to knight the Pain-Man with it. Then, with the skill of an executioner, he swept the sword around in a flashing arc and severed the Pain-Man's head.

A number of things happened instantaneously. The Pain-Man's head spun through the air for a split-second before dissolving into a scattering of black sparks like glittering ash. His body too broke down into a shimmering flurry of energy before simply winking out of existence. The black-light in the room seemed to devour itself, to curl and spin into its own heart like swirling water. His usefulness now exhausted, Carmichael collapsed, dying for the second time, his sword clattering from his nerveless fingers. And in unison Annie and Heather collapsed too, their knees buckling, their eyes closing, unconscious before they even hit the floor.

For a moment all was silent. Everyone simply stared, listening to the ringing fading in their ears, unable to believe the abruptness with which the chaos had simply vanished. Ian was the first to move. He stumbled towards Annie and Heather, dread chewing at his heart, not for the first time. His entire body felt pummelled as tenderised steak; his breath whistled in his throat. He reached the girls and dropped to his knees beside them. They looked pale, their lips tinged blue. They were not breathing.

'No,' he whispered, his voice as dry as the crunch of autumn leaves. He extended a shaking hand and placed his fingertips gently on Annie's throat. He felt the flutter of a pulse, weak and erratic, but gradually it strengthened as if he was imbuing her with life. He found that Heather's pulse, too, was strengthening. Colour was returning to the faces of both girls.

'Ian.'

419

The voice was gruff but surprisingly gentle. Ian turned to see Kaye standing awkwardly behind him, half-reaching out as though uncertain whether he should touch his shoulder.

'What is it?' he said, standing. The policeman's face seemed almost to be aching with compassion. Ian found the expression much more frightening than Kaye's anger.

'I think . . .' Kaye began, then stopped. Instead he half-turned and gestured behind him. Two young constables were standing by the main door of the Auditorium, holding a stretcher between them. On the stretcher was a blanket-covered form. Ian looked at Kaye, who wouldn't meet his eye. He walked over to the stretcher and pulled the blanket back.

Steph appeared to be sleeping peacefully. Her skin was pale but she did not look as bad as Annie had looked just a few minutes before. No one said anything to Ian as he reached out and placed his fingers on Steph's throat. There was no pulse. He listened to her chest. Nothing. Feeling numbed he pulled the blanket back up over her face and watched as the policemen carried her away. He swallowed, closed his eyes. Someone squeezed his shoulder (Kaye, he assumed) but he didn't acknowledge it and whoever it was moved away without a word.

'Ian,' said a voice from behind him. He opened his eyes and turned to see Annie looking at him. She was trying feebly to rise, using her elbows for leverage. Ian felt a jolt inside him, as if his life had been slowing and the sight of her had jump-started it again. His features cracked into a smile that felt strange and sad. As he approached her she managed to sit up, then reached out with both arms and said, 'Hold me.'

Epilogue

'So what happened?' said Ian.

It was the following day. He and Annie were sitting on an almost deserted bus travelling into Maybury. It was the first real chance they had had to talk alone together.

Annie shrugged. She looked pale and delicate as bone china. Her eyes appeared bruised and sunken from lack of sleep. After examination at Maybury District Infirmary, a Doctor Raiche had declared her 'A bit run down', and had prescribed a course of pills (which Ian suspected were simply placebos) and 'A few more early nights.' Ian waited for a moment, but it seemed as though a shrug was the only answer she was offering.

'Annie,' he said, and waited for her to look at him. 'Talk to me.'

She sighed. 'I'm confused, Ian,' she said at last. 'Even I'm not entirely sure what happened.' She turned and looked out of the window as if that would clarify her thoughts.

At last she continued, 'I was acting on instinct most of the time, going with the flow, using knowledge as soon as it was revealed to me. I knew *what* to do, but I didn't know *how* I knew or what the eventual outcome of my actions would be. It was strange, like ... like an inner me, one that I didn't even know existed, had suddenly taken over the controls. I felt strong and confident, but also scared. I felt that if I didn't concentrate utterly I'd fall apart.'

She pulled a face and shook her head, obviously dissatisfied with her explanation. 'It sounds so silly putting it into words,' she said. 'It sounds straightforward, but it wasn't; it was more ... more mystic than that. I wasn't dealing with words and pictures like our normal thoughts, but with instincts and a kind of emotional knowledge, and ... and femininity and ... I don't know ... cosmic awareness ... oh, it all sounds so stupid.'

Ian stroked the back of her head as though to soothe her distress away. 'It's okay,' he said, 'don't get upset. At least I understand something now.' A pause, and then, 'What about Latcher? And that ... that thing that appeared?'

Annie frowned, appearing to struggle for words or memories. 'Latcher was just a shell,' she said, 'a channel. A gateway, if you like. That thing was ... chaos. Misery. It created evil and suffering and then it feasted on the negative energy of all that pain.' She suddenly laughed and waved a hand at the fields, verdant with autumn sunlight. 'Can you believe we're talking about this?' she said. 'A day like today ...' She tailed off, the humour fading as quickly as it had appeared.

'So what happened to it?' asked Ian. 'All this evil, I mean. Did you kill it?'

Annie looked at him wearily. '*Can* you kill evil?'

Ian didn't reply and the two of them were silent for a few moments as the bus jolted towards Maybury. 'So it might come back?' Ian said finally.

'It always does, doesn't it? One way or another.' As if to comfort Ian, or perhaps both of them, she reached for his hand and squeezed it. She leaned across and kissed him lightly on the cheek. 'There's always a balance,' she said. 'It's the way it has to be, I suppose.'

They disembarked at the hospital. Ian spoke to the receptionist while Annie listened to the conversation two old men in wheelchairs were having about allotments. She felt soothed by the warm burr of their voices, felt an urge to drowse, to float. 'This way,' Ian said, coming back and pointing to his left.

They walked along corridors and up stairs, Annie hardly registering their progress. They stopped at a pair of large double doors propped open with wooden blocks, and stared into a long ward lined with beds that stretched to the far end like a study in perspective.

Neil was eleven beds up on the right. He had his family around him. There was a distinguished-looking father with a grey moustache, an anxious mother with fluttering hands, a younger brother, slim and solemn-looking behind his spectacles. When Neil saw them approaching he gave them a tired smile and murmured, 'Hi, guys, how's it going?'

'Fine,' said Ian, feeling slightly uncomfortable as the Gardeners turned to look at Annie and himself. 'How are you?'

'Okay,' said Neil. He touched his bruised throat. 'Sore, though. Can't talk too much.' Waving a hand around he said, 'This is my mum, dad, my brother Richard. This is Ian and Annie, two friends from Uni.'

Polite greetings were exchanged and Ian and Annie sat down, both feeling they were intruding. Annie looked at Neil and hoped the dismay she felt was not evident on her face. He knew nothing of last night's events; he was certainly ignorant of Steph's death. Annie knew he had awoken from his comatose state late last night, shouting and clawing as though shedding a nightmare. Though she hadn't had it confirmed, she felt as certain as she could be that he had woken the moment Carmichael had severed the head from the creature in the Auditorium. She remembered Neil and Steph together, laughing, less than a week ago, and lowered her eyes to conceal any tears that might fall.

'Anything happening about Latcher at the moment?' she heard Neil croak.

There was a silence, then Ian managed, 'We'll tell you all about it when you're better.'

Annie expected Neil to protest, but he didn't. Instead he said, 'I've never seen Dan Latcher, and yet I dreamed about him just before I woke up.'

Annie raised her head and looked at him. Neil seemed eager to share the experience. Even Ian's discouraging grunt failed to deter him.

'I was in darkness which I couldn't get out of, and then suddenly Latcher appeared, blazing with light. He took my hand and led me out of it. I woke up thinking that he really had done. It was strange.'

All five of Neil's visitors looked at him a moment in silence, then Annie reached out and took his hand and squeezed it, the world blurring as the first of her brimming tears crept down her cheek. Neil's voice was surprised and faintly embarrassed. 'Annie, what's the matter?'

Annie smiled through her tears, then managed to laugh, as though defying them. 'Just ignore me,' she said. 'I'm being silly.' When Ian touched her arm and asked her if she was okay, she nodded vigorously, for suddenly she was. She took the proferred handkerchief from Neil's father and blew her nose, trying to assimilate her own emotions. In a way she couldn't define even to herself, Neil's recounting of his dream had given her a sudden and intense surge of hope.